Mechanical Vibration and Shock Measurements

by

Professor Jens Trampe Broch
Dipl. Ing. E.T.H.

Revised by:

Joëlle Courrech, Dr. Ing.
John Hassall, M. Sc., M.I.O.A.
Philip Hollingbery, M.A., M.I.E.E.
Torben Licht, M.Sc.
Hans Mærsk-Møller, M.Sc.
R. B. Randall, B. Tech., B.A.
David Redfern, H.N.C. Mech.
Hans Jørgen Rindorf, M.Sc.
Jonathan Wort, M.Sc., M.I.Mech. E.

October 1980

ISBN 87 87355 36 1

2nd edition 1st impression

PRINTED IN DENMARK. K. LARSEN & SØN A/S. DK 2860 SØBORG

FOREWORD

The book "Mechanical Vibration and Shock Measurements" has long been a mainstay in Brüel & Kjær's series of books on the fundamentals of physical measurement and analysis. Although the basic theory is still valid, a great many developments have occurred since the book was last revised by Professor Jens Trampe Broch in May 1972, and it was decided in 1979 to bring the book fully up-to-date, partly by a revision of existing material, and partly by adding new chapters where relevant. It was decided to keep as closely as possible to Professor Trampe Broch's original text, and he has had the opportunity to approve the modifications. Even so, it is probably as well to make it clear how much of the present book is taken from the original, and how much is completely new.

Chapter 2 was revised by Bob Randall, and follows the original very closely. Some material has been added on digital frequency analysis, a field which has developed rapidly in the last few years.

Chapter 3 was revised by Joëlle Courrech and also follows the original quite closely. The discussion of non-linear systems has been expanded somewhat, and in addition to the exact treatment of the vibration of continuous structures, as given by Professor Trampe Broch, a brief introduction is given to two approximate methods which have increased in importance in recent years, viz. finite element techniques and statistical energy analysis.

The original Chapter 4 has been split into two, both revised by John Hassall. Chapter 4 covers that part of the original which considered the effects of vibrations and shock on mechanical systems, while Chapter 5 discusses the quite different topic of the effects of vibration and shock on man (Human Vibration). There have been included some new developments in both areas, for example a discussion of mean stress effects and acoustic fatigue in Chapter 4, and more detailed information on hand-arm vibration in Chapter 5, but otherwise these sections are based on the originals.

Chapter 6 on the selection of instrumentation is completely new and was written by David Redfern. Not only were very few of the instruments described in the original book still available, but there has also been a considerable expansion of the range of equipment available. The basic discussion of practical topics such as accelerometer mounting method and charge vs. voltage preamplifiers is adapted from the original.

Chapter 7 on the frequency analysis of shock and vibration is likewise completely new and was written by Bob Randall. Main emphasis is put on two topics which are considered to be currently most relevant; on the one hand analogue serial analysis using battery-operated portable equipment, and on the other hand digital real-time analysis which has now superseded analogue analysis in the laboratory.

Chapter 8 is a new addition, a discussion of a rapidly developing area of application of vibration measurement and analysis, viz. machine health monitoring. It was written by Hans Mærsk-Møller, and gives a guide to how the optimum economic benefit can be derived from the introduction of systematic and/or permanent assessment of the vibration of operating machines.

Acoustic Emission, which is treated in Chapter 9, is not a mechanical vibration in the classical sense, but has been included here because of its connection with Chapter 8. It represents another non-destructive testing technique, although its application tends to be more in the study of static stress situations, such as in pressure vessels, rather than rotating machines. Torben Licht, Hans Jørgen Rindorf and David Redfern all contributed to this chapter.

Chapters 10 and 11 cover topics which were discussed in the original book, but the arrangement has been altered somewhat. Both chapters were adapted by Jonathan Wort and Philip Hollingbery. Chapter 10 discusses the use of electrodynamic shakers for the application of vibration and shock signals to physical constructions both for endurance testing purposes, and also to measure their dynamic properties. It covers basically the same topics as Sections 7.3 and 7.4 of the original book on vibration and shock testing and also section 8.1 on mechanical impedance and mobility. Chapter 11 on balancing serves as an introduction to methods of vibration control. It has been adapted from the material of sections 4.2 and 7.5 of the original book, but includes discussions of both field balancing and special purpose balancing machines.

Chapter 12 discusses the remaining methods of shock and vibration control, viz, isolation and damping, treated in sections 7.1 and 7.2 of the original book. It has been adapted by John Hassall and follows the original quite closely.

Finally, the appendices have been revised by Bob Randall or Joëlle Courrech, depending on which section of the main text they are related to. Appendix E on electronic integration has been expanded to include the integration of impulses as well as continuous signals. The original Appendices F and G have been dropped, the first (on lowest measurable vibration levels) because this information can best be found from the product data of the much wider range of equipment now available (if not adequately covered by Fig.6.5) and the second (on the frequency analysis of impulses) because this topic is covered in Chapter 7 and in more detail in the B & K book "Frequency Analysis".

It is perhaps worth mentioning that the subjects cross correlation, cross-spectral density and coherence (Section 8.2 of the original book) have not been included because they are discussed in some detail in the B & K book "Frequency Analysis". Likewise, the topic of dynamic strain has not been included because it is covered in the B & K book "Strain Measurements".

R.B. Randall

CONTENTS

1. INTRODUCTION

Mechanical vibrations and shock are *dynamic* phenomena, — i.e. their intensity varies with time. Both the maximum intensity, however, and the rate of change in intensity with time, spread over wide measurement ranges and often require highly specialized equipment for their precise determination. Ground motions caused by far-off earthquakes (or explosions) may, for instance, be barely detectable while vibrations caused by large combustion engines can cause severe mechanical fatigue damage.

Although in most cases mechanical shocks and vibrations are undesired byproducts of otherwise useful processes, and great efforts are spent to reduce their effects, some vibrations are produced on purpose. Typical examples are the vibrations produced by conveying and screening machines, mechanical hammers, ultrasonic cleaning baths, etc., while desirable shock-effects are built into riveting hammers and pile-drivers.

As the same methods of description and measurement apply, in general, whether the vibrations or shocks being characterized are wanted or unwanted, no clear distinction has been made throughout this book. The various chapters have been laid out with a view mainly to describe measurement data and techniques necessary to characterize vibrations and shocks and to evaluate their effects on a responding medium. For more comprehensive treatments of theoretical aspects the reader is referred to standard textbooks and to literature cited in the bibliography.

Chapter 2 reviews briefly the basic characteristics of mechanical vibrations and shocks and the various quantities used to characterize them. Section 2.1 deals with periodic (discrete frequency) signals while section 2.2 extends the discussion to stationary random functions which must be described in terms of their statistical parameters. In both cases it is seen how description in terms of RMS (Root Mean Square) values can be advantageous because of their relation to the power content of the vibrations, and how the distribution of power with frequency can be determined using the Fourier transform. Sec-

13

tion 2.3 describes how the Fourier transform technique can also be applied to transient phenomena and shocks, although the spectra are then in terms of "energy" rather than "power". Finally, section 2.4 introduces the concept of non-stationary data and gives some typical examples.

Chapter 3 deals with the response of mechanical systems to vibrations and shocks, starting with a single-degree-of-freedom system and then extending the discussion to the more general case. Firstly, in section 3.1 it is shown that for deterministic excitation, the response of a system reduces in the frequency domain to the product of the excitation spectrum and the frequency response of the system, this corresponding in the time domain to a convolution of the excitation signal with the impulse response of the system. The concept of resonance is introduced and tied to the number of degrees of freedom of the system.

In section 3.2 there is a discussion of the various types of non-linearity and how they affect the simpler results obtained for linear systems. The most common case, of non-linearity in the spring element, is treated in most detail. Section 3.3 discusses torsional vibration, demonstrating the direct analogies with lateral vibration, while section 3.3 shows that the basic principles of section 3.1 also apply to stationary random signals, in that the power spectrum of a response can be obtained as the product of the input spectrum with the (squared amplitude of the) frequency response function.

Section 3.5 introduces another way of describing shock responses, the so-called *shock response spectrum*, which differs from the Fourier spectrum in that it takes some account of the damping of the excited structure and also of the maximum response before the system has settled down. The connection between them is made clear in Appendix D.

Sections 3.6, 3.7 and 3.8 all discuss extensions of the basic principles to the continuous structures normally met with in practice. Section 3.6 considers the exact equations of motion for which exact solutions only exist for a number of idealised cases, e.g. simple bars, beams and plates. Section 3.7 introduces *Finite Element techniques* which allow numerical solution of practical problems by modelling actual structures as assemblies of discrete elements, while section 3.8 briefly indicates that even greater simplifications can be made in the case where there is a high *modal density* so that it is no longer necessary to determine the individual modes but sufficient to average over a number of them, and also to make spatial averages.

Chapter 4 describes some effects of vibration and shock on mechanical systems, in particular with respect to fatigue. It is shown how results on fatigue life of metals, obtained with sinusoidal excitation, can be extended to random excitation, but warns at the same time that it may be more reliable in practice to actually generate the data using random signals. A section is included on mean stress effects, since most structural elements have to bear a steady load in addition to the dynamic one, and another section deals briefly with the case of intense acoustic excitation which has been found to cause failure of aerospace and other structures. Section 4.2 discusses briefly the damaging effects of shocks and transients, which may give sudden brittle failure as opposed to fatigue failure.

Chapter 5 summarises the most important effects of vibration and shock on man, ranging from *Kinetosis* (motion sickness) in the fractional Hertz range, through *Whole Body Vibration* in the range 1 — 80 Hz, and including *Hand-arm* vibration in the range 8—1000 Hz. Some criteria are included from the relevant standards.

Chapter 6 is a detailed guide to the proper selection of equipment for vibration and shock measurement and evaluation. After a brief introduction in section 6.1, sections 6.2 and 6.3 provide the necessary information to allow the optimum choice of accelerometer and preamplifier, now widely accepted as being the best all-round vibration transducer, even where parameters other than acceleration are to be measured. Sections 6.4, 6.5 and 6.6 cover the practical questions of calibration, choice of force and impedance transducers, and accelerometer mounting method, respectively.

Section 6.7 discusses the choice of portable battery-operated instruments, including vibration meters, tunable filters, graphic recorders, tape recorders, transport shock or "bump" recorders as well as stroboscopes and waveform analyzers. The tape recorder would often be used for field recording of signals which are to be analyzed in detail on sophisticated mains-operated equipment as discussed in section 6.8. The possibilities include frequency analysis using either sweeping or sequential filter analyzers and digital *real-time* analyzers based on the *FFT (Fast Fourier Transform)* or *digital filter* principles. Results can be written out graphically on an X-Y recorder, stored digitally on a digital cassette recorder for later processing or processed on a large scale using a desktop calculator or computer.

Chapter 7 gives specific information on how to optimise the frequency analysis of vibration and shock signals, this having already been shown to be the most important analysis technique. Section 7.1 gives an introduction to the mode of operation of typical analyzer systems, both analogue and digital, and to the choice of basic analysis parameters such as bandwidth and logarithmic vs. linear scales. Section 7.2 deals with the serial analysis of stationary signals, concentrating on what is probably the most important remaining application area, viz., field analysis using portable battery-operated equipment. Section 7.3, on the other hand, discusses the use of real-time digital analyzers for the more detailed analysis of both stationary signals and shocks and transients. Finally, section 7.4 discusses the analysis of non-stationary signals by a *moving time-window* approach, this being useful for treating non-stationarities such as changing speed (e.g. run-ups and run-downs) and where the signal itself is made up of discrete impulses, as in reciprocating machine vibrations.

Chapter 8 is a discussion of a rapidly growing area of application of the previously discussed measurement and analysis methods, viz., in *machine health monitoring.* Here, the vibration signal is considered basically as a carrier of information as to the internal condition of an operating machine, but the way in which the system is set up can be decisive in whether the procedures yield results. This chapter concentrates on information as to how to avoid the pitfalls which have prevented some people from realising the full potential of these procedures.

Chapter 9 covers a somewhat related topic, in that it represents another non-destructive evaluation technique, viz., *Acoustic Emission.* The basic difference is that it usually provides information on static stress conditions, such as in pressure vessels, as opposed to the condition of running machines discussed in Chapter 8. Because acoustic emission is a relatively new topic, for which specialised equipment has been designed, the chapter is self-contained, providing background information, details of transducers and instruments for signal conditioning and evaluation, and finally information on areas of application, including typical examples.

Chapter 10 discussed the use of electrodynamic shakers for the active generation of vibration and shock for a variety of purposes. Section 10.1 covers vibration generation both for *environmental testing* and for determination of the *dynamic properties of materials and structures.* After a discussion of the basic properties of exciters and their controls, the relative merits of sinusoidal vs random excitation are discussed. Finally, the basic concepts of *mechanical impedance and mobility* measurement are introduced and typical systems for their measurement are shown. Section 10.2 deals with shock testing both using electrodynamic shakers and other means, and concludes with a further discussion of the *Bump Recorder* introduced in Chapter 6.

Chapter 11 is entitled "Balancing of Rotating Machines" and serves as an introduction to methods of reducing vibrations. The concepts of static and dynamic unbalance of rigid rotors are first introduced and the importance of the bearing supports being "hard" or "soft" made clear. After a presentation of relevant standards for the degree of acceptable residual unbalance, it is discussed how the balancing can be achieved, either making use of specially designed *universal balancing machines* with associated electronics, or even using portable equipment *in situ* (Field Balancing). In the latter case the calculations involved can now be efficiently performed by pre-programmed pocket calculators (at least for the rigid rotors so far assumed). The chapter ends with a brief discussion of more difficult balancing tasks, viz., fine balancing,

balancing of flexible rotors (running above the critical speed) and multiple-span shafts, and crankshaft balancing for reciprocating machines.

The final chapter, Chapter 12, discusses the remaining methods for reducing the transmission of vibration and shocks, in cases where it is not possible to eliminate them at the source, and covers isolation, dynamic absorption, and damping.

The basic principle of *vibration isolation* consists in selecting a suitable spring mounting for the equipment so that the natural frequency of the spring-mass system is appreciably less than the lowest frequency to be isolated, assuring at the same time that the resonance will not be excited. With regard to *shock isolation*, also treated in section 12.1, this is treated on the basis of the *shock response spectrum* and it is found that similar conditions apply. However, in this case the choice of proper damping is more important, as are the non-linear properties of the mounts.

Section 12.2.1 discusses the application of *dynamic absorbers* which can be used to detune a resonance where there is one main excitation frequency. In combination with appropriate damping, a dynamic absorber can also be designed to have a limited response over a wide frequency range (including the resonances) and still attenuate at high frequencies.

Section 12.2.2 discusses the application of *damping treatments* in cases where it is impossible to avoid exciting resonances because of their number and close spacing. A guide is given as to the optimum way to apply damping material so as to obtain the best results from a given amount of treatment, and finally there is a discussion of the various methods available for determining the damping properties of materials.

1.1. GENERAL REFERENCES

Books:

BISHOP, R.E.D. and   *Mechanics of Vibration.* Cambridge University Press,
JOHNSON, D.C.:   1979

CREMER, L. and   *Körperschall.* Springer Verlag. Berlin/Heidelberg
HECKL, M.:   /New York 1967. Also English version *Structure-Borne Sound,* 1973

Den HARTOG, J.P.:   *Mechanical Vibrations.* McGraw-Hill Book Company, Inc. 1956

HARRIS, C.M. and CREDE, C.E.:	*Shock and Vibration Handbook.* McGraw-Hill Book Company, Inc. 1976
JACOBSEN, L.S. and AYRE, R.S.:	*Engineering Vibrations.* McGraw-Hill Book Company, Inc. 1958
MORROW, C.T.:	*Shock and Vibration Engineering.* John Wiley and Sons, Inc. 1963
MORSE, P.M.:	*Vibration and Sound.* McGraw-Hill Book Company, Inc. 1948
SNOWDON, J.C.:	*Vibration and Shock in Damped Mechanical Systems.* John Wiley and Sons, Inc. 1968
TIMOSHENKO, S.:	*Vibration Problems in Engineering.* John Wiley and Son, 1974
MEIROVITCH, L.:	*Elements of Vibration Analysis.* McGraw-Hill Book Company, Inc. 1975

Journals:

Acustica	Hirzel Verlag, Stuttgart
Akusticheskii Zhurnal	Published by the Academy of Science of the U.S.S.R. Moscow. (Also translated and published by the American Institute of Physics as : Soviet Physics, Acoustics)
Experimental Mechanics	Published by the Society of Experimental Stress Analysis, U.S.A.
J.A.S.A.	(Journal of the Acoustical Society of America). Published by the American Institute of Physics, New York
Journal of Sound and Vibration	Published by Academic Press, Inc. London
Journal of the Acoustical Society of Japan	(Japanese) Published by the Acoustical Society of Japan, University of Tokyo, Tokyo

Kampf dem Lärm	Published by Deutschen Arbeitsring für Lärmbekämpfung, E.V. Düsseldorf
Lärmbekämpfung	Verlag für angewandte Wissenschaften GmbH. Baden-Baden
Sound and Vibration	Published monthly by Acoustical Publications, Inc., Ohio, U.S.A.
The Shock and Vibration Bulletin	Published by The Shock and Vibration Information Center, Naval Research Laboratory, Washington, D.C.
The Shock and Vibration Digest	Published by The Shock and Vibration Information Center, Naval Research Laboratory, Washington, D.C.
Noise Control Engineering	Published by Ray W. Herrick Laboratories, Purdue University, West Lafayette, IN. 47907, U.S.A.

/

2. CHARACTERISTICS OF VIBRATION AND SHOCK

2.1. PERIODIC VIBRATION

Periodic vibration may be looked upon as an oscillating motion of a particle, or body, about a reference position, the motion repeating itself exactly after certain periods of time. The simplest form of periodic vibration is the so-called harmonic motion which when plotted as a function of time, is represented by a sinusoidal curve, Fig.2.1. Here T is the period of vibration, i.e. the time elapsed between two successive, exactly equal conditions of motion.

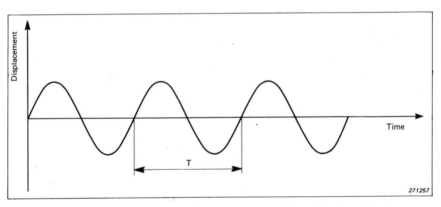

Fig.2.1. Example of a pure harmonic (sinusoidal) vibration signal

The *frequency* of the vibration is given by:

$$f = \frac{1}{T} \qquad (2.1)$$

Turning to the magnitude of the vibration this may be characterized by different quantities, all of which have definite mathematical relationships to each other *as long as harmonic motion is considered.*

If the vibration has the form of a pure translational oscillation along one axis (x) only, the instantaneous *displacement* of the particle (or body) from the reference position can be mathematically described by means of the equation:

$$x = X_{peak} \, sin\left(2\pi\frac{t}{T}\right) = X_{peak} \, sin\,(2\pi ft) = X_{peak} \, sin\,(\omega t) \qquad (2.2)$$

where

$$\omega = 2\pi f = \text{angular frequency}$$

$$X_{peak} = \text{Maximum displacement from the reference position}$$

$$t = \text{time}$$

As the *velocity* of a moving particle (or body) is the time rate of change of the displacement, the motion can also be described in terms of velocity (v):

$$v = \frac{dx}{dt} = \omega \, X_{peak} \, cos\,(\omega t) = V_{peak} \, cos\,(\omega t) = V_{peak} \, sin\,(\omega t + \pi/2) \qquad (2.3)$$

Finally, the *acceleration (a)* of the motion is the time rate of change of the velocity:

$$a = \frac{dv}{dt} = \frac{d^2x}{dt^2} = -\omega^2 \, X_{peak} \, sin\,(\omega t) = -A_{peak} \, sin\,(\omega t) = A_{peak} \, sin\,(\omega t + \pi)$$

$$(2.4)$$

From the above equations it can be seen that the form and period of vibration remain the same whether it is the displacement, the velocity or the acceleration that is being studied. However, the velocity leads the displacement by a phase angle of 90° $(\pi/2)$ and the acceleration again leads the velocity by a phase angle of 90° $(\pi/2)$. As characterizing values for the magnitude the peak values have been used, i.e. X_{peak}, V_{peak} and A_{peak}. The magnitude description in terms of peak values is quite useful as long as pure harmonic vibration is considered because it applies directly in the equations given above. If, on the other hand, more complex vibrations are being studied other descriptive quantities may be preferred. One of the reasons for this is that the peak value describes the vibration in terms of a quantity which depends only upon an instantaneous vibration magnitude regardless of the time history producing it.

A further descriptive quantity, which does take the time history into account, is the *average absolute* value, defined as (see also Fig.2.2):

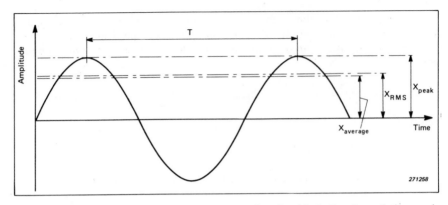

Fig.2.2. Example of a harmonic vibration signal with indication of the peak, the RMS and the average absolute value

$$X_{Average} = \frac{1}{T} \int_0^T |x|\, dt$$

Even though this quantity takes into account the time history of the vibration over one period (T) it has been found to be of limited practical interest. A much more useful descriptive quantity which also takes the time history into account, is the *RMS (root mean square)* value (Fig.2.2):

$$X_{RMS} = \sqrt{\frac{1}{T} \int_0^T x^2(t)\, dt} \qquad (2.5)$$

The major reason for the importance of the RMS-value as a descriptive quantity is its simple relationship to the power content of the vibrations.

For a *pure harmonic motion* the relationship between the various values is:

$$X_{RMS} = \frac{\pi}{2\sqrt{2}} X_{Average} = \frac{1}{\sqrt{2}} X_{peak}$$

A more general form of these relationships may be given by:

$$X_{RMS} = F_f\, X_{Average} = \frac{1}{F_c} X_{peak}$$

or

$$F_f = \frac{X_{RMS}}{X_{Average}}; \qquad F_c = \frac{X_{peak}}{X_{RMS}} \qquad (2.6)$$

22

The factors F_f and F_c are called "form-factor" and "crest-factor", respectively, and give some indication of the waveshape of the vibrations being studied.

For pure harmonic motion:

$$F_f = \frac{\pi}{2\sqrt{2}} = 1.11 \ (\approx 1 \, dB)$$

and
$$F_c = \sqrt{2} = 1.414 \ (= 3 \, dB)$$

Most of the vibrations encountered in daily life are not pure harmonic motions even though many of them may be characterized as periodic. A typical non-harmonic periodic motion is shown in Fig.2.3 (piston acceleration of a combustion engine). By determining the Peak, Average Absolute and RMS-value of this vibration as well as the form-factor and crest-factor a lot of useful information is obtained, and it can be clearly concluded that the motion is not harmonic. However, it will be practically impossible, on the basis of this information, to predict all the various effects that the vibration might produce in connected structural elements. Other methods of description must therefore be used.

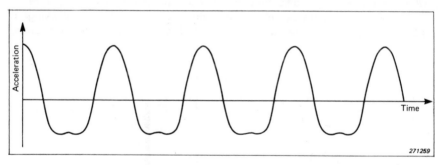

Fig.2.3. Example of a non-harmonic periodic motion (piston acceleration of a combustion engine)

One of the most powerful descriptive methods is the method of frequency analysis. This is based on a mathematical theorem, first formulated by FOURIER, which states that any periodic curve, no matter how complex, may be looked upon as a combination of a number of pure sinusoidal curves with harmonically related frequencies.

$$f(t) = X_0 + X_1 \sin(\omega t + \varphi_1) + X_2 \sin(2\omega t + \varphi_2)$$

$$+ X_3 \sin(3\omega t + \varphi_3) + \ldots + X_n \sin(n\omega t + \varphi_n) \quad (2.7)$$

23

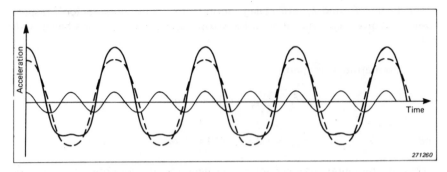

Fig.2.4. *Illustration of how the waveform shown in Fig.2.3 can be "broken up" into a sum of harmonically related sinewaves*

The number of terms required may be infinite, but in that case as the number of elements in the series is increased it becomes an increasingly better approximation to the original curve. The various elements constitute the *vibration frequency spectrum.* In Fig.2.4 the nonharmonic periodic motion of Fig.2.3 is redrawn together with the two most important harmonic curves representing its frequency spectrum. A somewhat more convenient method of representing this spectrum is shown in Fig.2.5 b, while Fig.2.6 shows some further examples of periodic time functions and their frequency spectra. A specific feature of periodic vibrations, which becomes clear by looking at Fig.2.5 and 2.6 is that their spectra consist of *discrete lines* when presented

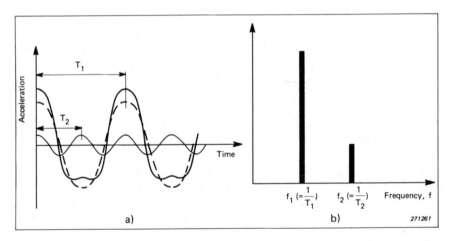

Fig.2.5. *Illustration of how the signal, Fig.2.3 can be described in terms of a frequency spectrum*
a) Description in the time domain
b) Description in the frequency domain

24

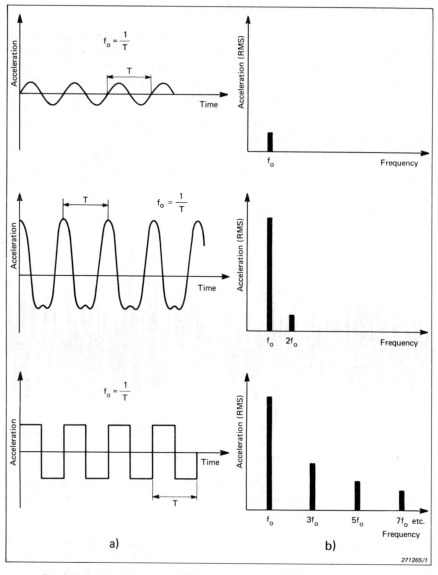

Fig.2.6. Examples of periodic signals and their frequency spectra
 a) Descriptions in the time domain
 b) Descriptions in the frequency domain

in the so-called frequency domain (Figs.2.5 b and 2.6 b). This is in contrast
to random vibrations which show continuous frequency spectra (section 2.2,
Fig.2.12).

2.2. STATIONARY RANDOM VIBRATION

Random vibrations are met rather frequently in nature and may be characterized as vibratory processes in which the vibrating particles undergo irregular motion cycles that never repeat themselves exactly, see Fig.2.7. To obtain a complete description of the vibrations, an infinitely long time record is thus theoretically necessary. This is of course an impossible requirement, and finite time records would have to be used in practice. Even so, if the time record becomes too long it will also become a very inconvenient means of description and other methods have therefore been devised and are commonly used. These methods have their origin in statistical mechanics and communication theory and involve concepts such as amplitude probability distributions and probability densities, and continuous vibration frequency spectra in terms of mean square spectral densities*.

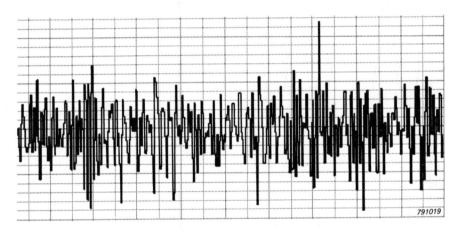

Fig.2.7. Example of a random vibration signal

Without going into too much mathematical detail the meaning of the above concepts should be briefly reviewed because of their importance in relation to practical vibration measurements.

The concept of probability is of a mathematical origin and denotes the chance of a particular event happening. If the event in question is absolutely certain to happen the probability of occurrence of the event is said to be 1. On the other hand, if the event in question is certain *not* to happen the probability of occurrence is said to be 0. Thus probabilities are, in the sense used here, positive real numbers between 1 and 0.

---

* Mean square spectral density is also often termed "Power Spectral Density" (P.S.D.) because the mean square is a quantity proportional to power.

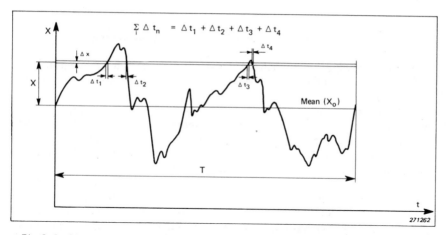

Fig.2.8. Sketch illustrating the concepts of probability and probability density

In the study of continuous processes such as stationary* random vibrations it is often convenient to use the concept of probability *density* instead of probability. Physically the probability density can be defined as the probability of finding instantaneous amplitude values within a certain amplitude interval, Δx, divided by the size of that interval (thus: density), see Fig.2.8. This means that while probabilities are dimensionless quantities the probability density is a quantity having a certain dimension.

Mathematically formulated the probability density at some specified amplitude level, x, is:

$$p(x) = \lim_{\Delta x \to o} \frac{P(x) - P(x + \Delta x)}{\Delta x} \tag{2.8}$$

Here $p(x)$ designates the probability density while $P(x)$ is the probability that any instantaneous amplitude value exceeds the level x and $P(x + \Delta x)$ is the probability of occurrence of instantaneous amplitude values exceeding the level $x + \Delta x$. By plotting the value of $p(x)$ for all values of x a probability density curve is obtained which has the feature that an integration of the curve from a value x_1' to a value x_2 immediately tells the probability of occurrence of instantaneous amplitude values within the interval $(x_2 - x_1)$, independent of the actual magnitude of x_1 and x_2. The presentation of experimental probability data in terms of probability density curves bears some advantages because it allows for a direct comparison of data between experiments (and between experimenters) independent of the width of the amplitude interval, Δx, used in the experiment. Finally, theoretical probability data are commonly presented

---

* Stationary random vibrations are defined as random vibrations whose *statistical* characteristics do not change with time.

27

in the form of probability density curves and this method of presentation must therefore be considered the most generally acceptable one.

From the definition of probability density it follows that by integrating the probability density curve over all possible amplitude values the magnitude of the integral will be 1 (because the probability of finding a certain amplitude value within all possible amplitude values is 1). The practical procedure involved in converting experimental and/or theoretical data into probability density data ensuring that the area under the probability density curve is 1, is called normalization. The most commonly known normalized probability density curve, the normal (Gaussian) curve, is shown in Fig.2.9.

Even though probability density data are very useful signal descriptions and give excellent information on how, on the average, the instantaneous amplitudes in a vibratory signal are distributed, they give little or no information as to the time history or frequency content of the process being studied. To try and remedy this, and to obtain further descriptive data, statistical physicists introduced a function called the *autocorrelation function, $\psi(\tau)$*. This function describes (on the average) how a particular instantaneous amplitude value depends upon previously occurring instantaneous amplitude values in that $\psi(\tau)$ is defined as:

$$\psi(\tau) = \lim_{T \to \infty} \frac{1}{T} \int_{-\frac{T}{2}}^{\frac{T}{2}} f(t) f(t + \tau) \, dt \qquad (2.9)$$

where $f(t)$ is the magnitude of the vibratory process at an arbitrary instant of

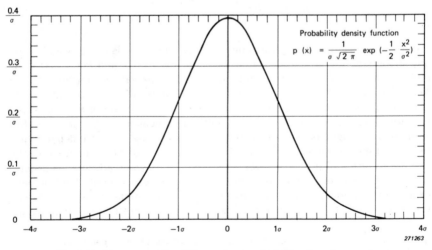

Fig.2.9. The normalized Gaussian probability density curve

time, t, and $f(t + \tau)$ designates the magnitude of the same process observed at a time, τ, later, see Fig.2.10.

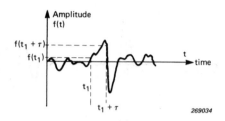

Fig.2.10. Basic concepts involved in deriving the autocorrelation function

In the case of an "ideal" stationary random process (white noise) the auto-correlation function would consist of an infinitely narrow impulse-function around zero ($\tau = 0$), see Fig.2.11 a), as in such a process each instantaneous amplitude value should be completely independent of all other instantaneous amplitude values.

However, in practice the autocorrelation functions associated with station-ary random vibrations cluster around $\tau = 0$, but are never "infinitely narrow" impulse-functions, Fig.2.11 b) and c). The reason for this spreading out of the curve around zero is that all practical random processes are frequency li-mited, and the narrower the frequency limits the more spread-out are the corresponding autocorrelation functions (because the rate at which a signal can change from its current value is much more limited).

From the autocorrelation function another, very important function in prac-tice, can be deduced, which has a certain resemblance to the Fourier fre-quency spectra described in section 2.1 for periodic vibrations. This function has been termed the *mean square spectral density function* (power spectral density function) and can be derived from the autocorrelation function as fol-lows: Assuming that the integral of $\psi(\tau)$ from $-\infty$ to $+\infty$ is finite (see Fig.2.11) one can write:

$$S(f) = \int_{-\infty}^{\infty} \psi(\tau) e^{-j2\pi f \tau} d\tau \qquad (2.10)$$

where f is frequency.

From the theory of Fourier integrals it is furthermore known that $\psi(\tau)$ can also be found from the above integral by inversion:

$$\psi(\tau) = \int_{-\infty}^{\infty} S(f) e^{j2\pi f \tau} df \qquad (2.11)$$

29

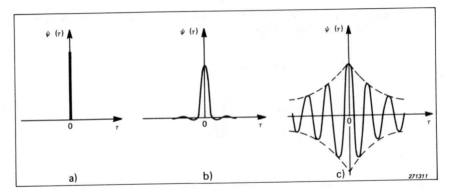

Fig.2.11. Examples of autocorrelation functions
  a) Autocorrelation function for an ideal stationary random process
  containing frequencies from 0 to ∞ (constant spectral density)
  b) Autocorrelation function for a "practical" wide band stationary
  random process
  c) Autocorrelation function for a narrow band stationary random
  process

The Fourier integral relations between $\psi(\tau)$ and $S(f)$ are often called the Wiener-Khinchin relations and play a very important role in the theory of random processes.

In physically realizable stationary processes one operates with positive frequencies only* and $\psi(\tau) = \psi(-\tau)$ whereby the integral for $\psi(\tau)$ becomes:

$$\psi(\tau) = 2\int_0^\infty S(f)\cos(2\pi f\tau)\,df$$

or, if a function $G(f)$ is defined so that

$$G(f) = 2S(f) \qquad \text{for } f>0$$

then
$$\psi(\tau) = \int_0^\infty G(f)\cos(2\pi f\tau)\,df \qquad (2.12)$$

---

* Note that frequency can be interpreted as rate of change of phase, in which case the concept of positive and negative frequencies is meaningful. A 2-sided frequency domain is useful analytically because of symmetry with the time domain, but in practical measurements it is most common to combine positive and negative frequency contributions to obtain a one-sided power spectrum. For a more detailed discussion see the B & K book "Frequency Analysis".

To interpret the function $G(f)$ consider the case where $\tau = 0$:

$$\psi(o) = \lim_{T \to \infty} \frac{1}{T} \int_{-\frac{T}{2}}^{\frac{T}{2}} f(t) f(t + o) \, dt = \lim_{T \to \infty} \frac{1}{T} \int_{-\frac{T}{2}}^{\frac{T}{2}} f^2(t) \, dt$$

and

$$\psi(o) = \int_0^\infty G(f) \, df$$

thus

$$\lim_{T \to \infty} \frac{1}{T} \int_{-\frac{T}{2}}^{\frac{T}{2}} f^2(t) \, dt = \int_0^\infty G(f) \, df \qquad (2.13)$$

Both of these integrals are measures of the power involved in the process, one in terms of the process time function, $f(t)$, and the other in terms of a frequency function, $G(f)$. Because of the squaring involved in the above time function description, $G(f)$ has been designated as the *mean square spectral density function* (or power spectral density function).

Traditionally, power spectra have been measured using analog frequency analyzers whose mode of operation may be understood as follows:

An ideal analog frequency analyzer will allow only that part of the signal to be measured which has frequency components within a narrow frequency band, B, see Fig.2.12. Assuming that no attenuation or amplification of these frequency components takes place in the analyzer the signal which is passed on to its indicating arrangement is:

$$\int_0^\infty G(f) \, df = \int_f^{f+B} G(f) \, df = \lim_{T \to \infty} \frac{1}{T} \int_{-\frac{T}{2}}^{\frac{T}{2}} f_B^2(t) \, dt$$

Here $f_B(t)$ is the above-mentioned part of the complete signal, $f(t)$, which has frequency components within B. If now B is made so small that $G(f)$ can be considered constant within this frequency range then

$$\int_f^{f+B} G(f) \, df = G(f) B$$

thus, in the limiting case when $B \to 0$, one obtains:

$$G(f) = \lim_{B \to 0} \lim_{T \to \infty} \frac{1}{BT} \int_{-\frac{T}{2}}^{\frac{T}{2}} f_B^2(t) \, dt \qquad (2.14)$$

31

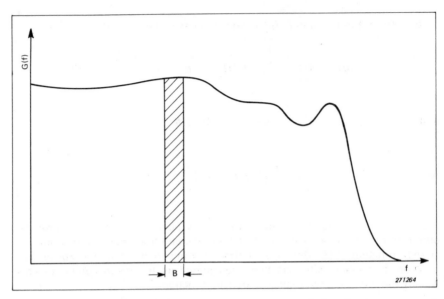

Fig.2.12. Determination of the mean square spectral density by means of ideal filters

This equation forms the basis of most analog experimental techniques used in the mean square spectral density analysis of random signals, although the actual bandwidth B used must of course be finite, in order that the measurement time T does not need to be infinite. The results (as a power spectral density) will only be valid, however, if B is sufficiently small that the above assumption is valid, i.e. that $G(f)$ is approximately constant within B. This will be the case for practical purposes if B is, say, less than $1/3$ of the width of any peaks in the spectrum being measured.

At one time, a digital alternative to analog analysis was based on the already-mentioned Wiener-Khinchin relationship. The autocorrelation function was first calculated digitally, and this then Fourier transformed by digital evaluation of the Fourier integral. It is only in the last few years, however, that digital alternatives to analog analyzers have been competitive in the sense that they could be incorporated as hardware in a portable standalone unit. One of the major factors here has been the increasing speed and miniaturization of digital components in general, resulting in continually reducing costs for a given calculation. Another major factor has been the development of the so-called Fast Fourier Transform (FFT) algorithm which has typically allowed savings of 100:1 in digital evaluation of the Fourier integral. This has in fact meant that it is now quicker to calculate the autocorrelation function by inverse transformation of the power spectrum, the latter being obtained by Fourier transforming the time signal.

The FFT procedure produces a constant bandwidth spectrum, but for constant percentage bandwidth (where the filter bandwidth is a constant percentage of its centre frequency) another digital analysis technique known as recursive digital filtering is found to be better. The choice of appropriate analysis method is discussed in Chapter 7.

Before closing the discussion on methods used to describe and analyze random vibration phenomena some important "practical" facts should be pointed out:

Returning to the equation (2.13)

$$\lim_{T \to \infty} \frac{1}{T} \int_{-\frac{T}{2}}^{\frac{T}{2}} f^2(t)\, dt = \int_0^\infty G(f)\, df$$

it can be seen that the expression on the left hand side of this equation has a close resemblance to the square of the expression previously used to define the RMS-value of a periodic vibration signal (Equation 2.5). This means that *the description of a complex signal in terms of its overall RMS-value is equally meaningful whether the signal has a periodic or a random character.*

When it comes to *spectral* description, however, a *periodic signal* may well be described in terms of *the RMS-values of its various components* (its frequency spectrum), while *random vibration signals* are best described in terms of *mean square spectral density functions*. This is due to the fact that random signals produce continuous frequency spectra and the RMS-value measured within a certain frequency band will therefore depend upon the width of the band. The detailed measurement evaluation techniques will, in view of the above, normally also differ, a fact which is more specially discussed in Chapter 7 of this book and in the B & K book "Frequency Analysis".

2.3. TRANSIENT PHENOMENA AND SHOCKS

Transient phenomena and mechanical shocks are, like random vibrations encountered relatively often in daily life. They may originate from such widely different releases of energy as rough handling of equipment, explosions and supersonic motion. However, common for this type of energy release is its short duration and sudden occurrence.

A simple shock may be defined as a transmission of kinetic energy to a system which takes place in a relatively short time compared with the natural period of oscillation of the system, while transient phenomena (also termed complex shocks) may last for several periods of vibration of the system.

Shocks and transient vibrations may be described in terms of force, acceleration, velocity or displacement and for a complete description it is necessary to obtain an exact time history record of the quantity in question.

In many cases the ultimate goal is not the waveform itself, but rather a means to estimate the effect that the corresponding shock or transient vibration would have on a certain mechanical system. A more useful method of description might then again be found in the form of Fourier analysis. If the time function for a shock is $f(t)$ then its Fourier transform is given by:

$$F(f) = \int_{-\infty}^{\infty} f(t) e^{-j2\pi ft} dt \qquad (2.15)$$

The analogy between this expression and the mean square spectral density function of stationary random vibrations (Equation (2.10)) is readily seen. There is, however, a very distinct difference in that the mean square spectral density function for stationary random vibrations is the Fourier transform of an already time-averaged, even function, the autocorrelation function, with the dimensions of amplitude squared. In the above Fourier integral for transient or shock functions the function $f(t)$ itself must be time-limited and has the dimensions of amplitude only. Because it in general is not an even function, its Fourier transform will be complex, but it is found that the square of the amplitude of the Fourier transform at each frequency gives a measure of the *energy* distribution of the transient.

It may be useful to see how this difference in dimensions influences the units in a particular case. Assuming that signal amplitude is expressed in volts (V), then the autocorrelation function for a stationary random signal would have units of volts squared (V^2) or power. The Fourier transform of this has the units $V^2 s$, or V^2/Hz, i.e. power per unit frequency or *power spectral density*. A shock or transient function, however, has units of Volts and its Fourier transform (amplitude) units of Volt-seconds (Vs). The amplitude squared thus has units $V^2 s^2$ or $V^2 s/Hz$, i.e. energy per unit frequency or *energy spectral density*. A transient of course has finite energy when integrated over all time, while a stationary random signal would have infinite energy, though finite power.

Most analyzers assume a signal is continuous and give a result in terms of power per analysis bandwidth. The conversion of this to the correct units is discussed in Chapter 7 and in more detail in the B & K book "Frequency Analysis".

In Fig.2.13 various shock time functions and the amplitudes of their Fourier spectra are given. It is seen from the figure that in general a shock pulse contains energy spread over all frequencies from zero to infinity, and that the spectra are continuous with no discrete frequency components.

34

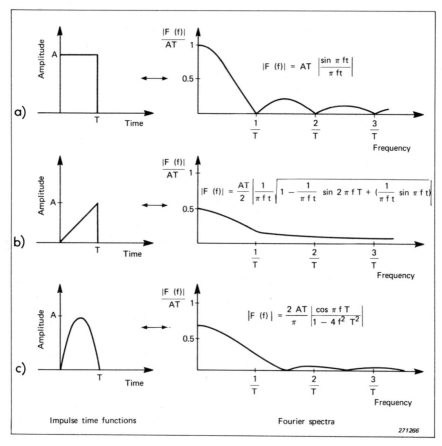

$$|F(f)| = AT \left| \frac{\sin \pi ft}{\pi ft} \right|$$

$$|F(f)| = \frac{AT}{2} \left| \frac{1}{\pi ft} \sqrt{1 - \frac{1}{\pi ft} \sin 2\pi fT + (\frac{1}{\pi ft} \sin \pi ft)} \right|$$

$$|F(f)| = \frac{2\,AT}{\pi} \left| \frac{\cos \pi fT}{1 - 4f^2 T^2} \right|$$

Impulse time functions   Fourier spectra

271266

Fig.2.13. Example of shock time functions and their Fourier transforms (amplitude spectra)
a) A rectangular shock pulse
b) A final peak sawtooth shock pulse
c) A half-sine shock pulse

In the expressions for F(f) given in the figure all the expressions within the parallel brackets approach unity as f goes to zero, so that at very low frequencies the magnitude of the spectrum component is equal to the area (amplitude-time integral) of the shock pulse, irrespective of the pulse shape. This fundamental relationship is of considerable practical importance, for example in shock testing. It means that so long as the shock pulse is short compared with the natural period of the mechanical system on which its acts, the severity of the shock is determined by the area of the shock pulse alone (see also Fig.3.13 b II).

35

In the case of transient phenomena the situation is somewhat different. Such phenomena, in the sense used in this book, may consist either of a single period "shock-wave", or of an oscillating transient. The Fourier spectrum function of a typical oscillating transient is shown in Fig.2.14 and it is seen that the magnitude of the spectrum components in this special case tends towards zero as the frequency f goes to zero. Also, a maximum magnitude of the spectrum is reached around f_o which corresponds roughly to the frequency of oscillation of the transient. This maximum is broader the quicker the transient phenomenon ceases.

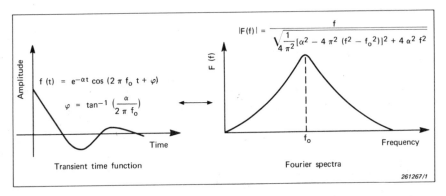

Fig.2.14. Example of an oscillating transient and its Fourier spectrum function

If the "transient" does not cease at all, i.e. when the "transient" is no longer a transient but a periodic phenomenon (in this case a harmonic vibration), the frequency spectrum degenerates into a discrete spectral line (infinitely narrow maximum at f_o).

2.4. NON-STATIONARY RANDOM VIBRATION

Theoretically all kinds of random vibrations encountered in practice are non-stationary because their statistical properties vary with time. However, from an engineering point of view this variation in statistical properties may be so slow, or of such a character, that many of the phenomena studied can be considered stationary in a practical sense.

Non-stationary random vibrations may therefore, in practice, be defined as random vibrations whose statistical properties vary with time within time intervals considered essential for their proper description. To analyze and describe such vibration data it is thus necessary to take their variation in statistical properties with time into account. A typical example of seriously non-stationary random vibrations is the vibrations induced in space vehicles during launch and re-entry.

To theoretically analyze non-stationary random vibrations properly it is necessary to introduce the concept of *ensemble averaging*. An ensemble average is an average taken over a large number (an ensemble) of repeated experiments, see Fig.2.15. As can be seen from the figure an ensemble average can be taken at any particular instant of time t_1, t_2, t_3 etc., and when the average values are plotted against time a more or less complete description of the vibration is obtained. There are, on the other hand, several reasons why this method of description is not very useful in practice. Firstly, it requires that the non-stationary process can be repeated a very large number of times. In the case of space vehicle launch and re-entry for instance this is not possible due to the cost of such experiments. Secondly, the amount of data necessary for a thorough description is so large that their proper measurement will pose serious problems.

It is therefore normally necessary to seek other methods of description, and in general some sort of time averaging is used. There are, however, certain limitations imposed upon this kind of time averaging in that the response and averaging time of the measurement equipment employed should preferably

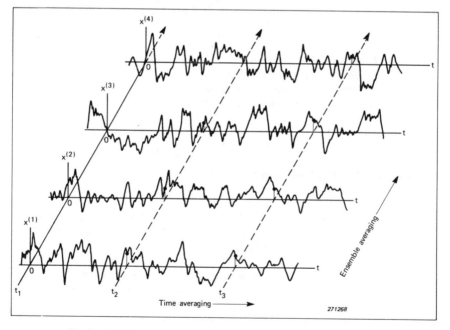

Fig.2.15. Illustration of an ensemble of random functions

be small relative to important time trends in the non-stationary data. This again may lead to considerable statistical uncertainties in the measurements.

Fig.2.16 illustrates some basic and important types of non-stationary random vibrations.

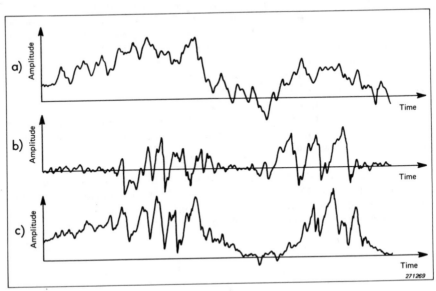

Fig.2.16. Examples of some basic types of nonstationary random vibrations
a) Time-varying mean value
b) Time-varying mean square value
c) Time-varying mean and mean square value

2.5. SELECTED BIBLIOGRAPHY

ANSI: S2. 10—1971 *Analysis and Presentation of Shock and Vibration Data.* A.S.A. 335 East 45th St., New York 10017

BENDAT, J.S.:   *Principles and Applications of Random Noise Theory.* John Wiley and Sons, Inc. New York, 1958

BENDAT, J.S. and PIERSOL, A.G.:   *Random Data, Analysis and Measurement Procedures,* John Wiley and Sons, Inc. New York, 1971

BLACKMAN, R.B. and
TUKEY, J.W.:
The Measurement of Power Spectra. Dover Publications, Inc. New York 1958

CRANDALL, S.H. and
MARK, W.D.:
Random Vibrations in Mechanical Systems. Academic Press, New York, 1963

DIN:
DIN 1311. (February 1970) *Schwingungslehre Kinematische Begriffe.* Beuth-Vertrieb GmbH, Berlin.

IEEE:
Special Issue on the Fast Fourier Transform. IEEE Trans. Audio & Electroacoustics Vol. AU-15, June 1967

KHARKEVICH, A.A.:
Spectra and Analysis. Fitzmatgiz, Moscow 1957 (in Russian). Also available in English translation published by Consultants Bureau, New York 1960

MORROW, C.T.:
Shock and Vibration Engineering. John Wiley and Sons, Inc. New York 1963

OPPENHEIM, A.V. and
SCHAFER, R.W.:
Digital Signal Processing. Prentice-Hall, New Jersey, 1975

PIERSOL, A.G.:
Spectral Analysis of Non-Stationary Spacecraft Vibration Data. NASA CR-341, Washington, D.C. December 1965

RICE, S.O.:
Mathematical Analysis of Random Noise. Bell System Tech. Journ. 23 (1944) and 24 (1945). Also contained in N. Wax: "Selected Papers on Noise and Stochastic Processes". Dover Publications, Inc. New York 1954

RUZICKA, J.E.:
Characteristics of Mechanical Vibration and Shock. Sound and Vibration. April 1967

SHARMAN, R.V.:
Vibrations and Waves. Butterworth, London 1963

THRALL, G.P. and
BENDAT, J.S.:
Mean and Mean Square Measurements of Non-stationary Random Processes. NASA CR-226, Washington D.C., May 1965

3. RESPONSE OF MECHANICAL SYSTEMS TO VIBRATIONS AND SHOCKS

3.1. RESPONSE OF LINEAR MECHANICAL SYSTEMS TO VIBRATIONS. RESONANCE

The motion of a mechanical system subjected to external forces is commonly termed the *response* of the system to the particular forces in question. Similarly, the external forces acting upon the system are termed the *exciting* forces, or simply the excitation. These terms are general and have to be specified closer when the behaviour of a particular system is being investigated.

To aid such specifications it is normally necessary to construct a somewhat simplified mechanical model and, on the basis of the model, to formulate the equations of motion for the system. This model can then be used as a basis for a further analysis.

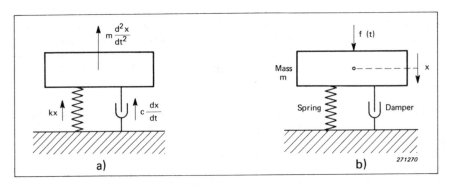

Fig.3.1. Models of a single degree-of-freedom system
a) System in free vibrations
b) System in forced vibrations

One of the simplest models of a vibrating system is shown in Fig.3.1.a), and consists of a mass, a spring and a damper. If the system behaves linearly (and time-invariant) the equation of free motion of the mass is (no external force applied):

$$m\frac{d^2x}{dt^2} + c\frac{dx}{dt} + kx = 0 \tag{3.1}$$

This system is called a *single degree-of-freedom system* in that it consists of *one* mass only, which moves along *one* axis only and its motion can thus be described by a *single* second order differential equation.

By applying an external force $f(t)$ to the system as indicated in Fig.3.1.b) the equation of motion becomes:

$$m\frac{d^2x}{dt^2} + c\frac{dx}{dt} + kx = f(t) \tag{3.2}$$

The solution of this equation gives directly the *displacement* response, $x(t)$, of the mass, m, produced by the excitation, $f(t)$. Other response quantities such as the *velocity response* or the *acceleration response* can be found from the well known relationships between the displacement, velocity and acceleration (see also Appendix B):

$$v(t) = \frac{dx}{dt} \quad \text{and} \quad a(t) = \frac{d^2x}{dt^2}$$

where $v(t)$ = velocity and $a(t)$ = acceleration of the mass, m, Fig.3.1.b).

The force $f(t)$, can have any dependency on time, and as long as the motion of the mass can be described by a linear differential equation of the type given above, it is, in principle, possible to obtain exact solutions for $x(t)$, $v(t)$ and $a(t)$. A very powerful tool in obtaining the required solutions is the *superposition principle*, which is applicable to linear differential equations. It states that *the effect of simultaneously super-imposed actions is equal to the sum of the effects of each individual action.*

Utilization of this principle can be made for instance by considering the function $f(t)$ as consisting of an infinite number of impulses, each with an infinitesimal width, $\Delta \tau$, and a height $f(\tau)$ and superimposing the responses produced by the action of each of these impulses, see Fig.3.2.

Mathematically this application of the superposition principle can be written:

$$x(t) = \int_{-\infty}^{t} f(\tau)h(t-\tau)d\tau \tag{3.3}$$

41

where $h(t - \tau)$ is the response of the system (Fig.3.1), at the time t to a unit impulse excitation acting at time τ. A unit impulse excitation is characterized by a force which is zero except at $t = \tau$ where it is infinite and encloses unit area:

$$\lim_{\varepsilon \to 0} \int_{-\varepsilon}^{\varepsilon} \delta(\tau) d\tau = 1$$

This is the exact response $x(t)$ to an excitation $f(t)$. This superposition integral is called a convolution. The function f is said to be convolved with h to produce x. The operation is commutative and by changing the variable we have the equivalent form

$$x(t) = \int_{-\infty}^{t} h(T)f(t - T) dT \qquad (3.4)$$

where $$T = t - \tau$$

Note that in this case the solution is built up from a superposition of *free vibration solutions.*

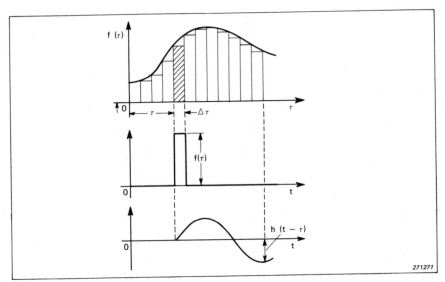

Fig.3.2. Illustration of the concepts involved in time domain superposition

Another method of utilizing the superposition principle is to determine the Fourier transform $F(f)$ of $f(t)$ and study the response of the system to each Fourier component separately. The impulse response function $h(t - \tau)$ defined above, then transforms into a complex *frequency response function,* H(f), and x(t) is obtained in terms of its Fourier transform, X(f):

$$X(f) = \int_{-\infty}^{\infty} x(t) e^{-j2\pi ft} dt = \int_{-\infty}^{\infty} e^{-j2\pi ft} dt \int_{-\infty}^{t} f(\tau) h(t-\tau) d\tau$$

$$= \int_{-\infty}^{\infty} dt \int_{-\infty}^{t} e^{-j2\pi f(t-\tau)} h(t-\tau) e^{-j2\pi f\tau} f(\tau) d\tau$$

By setting $t - \tau = \xi$ and expanding the regions of integration remembering that $h(t - \tau) = 0$ when $\tau > t$, X(f) can be written:

$$X(f) = \int_{-\infty}^{\infty} d\tau \int_{-\infty}^{\infty} e^{-j2\pi f\xi} h(\xi) e^{-j2\pi f\tau} f(\tau) d\xi$$

$$= \int_{-\infty}^{\infty} h(\xi) e^{-j2\pi f\xi} d\xi \int_{-\infty}^{\infty} f(\tau) e^{-j2\pi f\tau} d\tau$$

Thus: $$X(f) = H(f)F(f) \qquad (3.5)$$

The Fourier transform of the response is the product of the Fourier transform of the excitation and the frequency response function.

Note that in this case the solution is built up from a superposition of *steady state responses to simple harmonic excitations.*

The complex frequency response function H(f) of the system shown in Fig.3.1 is found simply by solving the equation of motion for an arbitrary Fourier component, $F_0 e^{j2\pi ft}$:

$$m\frac{d^2x}{dt^2} + c\frac{dx}{dt} + kx = F_0 e^{j2\pi ft} \qquad (3.6)$$

At this point the physical meaning of the *complex* frequency response function should be stated. A complex frequency response function means a response which gives information on *both the absolute value of the response quantity and the phase lag between the response and the excitation.* The general solution to the above equation is:

$$X(f) = H(f)F_0 e^{j2\pi ft} \qquad (3.7)$$

Here $$H\left(\frac{f}{f_0}\right) = \frac{1/k}{1 - \left(\frac{f}{f_0}\right)^2 + j\frac{1}{Q}\frac{f}{f_0}} \qquad (3.8)$$

43

$f_0 = \frac{1}{2\pi} \sqrt{\frac{k}{m}}$ the *resonant frequency* of the mechanical system and

$Q = \frac{1}{c} \sqrt{km}$ is a measure of the system's damping. Q is normally called the *quality factor* of the system and the larger the value of Q the smaller is the damping. For a completely undamped system $Q = \infty$ while for a critically damped system $Q = 1/2$. An approximate measure of Q is obtained in practice by measuring the width of the response curve, $|H(f)|$, at the half power points, see Fig.3.3.

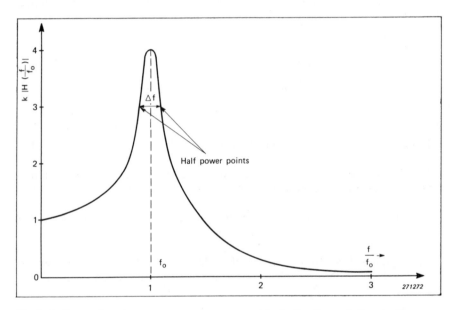

Fig.3.3. Example of a resonance curve with indication of the half power points $\left[|H(f)| = \sqrt{1/2|H(f_0)|^2} = 0.707|H(f_0)|\right]$

The half power points are the points on the curve where.

$$|H(f)|^2 = \frac{1}{2}|H(f_0)|^2$$

If this width is Δf then

$$Q = \frac{f_0}{\Delta f} \tag{3.9}$$

The frequency difference between the half-power points is often referred to as the *bandwidth* of the system.

44

For Q-values larger than 5, the error inherent in the approximation is smaller than some 3% (actually, even when Q is as low as 2 the error is of the order of 10%), see also Fig.3.4. Because of its direct relationship to the damping, the factor Q has become a very important quantity in the description of single degree-of-freedom linear systems.

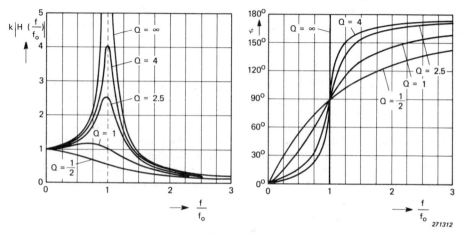

Fig.3.4. Examples of complex frequency response functions
a) Modulus (absolute value of the response)
b) Phase lag between response and excitation corresponding to a)

The phase lag between the response and the excitation is given by the expression:

$$\varphi = tan^{-1}\left[\frac{1}{Q\left(\frac{f}{f_o} - \frac{f_o}{f}\right)}\right] \tag{3.10}$$

and this function is plotted in Fig.3.4.b) for various values of Q.

A number of interesting facts can be seen from these curves.

Firstly, in the case of no damping (Q = ∞) the response and the excitation are *in phase* (ψ = 0) *below* resonance, while *above* resonance they are 180° out of phase. Because Q = ∞ the change in phase takes place in the form of a discontinuous jump.

Secondly, when Q ≠ ∞, i.e. damping is introduced in the system, the change in phase between response and excitation tends to take place gradually, and the larger the damping (the smaller Q) the slower is the phase change with frequency around resonance.

45

Thirdly, independent of the magnitude of the damping, the phase lag between the response and the excitation at *resonance* is 90°.

If the system being studied consists of several masses interconnected with spring and damper elements the approximate measure of Q stated above cannot be utilized unless the coupling between the different masses is so small that a unidirectional motion of one mass does not influence the motion of any of the others (or vice versa). In general, however, some coupling always exists, even though it might under certain circumstances be neglected in practice.

Systems in which a single mass moves in more than one direction or systems which consist of several, elastically interconnected masses, are commonly termed *multi-degree-of-freedom systems.* A linear multi-degree-of-freedom system can be mathematically described by a set of coupled second-order linear differential equations and when the frequency response curve of the system is plotted it will normally show one resonance "peak" per degree-of-freedom. *Thus a two degree-of-freedom* system shows *two* resonance peaks, *a three degree-of-freedom* system shows *three* resonance peaks, etc., see Fig.3.5.

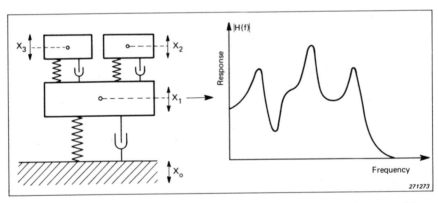

Fig.3.5. Example of a multi degree-of-freedom system (three degrees-of-freedom) and its frequency response function

3.2. SOME RESPONSE PROPERTIES OF NON-LINEAR SYSTEMS

In the previous section some important response characteristics of linear systems have been discussed, in particular their so-called frequency response functions. These functions can be derived mathematically from the linear differential equation of motion for the system. In the case of a single degree of freedom system this equation was given as

46

$$m\frac{d^2x}{dt^2} + c\frac{dx}{dt} + kx = f(t)$$

where m, c and k were considered constants, independent of x and t. This requirement is not always fulfilled in practice and the above equation may take the form:

$$m\frac{d^2x}{dt^2} + \beta\left(\frac{dx}{dt}\right) + F(x) = f(t) \qquad (3.11)$$

where

m = mass of the vibrating system

$\beta\left(\frac{dx}{dt}\right)$ = velocity dependent "damping" term

$F(x)$ = displacement dependent "stiffness" term

$f(t)$ = forcing function (see Fig.3.1).

Because this differential equation is no longer linear the principle of superposition cannot be applied and the derivations outlined in section 3.1 are therefore no longer valid. In principle each particular non-linear vibration problem has to be solved on its own. However, certain general properties which are of considerable practical interest may be discussed without actually solving the equation.

Consider for instance the case where only the "Stiffness" -term is non-linear. The motion of the mass m is then governed by the equation.

$$m\frac{d^2x}{dt^2} + c\frac{dx}{dt} + F(x) = f(t) \qquad (3.12)$$

The term kx has been substituted by $F(x)$ because the stiffness k which was constant in the linear equation depends now upon the vibration amplitude x. Several possible forms of $F(x)$ are sketched in Fig.3.6. In Figs.3.6.b, e and f, the system is said to possess a stiffening or hardening spring, while in Fig.3.6.c and d the system is said to possess a softening spring.

If the system has no excitation $f(t)$ and no damping term, the undamped free vibration is governed by the equation.

$$\frac{d^2x}{dt^2} + F(x) = 0 \qquad (3.13)$$

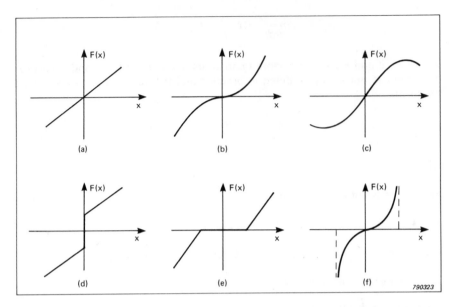

Fig.3.6. Force vs displacement characteristics for some symmetrical spring arrangements:
a) Linear
b) Linear plus cubic (Duffing)
c) Sinusoid (pendulum)
d) Pretensioned springs
e) Clearance
f) Asymptotic elasticity

The free oscillation is not sinusoidal unless $F(x)$ is linear. In the linear case the period and the shape of the oscillation are independent of the amplitude, but in the non-linear case both the period and the form of the oscillation vary with the amplitude.

The amplitude-period relation can be obtained by integrating Equation (3.13), by writing

$$\frac{dx}{dt} = v$$

then

$$v\frac{dv}{dx} + F(x) = 0$$

and one can integrate from the position of peak amplitude $x = a$ where $v = 0$ to the general position x where

$$\frac{dx}{dt} = v$$

48

i.e.
$$\frac{v^2}{2} + \int_a^x F(x)\, dx = 0$$

If one introduces the potential energy of the force $F(x)$

$$U(x) = \int_0^x F(\xi)\, d\xi \qquad\qquad (3.14)$$

then
$$\frac{dx}{dt} = v = \sqrt{2[U(a) - U(x)]}$$

Because of the symmetry the period of oscillation τ is four times the time interval required to move from $x = 0$ to $x = a$

$$\tau(a) = 4 \int_0^a \frac{dx}{\sqrt{2[U(a) - U(x)]}} \qquad\qquad (3.15)$$

The relationship between amplitude and natural frequency($f_0 = 1/\tau$) for the six types of non-linear springs from Fig.3.6 are shown in Fig.3.7. Note that the frequency of a stiffening system increases with amplitude while for a softening system it decreases.

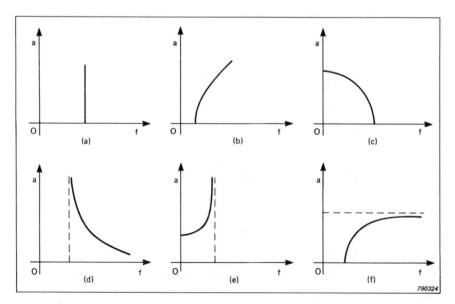

Fig.3.7. Amplitude versus natural frequency for undamped free vibrations of systems with the spring characteristics shown in Fig.3.6

49

When light damping and periodic excitation are added to the system, the steady-state response is generally periodic, with the same period as the excitation unless there is subharmonic resonance, as discussed later. The wave shape of the response oscillation is in general different from that of the excitation and also different from the free vibration wave shapes. Moreover, the response waveshape changes with the level of the excitation.

For fixed excitation amplitude and light damping, the response curves have the forms shown in Figs.3.8 and 3.9. They are like the corresponding curves for linear systems but the "backbones" of the resonant peaks are the non-linear free vibration amplitude-frequency relations shown in Fig.3.7.

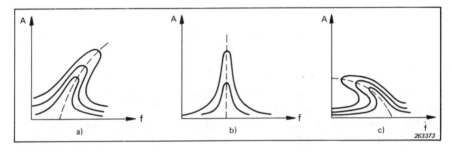

Fig.3.8. Typical resonance curves for various levels of excitation for:
a) A hardening spring type resonant system
b) A linear resonant system
c) A softening spring type resonant system

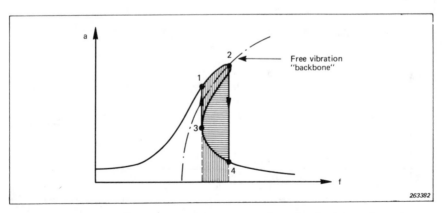

Fig.3.9. Theoretical frequency response curve for a hardening spring type resonant system. The hatched areas indicate the region of instability

We can see in the example shown in Fig.3.9 that there is a *hysteresis* effect on the steady-state response. The segment between points 2 and 3 is *unstable*. If the excitation frequency is slowly increased from zero, the quasi-steady response amplitude follows the curve in Fig.3.9 from 1 to 2 and jumps with an irregular transient to point 4. Now when the excitation frequency is slowly decreased, there is a sudden jump in steady-state response from 3 to 1. So in conclusion, the location of the peak response for a slowly sweeping input frequency is not the same for an upward sweep as it is for a downward sweep.

The response curve in Fig.3.9 has been for a fixed value of the damping parameter c and for fixed excitation amplitude. The effect of a decreasing damping is to extend the resonant peak further up the free vibration backbone while the effect of increasing the excitation amplitude is, as shown in Fig.3.8, to increase the response at all frequencies in a non-linear and non-uniform manner. The calculations of response curves is not simple and efforts have been made to devise approximate methods. Actual curves obtained from analog model studies are shown in Fig.3.10.

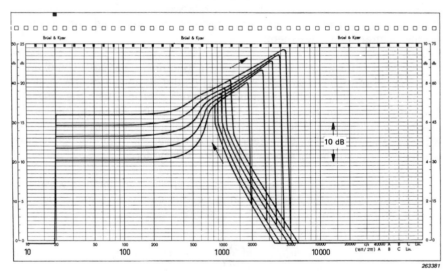

263381

Fig.3.10. Frequency response curves for a hardening spring type resonant system. The curves were measured for various levels of excitation of an analog model system

A property of non-linear systems is that they distort the wave-shape of the response signal, i.e. even if the force driving the system is purely sinusoidal the wave-shape of the response will not be sinusoidal (See Appendix C). Normally the response wave-shape will contain a number of frequency compo-

51

nents harmonically related to the frequency of the driving force. This can be confirmed mathematically, for instance, by approximating the solution to the non-linear differential equation by means of a series expansion, and experimentally by analyzing the response wave-shape by means of a frequency analyzer.

Under certain circumstances (very low damping) a very special phenomenon occurs in non-linear resonant systems of the type described above. This is the phenomenon of subharmonics. A subharmonic is a response vibration occurring at $1/2$, $1/3$, $1/4$, $1/5$ etc. of the frequency of the driving force. An intuitive explanation for the occurrence of subharmonics may be given in that the driving force supplies energy to one of the harmonics of the non-linear system and when energy is supplied it will start to oscillate. The higher harmonic then pulls all the other harmonics with it, as the specifically excited harmonic is an integral part of the whole motion.

While the occurrence of subharmonics in practice is relatively rare, "ordinary" harmonics (sometimes called superharmonics) are present to a greater or lesser extent in all non-linear systems. Even if their amplitude values are rather small they may play an important role when the vibration of complex (multi-degree-of-freedom) mechanical systems is considered. An example readily illustrates this statement:

Consider for instance the case where a non-linear spring element in a multi-degree-of-freedom system produces a third harmonic of the order of 1%. If the frequency of this harmonic by chance coincides with the resonant frequency of another resonance in the system which happens to have a resonance amplification factor $Q = 100$ this specific resonance will respond with the same amplitude as the actually excited frequency even though its frequency did not exist in the wave-shape of the driving force!

Another important case*, that will not be explained in detail is when the non-linearity is velocity-dependent only, i.e. the equation of motion for the system can be written:

$$m\frac{d^2x}{dt^2} + \beta\left(\frac{dx}{dt}\right) + kx = f(t) \tag{3.16}$$

A somewhat different situation then exists.

In this case also the production of harmonics varies with frequency and excitation level, but the resonant frequency itself remains practically constant.

---

* The case of non-linear masses in resonating systems has, to the author's knowledge, not seemed to be of any great interest in practice and is therefore not treated in this text.

A special case occurs when the damping is negative, in that in this case the system oscillates. Examples of systems where these kinds of selfsustained oscillations may take place are the flutter of aeroplane wings, oscillations in electrical transmission lines due to the action of the wind and some cases of Coulomb friction, e.g. hysteresis whirl in machine rotors. One of the most disastrous cases of damage caused by self-sustained oscillations is the failure of the Tacoma Bridge in 1940.

3.3. ROTATIONAL AND TORSIONAL VIBRATIONS

In the previous sections of this Chapter the vibration responses considered have been of the so-called *translational type* i.e. the vibrating masses have been oscillating rectilinearly along one (or more) axis only.

Another type of motion occurs when a body is forced to vibrate around one or more axes, such as is often the case for instance in rotating machinery or unsymmetrically loaded machine foundations. The simplest form of rotational vibrations may be that of torsional vibrations in a shaft, see Fig.3.11.a). Assuming that the inertia of the shaft itself is negligible compared with the inertia of the mass, m, and that the elastic behaviour of the mass can be neglected in comparison with the torsional elasticity of the shaft, the equation of free rotational motion for the system can be written:

$$I \frac{d^2 \varphi}{dt^2} + c' \frac{d\varphi}{dt} + k' \varphi = 0 \qquad (3.17)$$

Here I is the moment of inertia of the mass around its center of rotation, i.e. (around the shaft), ϕ is the angle of motion, c' is a damping constant and k' is the angular stiffness of the shaft, which depends upon the modulus of elasticity in shear and on the physical shaft configuration.

It can be seen that the differential equation governing the angular motion of the mass in Fig.3.11.a) has a completely analogous form to that governing rectilinear motion and which was given in Equation (3.1). This means that exactly the same mathematical treatment as discussed in section 3.1 can be applied to the rotational vibrations of the kind described above. The only differences are that the mass in section 3.1 must be substituted by the moment of inertia, and the (rectilinear) displacement, x, by the angle ϕ. If external forces are applied to the system their effects on the rotational motion are measured by the *Torque, M*, that they produce, Fig.3.11.b). The corresponding equation of motion is:

$$I \frac{d^2 \varphi}{dt^2} + c' \frac{d\varphi}{dt} + k' \varphi = M = F \cdot r \qquad (3.18)$$

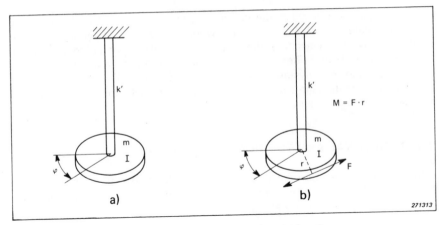

Fig.3.11. Examples of torsional vibration
   a) Free vibration
   b) Forced vibration

Thus, rotational motions are governed by torque equations, while rectilinear motions are governed by force equations.

A second example of rotational motion is, as mentioned above, that of an unsymmetrically loaded foundation. This case is illustrated in Fig.3.12, and plays an important role in the vibration and shock isolation of machines and equipment.

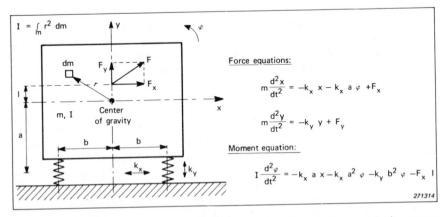

Force equations:

$$m\frac{d^2x}{dt^2} = -k_x\,x - k_x\,a\,\varphi + F_x$$

$$m\frac{d^2y}{dt^2} = -k_y\,y + F_y$$

Moment equation:

$$I\frac{d^2\varphi}{dt^2} = -k_x\,a\,x - k_x\,a^2\,\varphi - k_y\,b^2\,\varphi - F_x\,l$$

$$I = \int_m r^2\,dm$$

Fig.3.12. Model of an unsymmetrically loaded foundation, and the corresponding equations of motion

54

3.4. RESPONSE OF MECHANICAL SYSTEMS TO STATIONARY RANDOM VIBRATIONS

In section 3.1 it was shown that the response of any linear system to a prescribed excitation can be determined from a knowledge of the system's impulse response function or its complex frequency response function. If now the excitation consists of a Gaussian random process characterized by means of its auto-correlation function (or, what may be more common in practice, by means of its mean square spectral density function) what would the relationship between the excitation and the response then be?

Starting with the auto-correlation function representation of the response this can be formulated in terms of the system's impulse response function:

$$x(t)x(t+\tau) = \int_{-\infty}^{\infty} f(t-\tau_1)h(\tau_1)d\tau_1 \int_{-\infty}^{\infty} f(t+\tau-\tau_2)h(\tau_2)d\tau_2$$

$$= \int\int_{-\infty}^{\infty} f(t-\tau_1)f(t+\tau-\tau_2)h(\tau_1)h(\tau_2)d\tau_1 d\tau_2$$

(The formulation of the impulse response function is here slightly different from the one utilized previously. However, by studying Fig.3.2 and the connected mathematics it is easily seen that the two formulations are equivalent). As the auto-correlation function is by definition (Eqn. 2.9):

$$\psi_x(\tau) = \lim_{T\to\infty} \frac{1}{T} \int_{-\frac{T}{2}}^{\frac{T}{2}} x(t)x(t+\tau)dt$$

$$= \lim_{T\to\infty} \frac{1}{T} \int_{-\frac{T}{2}}^{\frac{T}{2}} \left[\int\int_{-\infty}^{\infty} f(t-\tau_1)f(t+\tau-\tau_2)h(\tau_1)h(\tau_2)d\tau_1 d\tau_2 \right] dt$$

then

$$\psi_x(\tau) = \int\int_{-\infty}^{\infty} \psi_f(\tau+\tau_1-\tau_2)h(\tau_1)h(\tau_2)d\tau_1 d\tau_2 \qquad (3.19)$$

which can be seen by setting $f(t+\tau-\tau_2) = f(t-\tau_1+\tau-\tau_2+\tau_1)$ where $\tau-\tau_2+\tau_1$ represents time lag in the multiplication process used to obtain the auto-correlation function for the excitation.

The response mean square spectral density function is found by taking the Fourier transform of $\psi_x(\tau)$:

$$S_x(f) = \int_{-\infty}^{\infty} \psi_x(\tau)e^{-j2\pi f\tau}d\tau \qquad (3.20)$$

or what is the same:

$$S_x(f) = \int_{-\infty}^{\infty} \psi_x(\tau) e^{-j2\pi f(\tau + \tau_1 - \tau_2)} e^{j2\pi f\tau_1} e^{-j2\pi f\tau_2} d\tau$$

and inserting the formula given above for $\psi_x(\tau)$ into this expression:

$$S_x(f) = \left[\int_{-\infty}^{\infty} h(\tau_1) e^{j2\pi f\tau_1} d\tau_1 \int_{-\infty}^{\infty} h(\tau_2) e^{-j2\pi f\tau_2} d\tau_2 \right] S_f(f)$$

as

$$S_f(f) = \int_{-\infty}^{\infty} \psi_f(\tau + \tau_1 - \tau_2) e^{-j2\pi f(\tau + \tau_1 - \tau_2)} d\tau$$

thus:

$$S_x(f) = H^*(f) H(f) S_f(f) = |H(f)|^2 S_f(f) \qquad (3.21)$$

where $H^*(f)$ is the complex conjugate of $H(f)$. This result is one of the most important ones in the theory of random processes and states that *the response mean square spectral density of a linear system at any frequency is equal to the excitation mean square spectral density times the squared modulus of the complex frequency response function at that frequency.* That a relationship of this kind was to be expected is also intuitively felt by considering the meaning of the mean square spectral density function and the relationship found in section 3.1 between the excitation and the response in terms of the complex frequency response function $H(f)$.

The response mean square spectral density function may, from a measurement point of view, be considered either as a frequency *spectrum* or as a system *response function* depending upon the problem at hand.

If the system being considered is non-linear the relationships stated above do, of course, no longer hold as these relationships were built on the general superposition principle, which is only valid for linear systems whose motion is governed by linear differential equations. The mean square spectral density function for the response is therefore no longer a unique function but changes with excitation level. Also the probability density function for instantaneous response amplitudes is no longer Gaussian and in general a vast amount of data is necessary to characterize the response of such systems to Gaussian random excitations.

If the non-linearity is situated in the stiffness element of the system considered, it is possible in some important cases to formulate and solve exactly the stochastic equations describing the probability density functions of the response. In general, however, some sort of linearization technique has to be used in a theoretical treatment. A considerable amount of theoretical and experimental work has been laid down in this area in the past decade or so and interested readers are referred to the literature listed at the end of this chapter for further studies.

3.5. SHOCK RESPONSE AND SHOCK SPECTRA

We have defined earlier a shock as a transmission of kinetic energy to a system, the transition taking place in a relatively short time compared with the natural period of oscillation of the system. A rectangular shock pulse may therefore constitute one or two shocks depending upon the natural period of oscillation of the system influenced by it and the duration of the pulse. This is illustrated in Fig.3.13.I) and II), and it should be noted that the maximum system response may in the case of Fig.3.13.I) reach a value which is twice the magnitude of the shock pulse.

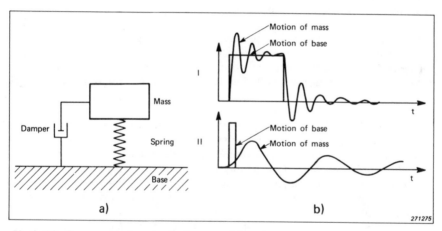

Fig.3.13. Response of a single degree-of-freedom system to shock excitation

Spectral decompositions are the most widely used procedure for the analysis of shock data. The two most common forms of spectral decomposition used are the *Fourier spectrum* and the *Shock spectrum.*

The *Fourier spectrum* is simply the forward Fourier transform of a time history. It can be calculated for either the excitation or the response time history. When dealing with shock data, it is often difficult to measure the response of the system under service conditions and the analysis is limited to that of the excitation time history. Generally one uses the Fourier spectrum of the shock input and the frequency response function of the system subjected to the shock in order to get information about the system response. The response being calculated in the frequency domain, the inverse Fourier transformation operation produces the response time history of the system.

The second spectral decomposition, which has proved to be of considerable value with respect to the comparison of shock motions, to the design of equipment to withstand shocks, and to the formulation of laboratory tests as a means to simulate environmental conditions, is the *shock response spectrum*, or briefly the *shock spectrum* (Note: This is not to be confused with the Fourier spectrum of the forcing shock pulse!). The shock spectrum is obtained by letting the shock pulse in question be applied to a series of linear, undamped single degree-of-freedom systems and plotting for example the maximum response of the system as a function of the system's natural frequency.

Various types of shock spectra are used depending upon the intended application of the information obtained. These may be the initial shock spectrum which is obtained from the maximum response while the shock pulse is still acting, or the residual shock spectrum which is obtained from the maximum response after the pulse has occurred.

Other definitions may be the overall or maximax spectrum which is plotted on the basis of the maximum response without regard to time, and the overall negative maximum shock spectrum which is obtained by considering the maximum response of the single degree-of-freedom system in the negative direction.

In practical measurement systems the requirement of zero damping in the responding single degree-of-freedom system may be difficult to achieve, but a selectable damping gives the advantage that the effect of the shock on various structures can be judged simply by considering the influence of damping. However, for relatively small amounts of damping the shock spectra will not be essentially different from the spectra obtained with no damping, since the response for the first few cycles will be virtually identical. The response of an undamped single degree-of-freedom system to a shock pulse can be calculated relatively easily for simple shock wave forms, using for example Laplace transform methods. Figs.3.14, 3.15 and 3.16 illustrate shock spectra obtained for a rectangular, sawtooth and halfsine shock pulse of duration T. The maximax shock spectra are found simply by taking the highest of the two spectrum values at any frequency.

Recently, the shock spectrum concept has been extended to multiple degree of freedom systems, non-linear systems etc. See the bibliography at the end of the chapter.

It may be worthwhile in connection with the discussion of shock spectra to

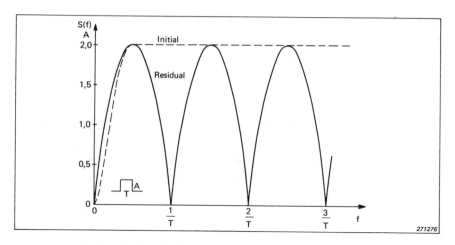

Fig.3.14. Shock spectra for a rectangular shock pulse

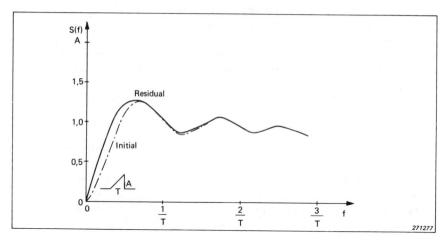

Fig.3.15. Shock spectra for a final peak sawtooth shock pulse

point out an interesting fact, namely that the Fourier spectrum of the shock pulse and the undamped residual shock spectrum are related by the formula:

$$S(f) = 2\pi f |F(f)| \qquad (3.22)$$

where $S(f)$ designates the residual shock spectrum and $F(f)$ is the Fourier spectrum of the shock (see also Appendix D).

Selection between the Fourier and the shock spectral methods of spectral decomposition is based on the application of the data. Fourier analysis is

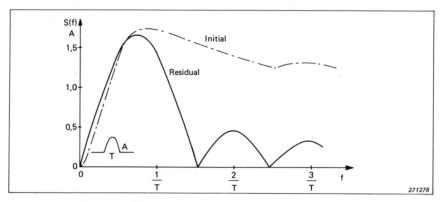

Fig.3.16. Shock spectra for a halfsine shock pulse

used to describe input data, response data or, if the both are measured simultaneously, it can be used to describe the frequency response function of the system. Once two of the three items are known the third can be calculated. Typically, the input time history and frequency response function are known and the response time history is to be determined. On the other hand, the primary application of shock spectral analysis is to predict peak response levels from input measurements, with only limited knowledge of the system response properties.

3.6. VIBRATIONS IN STRUCTURES. MECHANICAL WAVES

The mechanical systems considered in the preceding text have been of the so-called idealized lumped parameter type, i.e. masses have been assumed to be rigid bodies where all points within the body move in phase, and elastic elements have been assumed to have no mass. In practice all masses have a certain elasticity and all spring elements have masses. For instance a beam or a plate is a continuous combination of masses and springs.

As the number of degrees-of-freedom of a mechanical system was defined as the number of elastic movements of masses (resonances, see section 3.1) it follows that structures like beams and plates *have an infinite number of degrees-of-freedom*. The infinite number of "resonances" resulting from the infinite number of degrees-of-freedom are in the case of structures normally termed "natural modes", or simply "modes".

While in lumped parameter systems all points within a mass are supposed to move in phase, this is no longer true for continuous structures. A simple example illustrates this clearly: In Fig.3.17 the vibration of a beam clamped at one end and acted upon by an oscillating force in the other is shown. When the frequency of the oscillating force coincides with one of the beam's

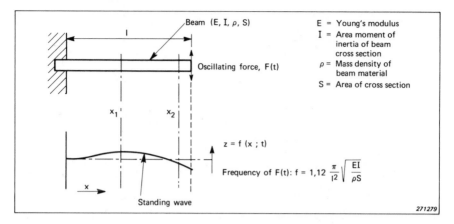

271279

Fig.3.17. Illustration of the response of a beam to an oscillating force the frequency of which coincides with one of the beam's natural vibration modes

modes, the vibration pattern of the beam forms a "standing wave", as shown in the figure. It is readily seen that the points within the beam at the place marked x_1 here move in opposite phase with respect to the points at the place marked x_2. One of the major differences between the motion of a lumped parameter system and a structure is thus that in the case of structures each resonance is associated with a (continuous) *mode shape*.

To describe for instance the motion of the beam in Fig.3.17 it is therefore not enough to describe the instantaneous vibration amplitude, z, as a function of t (time) only. It must also be described as a function of space co-ordinates, in this case x, i.e. $z = f(x; t)$.

In deriving the differential equation governing this motion it is necessary to apply partial differentials and the equation becomes a *partial differential equation*. Similarly the equation of motion for a plate, Fig.3.18, will be of the type: $z = f(x; y; t)$.

The examples shown in Fig.3.17 and 3.18 illustrate *transverse vibrations*. Also *compressional* and *torsional* vibrations may be excited in structures, (Fig.3.19) and a combination of all three types of vibrations may take place. The vibrations in structures may therefore be exceedingly complex and exact solutions to the differential equations of motion exist only for a few types of simple structures and load configurations. Some typical mode shapes for transverse vibrations of simple beams and plates are given in Figs.3.20 and 3.21.

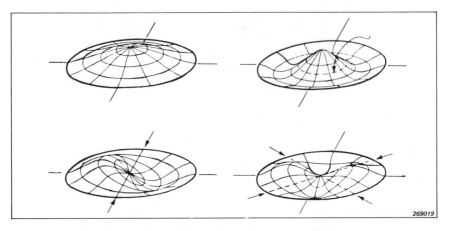

Fig.3.18. Shapes of a few of the normal modes of vibration of a circular plate clamped at its edge. (After Morse)

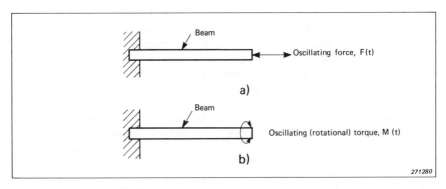

Fig.3.19. Illustration of compressional and torsional vibrations of a beam
a) Compressional vibration
b) Torsional vibration

From the theory of bending of beams and Newton's second law of motion the differential equation governing the free transverse vibrations of a beam can be found.

$$\varrho S \frac{\partial^2 z}{\partial t^2} + \frac{\partial^2}{\partial x^2}\left(EI\frac{\partial^2 z}{\partial x^2}\right) = 0 \qquad (3.23)$$

where

ρ = Mass density of the beam material

62

Beams of uniform section and uniformly distributed load

Natural frequencies $f_n = \dfrac{A}{2\pi}\sqrt{\dfrac{EI}{\rho Sl^4}}$

where E = Young's modulus
I = Area moment of inertia of beam cross section
l = Length of beam
ρ = Mass density of beam material
S = Area of cross-section
A = Coefficient from table below

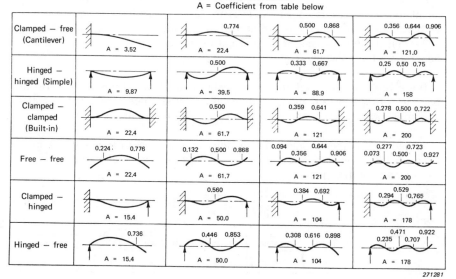

271281

Fig.3.20. Examples of boundary conditions and mode-shapes for various single uniform beam configurations

S = Cross-sectional area of the beam
E = Modulus of elasticity (Young's Modulus)
I = Moment of inertia of the cross-section.

This is a *fourth-order partial differential equation* the solution of which depends upon the boundary conditions, i.e. the way in which the beam is fastened. Fig.3.20 shows some examples of boundary conditions and corresponding mode shapes for the first four natural vibration modes.

The infinite number of degrees-of-freedom mentioned above manifest themselves by the fact that there is an infinite number of higher natural vibration modes. In general, however, only a few of the lower modes seem to be of great practical interest.

In the case of free transverse vibrations of plates the equation of motion is again a fourth-order differential equation, still more complicated to solve than the one governing the vibration of beams:

63

$$\frac{\partial^4 z}{\partial x^4} + 2\frac{\partial^4 z}{\partial x^2 \partial y^2} + \frac{\partial^4 z}{\partial y^4} + \frac{12\varrho(1-v^2)}{Eh^2}\frac{\partial^2 z}{\partial t^2} = 0 \qquad (3.24)$$

where h is the thickness of the plate and v is Poisson's ratio (about 0,3 for most metals.

Fig.3.18 illustrates the shapes of some of the first normal modes of a circular plate clamped at its edges, while examples of nodal lines of square plates with various edge conditions are shown in Fig.3.21. Note from Fig.3.20 and 3.21 that the frequencies of the normal modes in structural members are in general not harmonically related.

There are, however, other types of vibrations in structures which are, at least to a first approximation, harmonically related. These are compressional (longitudinal) vibrations, and in certain cases also torsional vibrations.

In setting up the equation of motion for compressional vibrations in a beam, Fig.3.22, it is noted that the result is a *second order partial differential equation* of the type:

$$\frac{\partial^2 \xi}{\partial x^2} = \frac{\varrho \partial^2 \xi}{E \partial t^2} \qquad (3.25)$$

	1st Mode	2nd Mode	3rd Mode	4th Mode	5th Mode	6th Mode
$\omega_n / \sqrt{D/\rho ha^4}$	3.494	8.547	21.44	27.46	31.17	
Nodal lines	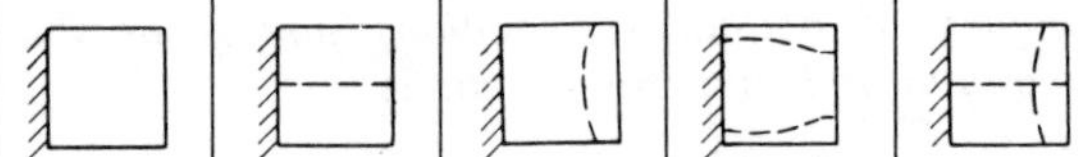					
$\omega_n / \sqrt{D/\rho ha^4}$	35.99	73.41	108.27	131.64	132.25	165.15
Nodal lines	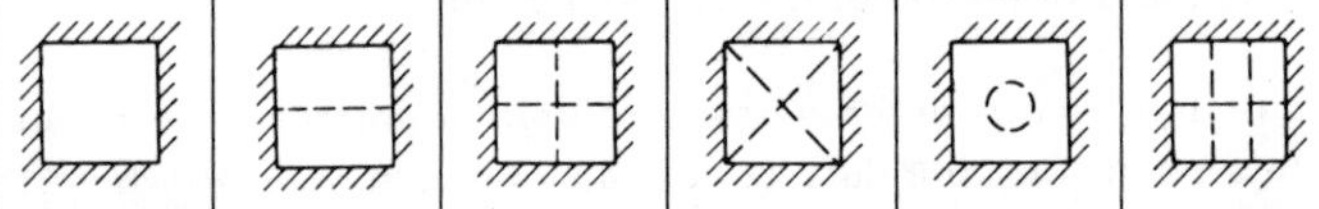					
$\omega_n / \sqrt{D/\rho ha^4}$	6.958	24.08	26.80	48.05	63.14	
Nodal lines	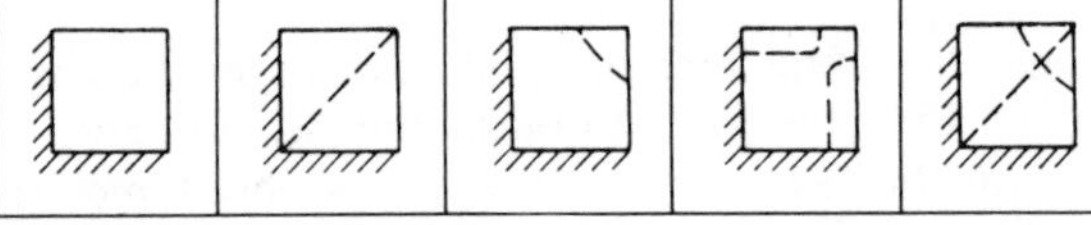					

$\omega_n = 2\pi f_n$ ρ = Mass density   a = Plate length

$D = Eh^3/12(1-v^2)$ h = Plate thickness

271282

Fig.3.21. Examples of modal line configurations for square plates under various edge conditions. (After D. Young)

64

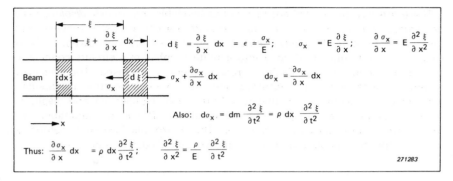

Fig.3.22. Sketch showing the derivation of the equation of motion for compressional (longitudinal) vibrations in a beam

This equation has the same form as the so-called wave-equation which governs various kinds of wave phenomena in theoretical physics. Compressional vibrations are therefore also often referred to as *mechanical waves* with a wave velocity (*v*) of:

$$\frac{1}{v^2} = \frac{\varrho}{E}; \qquad v = \sqrt{\frac{E}{\varrho}} \qquad (3.26)$$

The main reason for the inclusion of this brief section on structural vibrations in the book has been to illustrate that *the actual vibrations measured on a complicated construction may be widely different from point to point even if the measuring points considered are situated a relatively short distance apart from each other.* Also, the direction in space of the vibrations may vary and for thorough investigations it is therefore necessary to measure the vibrations both as a function of frequency and as a function of space coordinates at each measuring point.

3.7. SHOCK AND VIBRATION ANALYSIS USING FINITE ELEMENT TECHNIQUES

A more comprehensive theoretical treatment of structural vibration is outside the scope of this book and can be found in many excellent textbooks on the subject. We will however discuss the finite element method for shock and vibration analysis which is becoming more and more used due to the advancement in sophisticated digital computers. Several finite element programs are currently available from various sources. While we have until now only discussed the exact solution of the dynamic problems, the finite element method is an approximate solution.

65

There are two finite element techniques available: *the matrix displacement or stiffness method* where the displacements are chosen as unknowns, and the *matrix force or flexibility method* where forces are unknowns. In both cases, the continuum is divided into a finite number of elements connected only at the node points. Each discrete element is idealised. The displacements of these points are assumed and the complete solution is obtained combining displacements so that it satisfies force equilibrium and displacement compatibility at the joints of the elements. The matrix equations are then solved numerically by a computer. The matrix displacement method is currently the most popular and is the one we will discuss in this section.

Static analysis

The equation is of the form,

$$[F] = [K][U] \tag{3.27}$$

$[F]$ = vector of forces
$[U]$ = vector of displacements
$[K]$ = stiffness matrix for the entire structure.

The matrix $[K]$ is generally singular because rigid body motion is not prevented.

— For one spring element

$$F_1 = k(u_1 - u_2)$$

$$F_2 = k(u_2 - u_1)$$

$$\begin{bmatrix} F_1 \\ F_2 \end{bmatrix} = \begin{bmatrix} k & -k \\ -k & k \end{bmatrix} \begin{bmatrix} u_1 \\ u_2 \end{bmatrix}$$

where F_i are forces and u_i displacements

—For two spring elements

$$\begin{cases} F_1 = k_1(u_1 - u_2) \\ F_2 = k_1(u_2 - u_1) + k_2(u_2 - u_3) \\ \quad = -k_1 u_1 + (k_1 + k_2)u_2 - k_2 u_3 \\ F_3 = k_2(u_3 - u_2) \end{cases}$$

$$\begin{bmatrix} F_1 \\ F_2 \\ F_3 \end{bmatrix} = \begin{bmatrix} k_1 & -k_1 & 0 \\ -k_1 & k_1+k_2 & -k_2 \\ 0 & -k_2 & k_2 \end{bmatrix} \begin{bmatrix} u_1 \\ u_2 \\ u_3 \end{bmatrix}$$

However, the stiffness matrix can also be assembled from the stiffness of the individual elements

$$[K]^{(1)} = \begin{bmatrix} k_1 & -k_1 \\ -k_1 & k_1 \end{bmatrix} \qquad [K]^{(2)} = \begin{bmatrix} k_2 & -k_2 \\ -k_2 & k_2 \end{bmatrix}$$

$$[K] = \begin{bmatrix} k_1 & -k_1 & 0 \\ -k_1 & k_1 & 0 \\ 0 & 0 & 0 \end{bmatrix} + \begin{bmatrix} 0 & 0 & 0 \\ 0 & k_2 & -k_2 \\ 0 & -k_2 & k_2 \end{bmatrix}$$

Thus $$[K] = \begin{bmatrix} k_1 & -k_1 & 0 \\ -k_1 & k_1+k_2 & -k_2 \\ 0 & -k_2 & k_2 \end{bmatrix}$$

The stiffness matrix can be obtained by assuming a unit displacement in one degree of freedom (keeping the other displacement zero) and finding the force required to cause a unit displacement.

Dynamic Analysis

The dynamic equation of motion can be written in matrix form as,

$$[M]\,[\ddot{X}] + [C]\,[\dot{X}] + [K]\,[X] = [F(t)] \tag{3.28}$$

where

$[M]$ = mass matrix
$[C]$ = damping matrix
$[K]$ = stiffness matrix
$[F(t)]$ = external force vector

We see that two additional terms, the mass and the damping, are needed.

The mass matrix can be found in different ways

— *The lumped mass approach:* the mass of an uniform bar can for instance be lumped at two nodes and the mass matrix becomes

$$[M] = \begin{bmatrix} m/2 & 0 \\ 0 & m/2 \end{bmatrix}$$

or at three nodes

$$[M] = \begin{bmatrix} m/3 & 0 & 0 \\ 0 & m/3 & 0 \\ 0 & 0 & m/3 \end{bmatrix}$$

This gives a diagonal matrix which is particularly suitable for computer calculations. However, this approach is not accurate and the structure has to be divided into a large number of elements to give reasonable results.

— *The consistent mass approach:* the mass matrix is derived using the same displacement function as the stiffness. The matrix here is non-diagonal and is a better representation of the actual mass distribution.

In these two first approaches the mass is independent of the frequency.

— *The distributed mass approach:* this uses exact mathematical expressions for mass distribution and yields better results but mass and stiffness matrices are functions of frequency and the method is therefore generally too expensive in computer time.

The finite element method with damping is complex and such assumptions as *proportional damping* have to be made to include the contribution due to the damping. This assumption is generally not realistic except in lightly damped structures. When damping is predominant, the exact modal contribution of damping is important and experimental modal analysis may be useful.

When the matrix equations of motion are written the computer will solve them using standard methods.

The dynamical problem can be solved using four diferent techniques:

— normal modes method
— frequency response method
— direct integration for transient response
— statistical technique for response to random vibration.

68

Details about these different methods and their advantages can be found in the references given at the end of the chapter.

To represent complex structures by using finite elements one must have various shapes of elements available. Below are listed some of the most commonly available elements in the computer programs:

— the beam element
— shear panel (quadrilateral element)
— plane stress and strain element (triangular or quadrilateral shape)
— bending plate element (triangular or quadrilateral shape)
— shell and ring element
— solid element (tetrahedron, wedge or hexahedron elements).

The finite element method is in constant evolution and newer and better elements are continually being developed. Its important place is due both to its ease of application and its universality in solving both structural and non-structural problems such as heat transfer, fluid flow etc.

3.8. STATISTICAL ENERGY ANALYSIS

It is possible at relatively high frequencies to get reasonably accurate predictions of the mean response by averaging over space as well as over frequency bands which include many modes, instead of considering each particular mode at one time. This method, known as statistical energy analysis (SEA), is explained in more detail by Lyon in the reference given at the end of the chapter. It circumvents problems like boundary conditions (which are not known anyway) and exact shape of the individual elements. It is based on the average over the structural area, a panel, for example, and the average over a frequency band, such as 1/3 octave. It assumes a knowledge of the modal density $n(f)$ i.e. the number of modes per unit frequency, defined as

$$n(f) = \frac{\Delta N}{\Delta f} \qquad (3.29)$$

where ΔN is the number of modes within the frequency band Δf.

When the number of modes is high, it is easier to predict a response averaged over space than individual values but it is then difficult to predict the vibration at a given point. The method assumes the orthogonality of the normal modes and that the damping of the normal modes is very low. It should be mentioned that the use of statistical energy analysis for vibration prediction requires considerable experience and that the procedure is very sensitive to violation of the basic assumptions.

3.9. SELECTED BIBLIOGRAPHY

BENDAT, J.S. and PIERSOL, A.G.: *Measurement and Analysis of Random Data.* John Wiley and Sons, Inc. New York 1971

BOURGINE, A.: *Sur une Approche Statistique de la Dynamique Vibratoire des Structures.* Office National d'Etudes et de Recherches Aerospatiales 1973

BROCH, J.T.: *Selected Reprints from Technical Review* — Non Linear systems and random vibration 1972

CRANDALL, S.H. and MARK W.D.: *Random Vibrations in Mechanical Systems.* Academic Press. New York 1963

CRANDALL, S.H. et al.: *Random Vibrations I and II.* The M.I.T. Press and John Wiley and Sons, Inc. 1958 and 1963

Den HARTOG, J.P.: *Mechanical Vibrations.* McGraw-Hill Book Company, Inc. 1961

KARMAN, T. and BIOT, M.A.: *Mathematical Methods in Engineering.* McGraw-Hill Book Company, Inc. 1940

KELLY, R.D. and RICHMAN G.: *Principles and Techniques of Shock Data Analysis.* The Shock and Vibration Information Center. United States Department of Defense 1969

KITTELSEN, K.E.: *Measurement and Description of Shock.* Brüel & Kjær. Tech. Rev. No.3-1966

LYON, R.H.: *Statistical Energy Analysis of Dynamical Systems, Theory and Applications.* MIT Press, Cambridge MA, 1975

MINORSKY, N.: *Introduction to Non-Linear Mechanics.* Edwards Bros., Ann Arbor, Mich. 1947

MORROW, C.T.: *The Shock Spectrum as a Criterion of Severity of Shock Impulses.* J.A.S.A. Vol.29, No.5, May 1957

MORROW, C.T.: *Shock and Vibration Engineering.* John Wiley and Sons, Inc. 1963

MORSE, P.M.: *Vibration and Sound.* McGraw-Hill Book Company, Inc. 1948

PILKEY, W. and PILKEY, B.:	*Shock and Vibration Computer Program Reviews and Summaries.* The Shock and Vibration Information Center. United States Department of Defense. 1975
ROBSON, J.D.:	*An Introduction to Random Vibration,* Edinburgh University, Press 1963
SALTER, J.P.:	*Steady State Vibration,* Kenneth Mason Book Co., England 1969
SESHADRI, T.V.:	*Shock and Vibration Analysis using Finite Element Techniques.* The Shock and Vibration Digest. July 1975
SESHADRI, T.V.:	*Shock and Vibration Analysis using Finite Element Technique.* Journal of Sound and Vibration. Dec. 1978
SMITH, P.W. Jr., and LYON, R.H.:	*Sound and Structural Vibration.* National Technical Information Service. U.S. Department of Commerce 1965
THOMSON, W.T. and BARTON, M.V.:	*The Response of Mechanical Systems to Random Excitation.* J. Appl. Mech. Vol.24, p.248 — 251, 1957
VIGNESS, I.:	*Elementary Considerations of Shock Spectra.* Shock, Vibration and Associated Environments, Bulletin 34, 1965, Part 3
YOUNG, D.:	*Vibration of Rectangular Plates by the Ritz Method.* J. Appl. Mechanics. Vol.17, p.448 1950
ZIENKIEWICZ, U.C.:	*The Finite Element Method in Engineering Sciences.* McGraw-Hill 1971

4. EFFECTS OF VIBRATIONS AND SHOCK ON MECHANICAL SYSTEMS

4.1. DAMAGING EFFECTS OF VIBRATIONS. MECHANICAL FATIGUE

Even though mechanical failure due to material fatigue is by far the most commonly known deteriorating effect of vibrations, a vibrating mechanical construction may fail in practice for other reasons as well. Failure may, for instance, be caused by the occurrence of one, or a few, excessive vibration amplitudes (brittle materials, contact-failures in relays and switches, collisions between two vibrating systems etc.), — or by the fact that a certain vibration amplitude value is exceeded for too great a time.

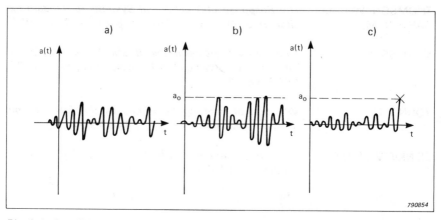

Fig.4.1. Possible modes of failure under practically experienced random excitation

    a) Normal fatigue, where failure occurs after a time which is dependent on the total number of cycles and their peak values

    b) Failure occurs if a(t) is greater than a_0 for a certain total time

    c) Failure occurs when a(t) first exceeds the level a(t) = a_0

However, the importance of mechanical fatiguing effects has initiated a considerable amount of research and testing around the world. It has therefore been deemed appropriate to include a section here which deals with this particular topic.

The fatigue phenomenon is today deemed to originate from local yield in the material or, in other words, from a *sliding of atomic layers*. This sliding is caused by a combination of so-called "dislocations" (irregularities in the crystalline structure of the material) and local stress concentrations. It is now assumed that each slip, no matter how small, is connected with a small deterioration of the material, independent of the direction of the slip. The deterioration stops only when the slip stops. Some definite proof for this hypothesis has, to the author's knowledge, not been established as yet. It gives however, a logical and reasonable explanation for the formation of the microscopic "slip bands" which are the first visible signs of material fatigue.

When slip bands have been formed they are, under continuous vibration loading, observed to progress and form minute cracks which eventually join together and produce major cracks. As soon as a crack has reached a certain size it will propagate through the material according to a mathematical law of the form:

$$\frac{dx}{dN} = c e_r^{\,m} x^n \tag{4.1}$$

where
$x =$ crack length
$N =$ number of stress reversals
$c, m, n =$ constants dependent upon the material properties (a reasonable assumption seems in many cases to be $m = 2, n = 1$)
$e_r =$ relative strain

Finally the crack will become so large that the stress in the remaining material becomes too great, whereby the crack propagation becomes unstable, and fatigue failure occurs.

Even though it is possible to describe a certain part of the fatiguing process by means of a relatively simple mathematical expression (see formula above) both the formation of "slip bands" and the final crack instability stages are of a highly statistical nature. Taken as a whole, therefore, *fatigue failures must be regarded as statistical phenomena.*

The statistical nature of the phenomenon manifests itself as a considerable spread in the results of fatigue experiments. As an example of the result of such experiments Fig.4.2 shows a histogram made from investigations on

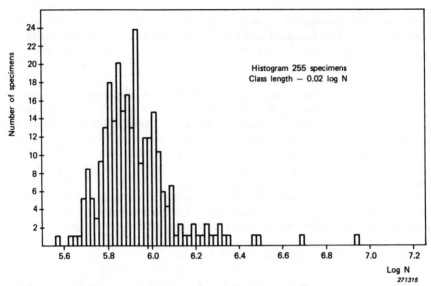

Fig.4.2. *Typical histogram obtained from fatigue experiments (after Bloomer and Roylance)*

the fatigue life of notched aluminium specimens. The results shown were obtained from tests at a single vibration stress level.

By making similar tests at a number of vibration stress levels, a curve, commonly termed the *S-N* curve (Wöhler-Kurve) can be obtained, which shows the relationship between *the average number of stress reversals to failure and the vibration stress level*.

The actual *S-N* curve for a material does not only depend upon the vibrational effects, but is also affected by factors such as temperature, atmospheric conditions (corrosion effects), pre-treatment of the material, etc. Fig.4.3 illustrates a set of *S-N* curves valid for 4340 steel under normal atmospheric conditions. The curves shown are based on pure harmonic vibration loading only. In practice, however, a mechanical part, or material, is very rarely, if ever, subjected to pure harmonic vibrations of constant maximum amplitude during its complete "life".

In order to take varying amplitudes into account in theoretical estimations of the average fatigue life, a "rule" of linear accumulation of damage has been suggested (Palmgren, Minor):

$$D = \sum \frac{n_i}{N_i} \qquad (4.2)$$

74

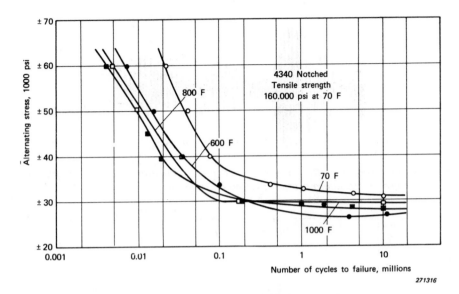

Number of cycles to failure, millions

271316

Fig.4.3. Fatigue strength curves for notched 4340 steel (from Metals Hand-book)

Here n_i is the actual number of stress reversals at a vibration stress level which requires a total number of stress reversals, N_i, to failure. Failure should thus occur when $D = 1$. By using the above expression, and a mathematical approximation to the S-N curve of the form

$$NS^b = a \qquad (4.3)$$

it is sometimes possible to establish a closed mathematical formula for D. Two conditions which have to be fulfilled when use is to be made of the formulae for D and the S-N curve are, however, that each stress reversal has an approximately sinusoidal wave-shape and that the mean stress is zero. These conditions are fulfilled, for instance, by the vibrational stresses occurring in a linear single degree-of-freedom system excited by random vibrations, see Fig.4.4.

Furthermore, in such systems the statistical distribution of maximum vibration amplitudes (peaks) can be mathematically described by means of the so-called *Rayleigh-distribution,* Fig.4.5:

$$p(x)\,dx = \frac{x}{\sigma^2} e^{-\frac{x^2}{2\sigma^2}}\,dx \qquad (4.4)$$

where $p(x)dx$ is the probability of occurrence of peaks within the infinitely

75

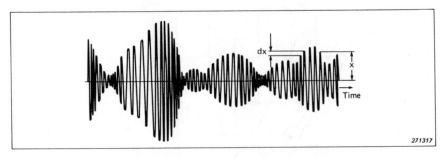

Fig.4.4. Illustration of the stress-versus-time trace produced in a single degree-of-freedom system excited by random vibrations

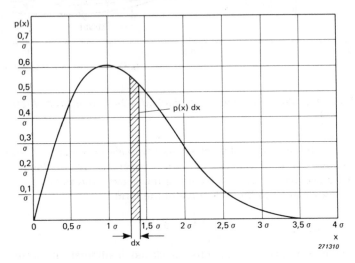

Fig.4.5. Typical peak probability density curve for narrow band random vibrations (Rayleigh distribution)

small amplitude "window" dx (Figs.4.4 and 4.5). As the total number of
peaks occurring within dx is $n(x) = f_o \cdot T \cdot p(x)dx$, and the partial fatigue damage caused by these stress reversals around the vibration level x is

$$Dx = \frac{n(x)}{N(x)} = f_o \cdot T \frac{p(x)dx}{N(x)}$$

the accumulated damage over all vibration peak levels during the period of
time, T, is:

76

$$D = \sum \frac{n(x)}{N(x)} = f_0 T \int_0^\infty \frac{p(x)\,dx}{N(x)}$$

Utilizing now the mathematical approximation to the S-N curve as well as the expression for the Rayleigh distribution of stress reversals given above, the total time to failure ($D = 1$) can be estimated by solving the integral in the formula for D:

$$T = \frac{a}{f_0 (\sqrt{2}\sigma)^b \cdot \Gamma\left(1 + \frac{b}{2}\right)} \qquad (4.5)$$

where Γ is the gamma-function tabulated in most reference books on mathematical functions.

In the case of common engineering materials, b takes values between 3 and 8 (Steel, $b = 3,5$; Tinbronze (Cu, Sn, Pb), $b = 7,5$).

The formula for T in the above equation has been derived on the basis of narrow band random stress/time histories of the type shown in Fig.4.4 and constant amplitude generated S-N curves. The same formula has also been applied to wideband random signals such as shown in Fig.4.6, using an "average frequency" determined from counting zero crossings. Recent work, however, has shown these techniques to be anti-conservative compared with actual random fatigue data. This tendency increases with increasing bandwidth leading to significant overestimation of the fatigue life when dealing with wide band random data. New prediction techniques employing random vibration generated S-N curves and advanced peak counting methods, which only

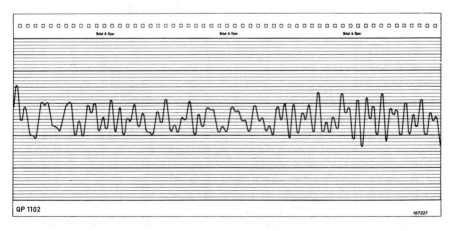

Fig.4.6. Typical stress-versus-time trace at a "critical point" on a complicated structure

77

take the significant peaks into consideration, agree more closely with practice. Unfortunately, much of this is proprietary information and not generally available in the open literature at the time of writing.

4.1.1. Effect of mean stress

In practice, fatigue problems are not usually associated with only a single stress varying around a mean value of zero. The stress which causes a failure is usually composed of at least two major components; a mean stress, with a varying stress superimposed upon it. A diagrammatic stress-time curve for this type of loading including a sinusoidally varying and a mean stress is shown in Fig.4.7 with the important parameters labelled. The S-N information can be expressed in a number of different ways using various combinations of these parameters. S-N curves may be plotted for a range of stress ratios, R, the ratio of the minimum stress (S_{min}) to the maximum stress (S_{max}), as in Fig.4.8, producing a family of curves from which the fatigue life can be found for a combination of mean and sinusoidally varying stresses over a wide range of ratios. The value R = —1,0 represents the case of a cycle with a zero mean, the condition of Fig.4.3.

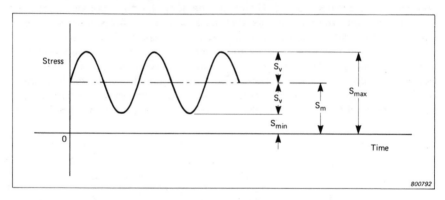

Fig.4.7. Stress composed of both steady and varying components

Several other methods of presenting this data are commonly used, one of which is shown in Fig.4.9. In this case the number of cycles to failure is plotted as a relationship between the varying stress S_v, and the mean stress S_m.

For the case of a random signal varying about a mean stress, the problems associated with the randomness of the signal and those associated with the steady stress can be considered to be independent of each other. A two part procedure is therefore normally employed; one part dealing with the randomness of the fluctuation, and one dealing with the effect of the steady component. Firstly, the randomly fluctuating component is reduced to an equivalent

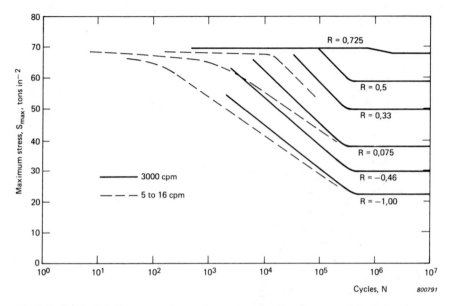

*Fig.4.8. Typical S-N curves for various stress ratios for unnotched specimens
(ASTM)*

sinusoidal stress giving the same fatigue life, as described in some detail at the beginning of the chapter. Secondly, the combined stresses are then evaluated together using curves of the types shown in Figs.4.8 and 4.9, to give an estimate of the lifetime. Also in this case, more reliable results can be obtained using S-N data generated using random excitation.

In the practical case of a real structure, the actual mode of failure and time to failure are dominated by the local physical features of the structure as well as the external factors such as corrosion, temperature, pre-treatment, etc. mentioned previously. The failure of a structure is therefore dominated by the weakest links in the failure chain and much effort is required to identify and eliminate them. Fatigue cracks may begin from stress concentrations at sharp corners, surface irregularities or damage, or welds. Large welded structures in a corrosive environment under the action of continuous random excitation are particularly susceptible to failures emanating from discontinuities in welds. Ships, offshore structures, turbine casings, and pressure vessels in chemical process plants are typical examples.

4.1.2. Acoustic Fatigue

A rather different type of fatigue failure has become of particular interest in

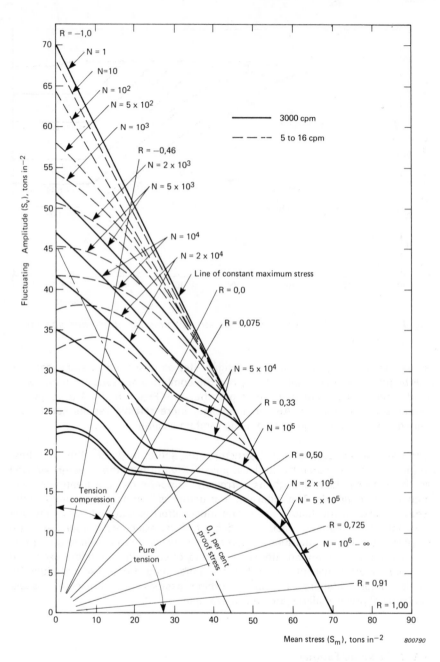

Fig.4.9. *Typical variable/mean stress curves for unnotched specimens (ASTM)*

recent years; the failure of structures excited by direct acoustic radiation rather than by structure-borne vibration. The problem has been most acute in aerospace structures where acoustic loading is caused both by direct radiation from the power plant, and by the generation of intense acoustic disturbances in the boundary layer during high speed flight. For many aircraft and rocket components, the acoustic fatigue requirements, and not the static strength requirements, determine the design of the structure.

Jet exhaust noise is highly directional, having a maximum intensity at angles of between 30° and 45° from the jet exhaust axis. Some parts of the air frame inevitably fall on this line of maximum radiation. Apart from the understandable case of engine exhaust and nacelle components, trailing edge wing panels and rear fuselage panels are often seriously affected. As the total acoustic power radiated by a jet exhaust is proportional to the eighth power of the jet efflux velocity (between the cube and the fifth power of the jet efflux velocity for rockets), and the square of the jet diameter, the magnitude of the acoustic fatigue problem on high powered lightweight structures can be readily appreciated.

The incident acoustic wave generates various modes of vibration in the structure, causing the stress concentrations which lead to eventual failure. In a structural panel, the resonances are usually very lightly damped and the response to the excitation very peaky in nature. (See Fig.4.10). The mode of failure is therefore very dependent upon the details of both the excitation spectrum and the structure's response to it. Sufficient information can normally only be gathered from extensive tests in a special chamber. The sound source must be capable of producing noise at very high levels, in excess of 150 dB, usually by means of an exponential horn. Signal generation, measuring, and analysis instrumentation is, however, similar to that described elsewhere in this volume.

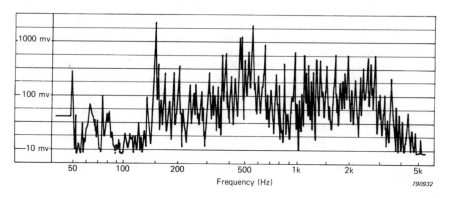

Fig.4.10. Response of a panel to acoustic excitation (after Yeh)

Further important areas where acoustic fatigue is a problem are air-moving equipment, power station generating equipment, and nuclear power plant.

The problem of random load fatigue has been studied quite extensively over the past 15 to 20 years, and interested readers are referred to the selected bibliography cited at the end of the Chapter, in particular to the Brüel & Kjær Technical Reviews No.1—1968 and No.4—1968 (included in "Selected Reprints").

4.2. DAMAGING EFFECTS OF SHOCK AND TRANSIENTS

As discussed earlier in sections 2.3 and 3.5, a shock is characterised by a sudden, not always expected, occurrence, and a short duration in relation to the natural frequency of the system on which the shock is acting. A transient, however, may last for a time which corresponds to several cycles at the natural frequency of the system. Whatever parameter is used to describe the rapid transfer of energy which constitutes a shock i.e. force, acceleration, velocity, or displacement, it is always necessary to obtain a time history of the shock in the units chosen. This information is required, not as a result in itself, but as a means of estimating the effect that the shock has on a particular system. The engineer is more interested in the response of his system to the application of a shock, e.g. from rough handling, explosions, impact, collision, etc. than he is in the shock itself. The length, rise time, and specific shape of the shock pulse, all have an influence on the ultimate response of the structure in question. It is for this reason that the concept of the shock response spectrum has been widely used to compare shock motions, to formulate laboratory tests, and to design equipment to withstand shock inputs. The motion of the system on which the shock acts is dependent upon the frequency of both the shock excitation and the natural frequency of the system.

Mechanical shocks are of particular importance in the design and operation of machinery and structures, because instantaneous input levels are frequently an order of magnitude greater than steady state levels. Shock and transient analysis are normally concerned with the design of the system to survive the environment, or with the attenuation of the input to the system by means of packaging or isolators to reduce the damaging effect of the shock input. Damage caused by shock loading will usually fall into failure categories b) and c) in Fig.4.1. Category b) may be considered a form of "fatigue" failure for which only shocks are counted and for which the life can be defined simply as the number of shocks to failure. Category c) implies instant catastrophic failure as soon as a_o is exceeded, i.e. the design shock occurs. Depending on the application, two different meanings can be attached to the word survival:

1. the system exhibits no permanent damage after a shock or a known or expected number of shocks, or

2. the system suffers no deterioration of performance either during or after the shock or series of shocks.

Permanent damage need not necessarily take place for a mechanical or structural system to fail a shock test, so a simple test to destruction may not always be sufficient to ensure survivability. In addition, the characteristics of the shock environment must be known with reasonable accuracy in order to ensure that environmental tests are valid. For this reason, measured time histories are often used as laboratory test excitations in order to reproduce as closely as possible the actual conditions experienced in use.

Methods of isolation and control are discussed in more detail in Chapter 12.

4.3. SELECTED BIBLIOGRAPHY

ASTM   STP 338—1963

BLOOMER, N.T. and   *A Large Scale Fatigue Test of Aluminium Specimens.*
ROYLANCE, T.F.:   The Aeronautical Quarterly, Vol. XVI, Nov. 1965

BROCH, J.T.:   *Selected Reprints from Technical Review: Non-Linear Systems and Random Vibration.* B & K Publication, June 1975

FORSYTH, P.J.E.:   *The Physical Basis of Metal Fatigue.* Blackie and Son, London 1969

HARRIS, C.M., and   *Shock and Vibration Handbook.* McGraw-Hill Book
CREDE, C.E. (eds.):   Company, Inc. New York, 2nd Ed. 1976

KACENA, W.J., and   *Fatigue Prediction of Structures subjected to Random*
JONES, P.J.:   *Vibration.* Shock and Vibration Bulletin, No.46, Part 3, 8/1976, pp. 87-96

KELLY, R.D., and   *Principles and Techniques of Shock Data Analysis.*
RICHMAN, G.:   Published by the Shock and Vibration Information Center, U.S. Department of Defence, 1969

LITTLE, R.E. and   *Statistical Design of Fatigue Experiments.* Applied
JEBE, E.H.:   Science Publishers, London 1975

MADAYAG, A.E. Ed.:   *Metal Fatigue: Theory and Design.* John Wiley and Sons 1969

McLEAN D.:   *Mechanical Properties of Metals.* John Wiley and Sons, 1962

MINER, M.A.:   *Cumulative Damage in Fatigue.* Journal of Appl. Mech. Vol. 12—1945

NATO AGARD: *Proceedings of a Symposium on Random Load Fatigue* — 1972

NATO AGARD: *Proceedings of a Symposium on Acoustic Fatigue* — 1973

PALMGREN, A.:   *'Die Lebensdauer von Kugellagern',* VDI Vol.68, 1924, 339—41

ROLFE, S.T., and   *Fracture and Fatigue Control in Structures.* Prentice-
BARSOM, J.M.:   Hall 1977

SANDOR, B.I.:   *Fundamentals of Cyclic Stress and Strain.* University of Wisconsin Press 1972

TRAPP, W.J., and   *Proceedings of the 2nd International Conference
FORNEY, D.M. Jnr. Ed.: of Acoustical Fatigue in Aerospace Structures.* Dayton Ohio, April 29th — May 1st 1964. Syracuse University Press

WEIBULL, W.:   *Fatigue Testing and Analysis of Results.* AGARD-Publication by Pergamon Press. Oxford — London — New York — Paris 1961

YEH, L.:   *Structure Life Prediction using Broad Band Acoustic Fatigue Theory.* Proceedings of the Noise, Shock and Vibration Conference at Monash University, Melbourne, Australia, May 22—25, 1974 Pages 113—129

Journal: *The Shock and Vibration Bulletin,* The Naval Research Laboratory, Washington DC

5. EFFECTS OF VIBRATIONS AND SHOCK ON MAN

5.1. WHOLE-BODY VIBRATION

The human body is both physically and biologically a "system" of an extremely complex nature. When looked upon as a mechanical system it contains a number of linear as well as non-linear "elements", and the mechanical properties are quite different from person to person.

Biologically the situation is by no means simpler, especially when psychological effects are included. In considering the response of man to vibrations and shocks it is necessary, however, to take into account both mechanical and psychological effects.

Because experiments with human beings are difficult, time-consuming and in extreme cases unesthetical, much of the knowledge gained to date has been obtained from experiments on animals. It is, of course, not always possible to "scale" results obtained from animal experiments to reactions expected from man, but nevertheless such experiments often result in valuable information.

As the purpose of this Chapter is more to review some of the present knowledge than to discuss particular experiments in detail, the following pages contain a brief description of some major facts which are now known about man's response to vibrations and shocks.

Considering first the human body as a mechanical "system" it may, at low frequencies and low vibration levels, be roughly approximated by a linear lumped parameter system of the type shown in Fig.5.1. One of the most important "parts" of this system with respect to vibration and shock effect seems to be the part marked "thorax-abdomen system". This is due to a distinct resonance effect occurring in the 3—6 Hz range as indicated on Figs.5.2 and 5.3 and which makes efficient vibration isolation of a sitting or standing person very difficult. A further resonance effect is found in the 20 to 30 Hz region and is caused by the head-neck-shoulder system, Fig.5.3.

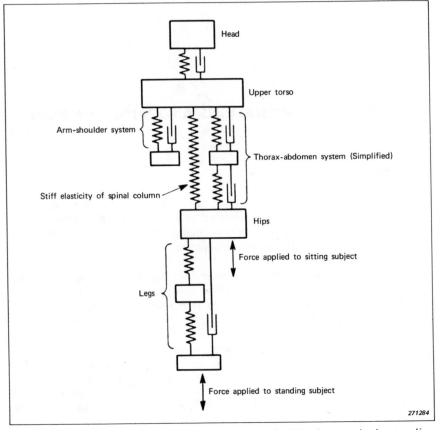

Fig.5.1. Simplified mechanical system representing the human body standing on a vertically vibrating platform. (After Coerman et al.)

Also in the region 60 to 90 Hz disturbances are felt which suggest eyeball resonances, and a resonance effect in the lower jaw-skull system has been found between 100 and 200 Hz.

Above 100 Hz, simple lumped parameter models like that shown in Fig.5.1 are not very useful. It is then necessary to apply continuous structural analysis methods which become very complex. By such methods, however, it has been shown that for the skull itself the fundamental mode of vibration seems to be in the region of 300 — 400 Hz with resonances for higher modes around 600 to 900 Hz. At still higher frequencies use must be made of wave theory both in the form of shear waves and of compressional waves (sound waves).

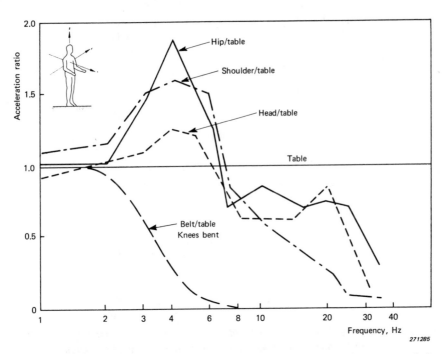

Fig.5.2. Transmissibility of vertical vibration from table to various parts of the body of a standing human subject as a function of frequency. (After Dieckmann; data for transmission to belt, after Radke)

From a shock and vibration point of view the low frequency range may be considered most important. Some very interesting measurements have here been made by von Bekesy and concern the attenuation of vibration along the human body. In Fig.5.4 the results obtained at 50 Hz are reproduced and show that the attenuation from foot to head is of the order of 30 dB. Similarly, the attenuation from hand to head is roughly 40 dB.

Apart from the mechanical responses mentioned above, both physiological and psychological effects are observed. Although these effects are rather complex and difficult to measure, it seems that physiological results obtained from animal experiments also apply to man to a certain extent. These experiments have been mostly concerned with changes in food assimilation, muscular activity, reproductive activity etc. as well as actual internal injury.

Psychological effects such as perception, discomfort, and pain, have recently been studied in some detail. Most of the studies have been carried out on vehicle drivers and aircraft pilots, whose ability to perform complex tasks under adverse environmental conditions, including vibration, is particularly

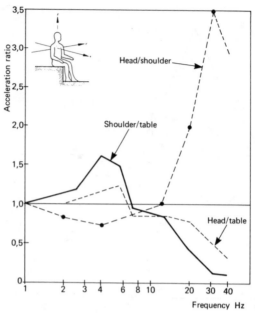

Fig.5.3. Transmissibility of vertical vibration from table to various parts of a seated human subject as a function of frequency. (After Dieckmann)

important. The data available is therefore mainly for sitting or standing subjects. The recent ISO 2631 — 1978 brings this data conveniently together as a set of vibration criteria curves for vertical and lateral vibration over the frequency range 1 to 80 Hz. These are shown in Figs.5.5 (vertical) and 5.6 (lateral), and apply to vibration transmitted to the torso of a standing or sitting person in the axis system indicated.

Vibration at frequencies below 1 Hz occurs in many forms of transport and produces effects, e.g. Kinetosis (motion sickness), which are completely different in character from those produced at higher frequencies. These effects cannot be simply related to the three parameters of the exciting motion, intensity, duration, and frequency, as has been possible in the range from 1 Hz to 80 Hz. In addition, human reaction to vibration below 1 Hz is extremely variable and seems to depend on a large number of external factors which have nothing to do with the motion, e.g. age, sex, vision, activity, odours. Despite this variability and the limited amount of data available, an attempt has been made to formulate tentative standards for the frequency range from 1 Hz down to 0,1 Hz in an addendum to the previously mentioned Standard for whole-body vibration i.e. ISO 2631. Recommendations are made only for linear motion in the vertical plane, the acceleration — time relationship following a "constant energy" law, i.e. $accn^2 \times time = constant$. It should be noted that this is the case for neither whole-body vibration (ISO 2631) nor hand-

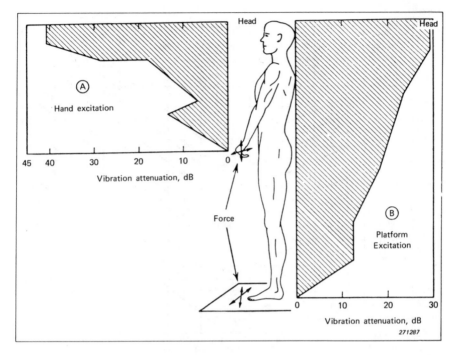

Fig.5.4. Attenuation of vibration at 50 Hz along human body. The attenuation is expressed in decibels below values at the point of excitation. For excitation of (A) hand, and (B) platform on which subject stands. (After von Bekesy)

arm vibration (Draft ISO 5349), which follow a non-linear acceleration-time relationship.

Above 80 Hz, the sensations and effects are very dependent upon local conditions at the point of application, e.g. the actual direction, position and area over which the vibration is transmitted, and upon the damping at this point, e.g. due to clothing or footwear. These external factors heavily influence the response of the skin and superficial tissue chiefly affected by frequencies above 80 Hz. It is thus generally not possible at present to state valid criteria outside the stated range, 1 Hz to 80 Hz.

The vibration levels indicated by the curves in Figs.5.5 and 5.6 are given in terms of *RMS acceleration levels which produce equal fatigue-decreased proficiency*. Exceeding the exposure specified by the curves will, in most situations cause noticeable fatigue and decreased job proficiency in most tasks. The degree of task interference depends on the subject and the complexity of

89

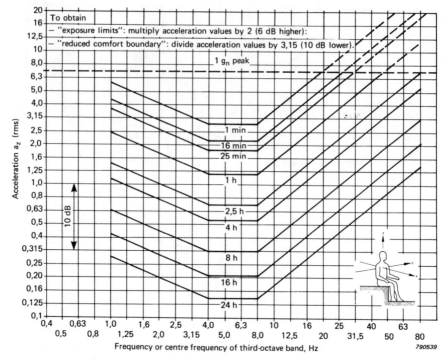

Fig.5.5. Vertical vibration exposure criteria curves defining equal fatigue-decreased proficiency boundaries

the task but the curves indicate the general range for onset of such interference and the time dependency observed.

An *upper bound to exposure* considered acceptable (hazard to health as well as performance) *is taken to be twice as high as (6 dB above)* the "fatigue-decreased proficiency" boundary shown in Fig.5.5 while the "reduced comfort boundary" is assumed to be about one third of (10 dB below) the stated levels.

These criteria are presented as recommended guidelines or trend curves rather than firm boundaries classifying quantitative biological or psychological limits. They are intended only for situations involving healthy, normal people considered fit for normal living routines and the stress of an average working day.

There are, as yet, no firm criteria for purely angular vibration equivalent to those for purely translational vibration as described above. In practice, angu-

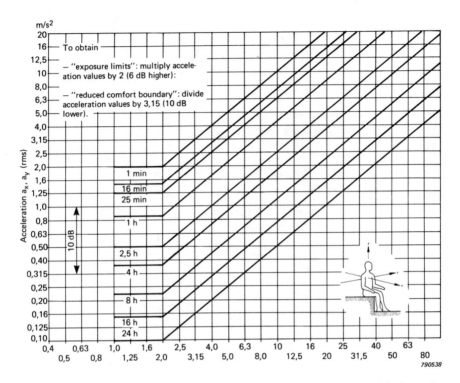

Fig.5.6. Lateral vibration exposure criteria curves defining equal fatigue-decreased proficiency boundaries

lar motion (i.e. in yaw, roll and pitch) whose centres of rotation lie at a distance from the point of application to the body, can be adequately approximated by purely translatory motion. However, there is much current work aimed at the eventual definition of criteria curves similar to those of Figs.5.5 and 5.6 for translatory vibration.

Finally, Fig.5.7 indicates the tolerance of human subjects to single shock acceleration pulses of the type produced in the floor near drop forges or similar equipment (results from a single study).

5.2. HAND-ARM VIBRATION

Hand-arm vibration is the second large problem area where transmission into the human body is concerned. It is, however, rather different from whole-body vibration in the type of problems to which it gives rise. Whereas vibration transmitted into the standing or seated body normally gives rise to problems of a general nature e.g. motion sickness, discomfort, reduced-work-

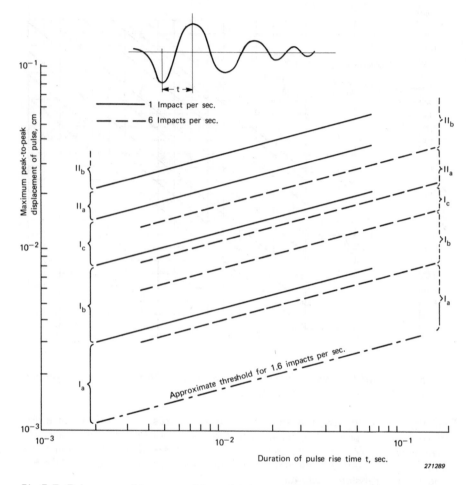

Fig.5.7. Tolerance of human subjects in the standing or supine position to re-petitive vertical impact pulses representative of impacts from pile drivers, heavy tools, heavy traffic, etc. Subjective reaction is plotted as a function of the maximum displacement of the initial pulse and its rise time. The numbers indicate the following reactions for the areas between the lines: I a, threshold of perception; I b, for easy per-ception; I c, of strong perception, annoying; II a, very unpleasant, pot-ential danger for long exposures; II b, extremely unpleasant, defin-itely dangerous. The decay process of the impact pulses was found to be of little practical significance. (After Reiher and Meister)

ing efficiency, etc, vibration applied to the hand-arm may, in addition, produce actual physical damage locally if the level and exposure times are sufficiently high.

Vibration levels encountered in many commonly used power tools are sufficiently high to cause damage when operated for durations common in industry. Typical of these power tools are chipping hammers, power grinders, hammer drills, and chain saws, found in widespread use in the mining, construction, manufacturing and forestry industries. Vibration may be transmitted into the body from a vibrating tool or hand-held workpiece via one or both arms simultaneously, causing, at lower levels, discomfort and reduced working efficiency. At higher levels and longer exposure periods, diseases affecting the blood vessels, joints and circulation occur. Severe exposure leads to a progressive circulation disorder in the part of the body suffering the highest level of vibration, usually the fingers or hand where hand-held tools are con-

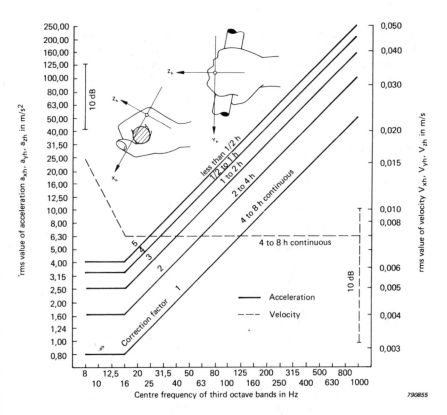

Fig.5.8. Exposure guidelines for vibration transmitted to the hand

cerned. This is variously known as "dead hand", vibration-induced white finger, or Raynaud's disease. In extreme cases this leads to permanent damage or gangrene. These diseases and their causes are currently being extensively investigated both by medical and engineering researchers.

A very recent ISO draft publication (5349) attempts to gather current knowledge into a convenient form and to enable conclusions to be drawn about the damage risk of practically measured vibration exposures. The suggested guideline levels are shown in Fig.5.8 and cover the frequency range from 8 Hz to 1 kHz. Although exposure curves for both third octave and octave bands are presented, third octaves are recommended as these are likely to be more stringent than octaves when applied to the discrete frequency spectra often encountered in rotating hand-held tools. Intermittent use is covered by a series of curves which allow greater levels of vibration for shorter exposure times, via a non-linear relationship which demands increasingly shorter exposure times at the highest levels, in a manner similar to that for the whole-body vibration curves. Compare Figs.5.5 and 5.8.

Most of the data used to derive the curves were from pure sine or narrow band investigations and they are therefore mainly applicable to that type of excitation. However, they may be provisionally applied to repeated shock and other types of markedly non-sinusoidal excitation, in which case a measure of the crest factor should be determined.

5.3. SELECTED BIBLIOGRAPHY

AGATE, J.N. and DRUETT, H.A.: *A Study of Portable Vibrating Tools in Relation to the Clinical Effects which they Produce*. Brit. J. Industr. Med., 1947, 4, 141—163

AXELSSON, SVEN ÅKE:*Analysis of Vibrations in Power Saws*. Studia Forestalia Suecica. Nr.59 1968

ALLEN, G.R.: *Proposed Limits for Exposure to Whole-Body Vertical Vibration 0,1 to 1,0 Hz*, AGARD — CP 145, 1975

COERMANN, R. et al: *The Passive Dynamic Mechanical Properties of the Human Thorax — Abdomen System and of the Whole Body System*. Aerospace Med. Vol.31, p. 443, 1960

COERMANN, R.: *Einwirkung stoßförmiger Beschleunigungen auf den Menschen*. VDI-Berichte Nr. 135, 1969

DIECKMANN, D.: *Einfluß vertikaler mechanischen Schwingungen auf den Mensch.* Arbeitsphysiol. Vol. 16, S. 519, 1957

DUPUIS, H., *Biomechanisches Verhalten, Muskelreaktion und sub-*
HARTUNG, E. and *jektive Wahrnehmung bei Schwingungserregung der*
HAMMER, W.: *oberen Extremitäten zwischen 8 und 80 Hz.* Archives of occupational and environmental health 37, 9-34 (1976)

GOLDMAN, D.E. and *The Effect of Shock and Vibration on Man.* No.60 —
VON GIERKE, H.E.: 3, Lecture and Review Series. Naval Medical Research Institute, Bethesda, Maryland, U.S.A. 1960

HARRIS, C.M. and *Shock and Vibration Handbook,* McGraw-Hill Book
CREDE, C.E. (Eds.): Company, Inc. New York 2nd Ed. 1976

O'HANLON, F.J. and *Motion Sickness Incidence as a Function of the Fre-*
McCAULEY, M.E.: *quency and Acceleration of Vertical Sinusoidal Motion.* Aerospace Medicine April 1974

I.S.O. 2631-1978: *Guide for the evaluation of human exposure to whole-body vibration*

I.S.O. Draft Addendum *Evaluation of Exposure to Whole-Body, z-axis, Verti-*
to I.S.O.-2631: *cal Vibration in the frequency range 0,1 to 1,0 Hz*

I.S.O./DIS 5349: *Principles for the measurement and the evaluation of human exposure to vibration transmitted to the hand*

MIWA, T.: *Evaluation Methods for Vibration Effect (Part 1 — 9).* Ind. Health (Japan) 1967 — 1969

RATHBONE, T.C.: *Vibration Tolerance.* Power Plant Engineering 43, p. 721 — 724, 1939

REASON, J.T. and *Motion Sickness.* Academic Press, London 1976
BRAND, J.J.:

REIHER, H. und *Die Empfindlichkeit des Menchen gegen Stöße.* For-
MEISTER, F.J.: schung auf dem Gebiete des Ingenieurwesens. Vol. 3, S. 177, 1932

REYNOLDS, D.D. and *Analytical Vibration Analysis of Non-Isolated Chain*
SOEDEL, W.: *Saws.* J.S.V. Vol.44, No.4, 1976 pp 513—523

REYNOLDS, D.D. et al.: *Hand-Arm Vibration Parts I, II and III.* J.S.V. Vol. 51, No. 2, 1977, pp 237—282

TAYLOR, W. (Ed.): *The Vibration Syndrome.* Proceedings of a Conference on the Medical Engineering and Legal Aspects of Hand-Arm Vibration, at the University of Dundee from 12 to 14 July, 1972. B.A.S. special volume No. 2, published by Academic Press, 1974

TELFORD, E.D., McCANN, M.B. and MacCORMACK, D.H.: *"Dead hand" in Users of Vibrating Tools.* The Lancet Sept. 22, 1945. 1:359

TEMPEST, W. (Ed.): *Infrasound and Low Frequency Vibration.* Academic Press, London 1976

VDI 2056: *Beurteilungsmaßstäbe für mechanische Schwingungen von Maschinen.* Oktober 1964, Beuth-Vertrieb, Berlin

VDI 2057: *Beurteilung der Einwirkung mechanischer Schwingungen auf den Menschen.* Oktober 1963, Beuth-Vertrieb, Berlin

WIKSTRÖM, B.O. and ISAKSSON, A.: *Undersöknings rapport,* 1978: 28. Arbetarskyddsstyrelsen, Fack, Stockholm, Sweden

SHOENBERGER, R.W.: *Subjective Response to very Low-Frequency Vibration,* Aviation Space and Environmental Medicine Vol. 46, No. 6, June 1975

6. VIBRATION MEASURING INSTRUMENTATION AND TECHNIQUES

6.1. GENERAL MEASUREMENT CONSIDERATIONS

As indicated previously in this book there are three quantities which are of interest in vibration studies, the vibratory displacement, velocity and acceleration (peak or RMS values). These three quantities are related simply, as described in Chapter 2. If the phase relationships between the three parameters are neglected as is always the case when making time-average measurements, then the velocity at a given frequency can be obtained by dividing the acceleration by a factor proportional to the frequency, and the displacement can be obtained by dividing the acceleration level by a factor proportional to the frequency squared. This operation is performed in electronic measuring instruments by an integration process. The relationship between the three parameters as a function of frequency is shown in Fig.6.1. Note that the axes are logarithmic.

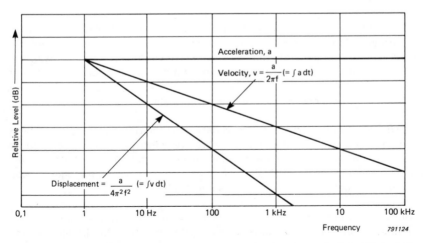

Fig.6.1. The integration and double integration of acceleration to obtain velocity and displacement respectively

The first vibration pickups producing an electrical output were rather bulky velocity sensitive devices. During the last few years there has been a marked move towards the use of acceleration sensitive transducers, called accelerometers. Reasons for this transfer of preference are that accelerometers are generally much smaller physically than velocity pick-ups and that their frequency and dynamic ranges are significantly wider, even after integration to velocity. A wider dynamic and frequency range is a prime requirement of the modern vibration pickup, particularly to cater for the growing interest in high frequency vibration as a carrier of information on the running condition of machinery and the corresponding wide range of vibration levels to be detected. An additional factor which underlines the benefits of accelerometers is the fact that an acceleration signal can be easily and validly integrated electronically to obtain velocity and displacement whereas electronic differentiation used with velocity and displacement transducers is a more complex and dubious affair.

In theory it is irrelevant which of the three parameters, acceleration, velocity or displacement are chosen to measure vibration. If one plotted a narrow-band frequency analysis of a vibration signal in terms of the three parameters, they would all show the same frequency components but would have different average slopes as seen in Fig.6.1. It can be seen that displacement measurements give low frequency components most weight and conversely acceleration measurements weight the high frequency components. This leads to a practical consideration that can influence the choice of parameter. It is advantageous to select the parameter which gives the flattest frequency spectrum in order to best utilise the dynamic range of the measuring instrumentation.

The nature of mechanical systems is such that appreciable displacements only occur at low frequencies, therefore displacement measurements are of limited value in the general study of mechanical vibrations. Displacement is often used as an indicator of unbalance in rotating machine parts because relatively large displacements usually occur at the shaft rotation frequency, which is the frequency of primary interest for balancing purposes.

RMS velocity measurements are widely used for vibration "severity" measurements. This is due to the fact that vibratory velocity is simply related to vibratory energy and is therefore a measure of the destructive effect of vibration. A given velocity level also signifies constant stress for geometrically similar constructions vibrating in the same mode.

Because acceleration measurements are weighted towards high frequency vibration components, this parameter is preferred where the frequency range of interest covers high frequencies.

Vibration pickups of small size and weight are desirable because the pickup should load the structural member on which it is mounted as little as possible and because it is often required to measure vibration at a point on a structure rather than over an area.

The frequency range of interest in vibration measurements has been increasing steadily over the past two or three decades. Today many vibration measurements are carried out up to 10 kHz, and often higher. The increased interest in higher frequencies has been prompted by the development of high-speed machinery and the recognition that high frequency vibrations carry valuable information about the condition of rolling element (ball, roller, needle) bearings, gear teeth, turbomachinery blading etc.

The vibration associated with fluid flow, jet noise, cavitation etc. is essentially random in nature and must often be measured either alone or together with periodic vibration components. This again calls for more complicated measurement techniques than was common in earlier days.

To be able to predict the effects of vibration on mechanical structures and man, it is not normally sufficient to measure the overall vibration level over the frequency range of interest. Frequency analysis is necessary to reveal the individual frequency components making up the wide band signal. For this purpose a filter is contained in or attached to the vibration measuring instrument, thus making a frequency analyzer. The filter allows only frequency components to be measured which are contained in a specific frequency band. The pass band of the filter is moved sequentially over the whole frequency range of interest so that a separate vibration level reading can be obtained at each frequency.

The filter section can consist of a number of individual contiguous fixed frequency filters which are scanned sequentially or a tunable filter which can be tuned continuously over the frequency range. A third alternative, which is becoming rapidly widespread due to advances in digital signal handling technology, is the use of real-time analyzers which present a continuously updated complete frequency spectrum on a display screen. Another fundamental difference between the various filter and analyzer types is in the filter bandwidth, narrow or wide and whether it is a fixed percentage of the tuned frequency or is a constant number of Hz absolute bandwidth independent of tuned frequency.

It is very often necessary in practical vibration work to use analyzers with an exceedingly narrow bandwidth in order to separate closely spaced sinusoidal components or because the structures excited by vibration often contain mechanical resonances with large Q-values (lightly damped resonances).

Which type of instrumentation should be used in a particular measurement situation must be decided upon by the ultimate use of the data obtained and the measuring equipment available. This and the following chapters will demonstrate the facilities provided by a wide range of instruments and discuss their application to practical problems.

6.2. SELECTION OF ACCELEROMETER

An accelerometer is an electromechanical transducer which produces at its output terminals, a voltage or charge that is proportional to the acceleration to which it is subjected. Piezoelectric accelerometers exhibit better all-round characteristics than any other type of vibration transducer and are more-or-less universally preferred for measurements covering a wide frequency range.

The heart of the accelerometer is its piezoelectric elements which are usually made from an artificially polarized ferroelectric ceramic. These piezoelectric elements have the property of producing an electrical charge which is directly proportional to strain and thus the applied force when loaded either in tension, compression or shear. In practical accelerometer designs the piezoelectric elements are arranged so that they are loaded by a mass or masses and a preloading spring or ring. When subjected to vibration the masses exert a varying force on the piezoelectric elements which is directly proportional to the vibratory acceleration. For frequencies lying well under the resonant frequency of the assembly, the acceleration of the masses will be the same as the acceleration of the base, and the output signal level will be proportional to the acceleration to which the accelerometer is subjected.

Two accelerometer configurations are in common use, the compression and the shear types which are shown in the schematic drawings in Fig.6.2.

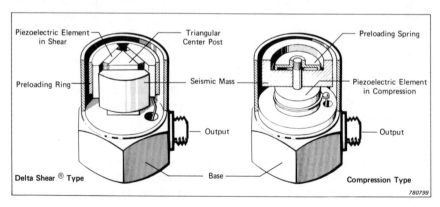

Fig.6.2. The two accelerometer configurations in common use

Accelerometer Type	Weight (gram)	Charge Sensitivity (pC/ms^{-2})*	Mounted Resonance Frequency (kHz)	Important Characteristics	Application Areas
4366 △	 28	~4,5	27	Delta Shear® Construction having good all-round characteristics and particularly low sensitivity to temperature transients and base strains	General shock and vibration measurements. Vibration testing and control.
4367 △	13	~2	32		
4368 △	 30	~4,5	27		
4369 △	 14	~2	32		
4371 △	 11	1 ± 2%	35	Delta Shear® types as above. Also have Uni-Gain® sensitivity for simple system calibration and Interchangeability	
4370 △	 54	10 ± 2%	18		General vibration measurements. High sensitivity for low-level measurements
4375 △	2 excl. cable	~0,3	60	Miniature size, low weight Delta Shear® type. High resonance frequency	High level and high freq. vibr. measurements. Ideal for delicate structures, panels etc. and in confined spaces
4374 △	0,7 excl. cable	~0,1	75	Submiature size, low weight shear type. Very high resonant frequency	
8309 □	3 excl. cable	~0,004	180	Miniature size. Integral fixing stud. Integral cable.	Shock measurements up to 1 million ms^{-2} High frequency vibr. measurements
4321 △	 55	1 ± 2%	40	Three Delta Shear® Uni-Gain® accelerometers combined in one unit	Vibration measurements in three mutually perpendicular directions
8305 □	 40	~0,12	30	Quartz element for high stability. Laser calibrated to ± 0,5% accuracy	Reference standard for comparison calibration of accelerometers
8306 □	 500	1000	1 kHz LP filter built in	Very High Uni-Gain® sensitivity. Built-in Preamp and LP filter. Requires 28V 2mA DC power supply	Ultra low-level (down to 0,000 002 g) and low freq. vibration measurements on large structures
8308 □	 100	1 ± 2%	30	Robust-construction. Balanced Uni-Gain® output. Max. Temp. 400°C	Permanent vibration monitoring. High temp. vibr. measurements.
8310 □	 100 excl. cable	1 ± 20%	30	As Type 8308 but with integral high temp (800°C) cable	Aeronautical, industrial and nuclear use. Used with preamp. Type 2634

*Multiply by 9.81 for sensitivity in pC/g   △ Shear Types   □ Compression Types   791117

Fig.6.3. Main characteristics and application areas for B & K accelerometers

In general, it can be said that the shear configuration gives the best all-round results for general purpose accelerometers and the compression design is used for accelerometers which are aimed at particular applications.

The table in Fig.6.3 indicates the application and main characteristics of the B & K accelerometer range. At first glance there may seem to be a confusingly large range of accelerometers available. But it will be seen, after closer inspection, that they can be divided into two main groups. A group of general purpose types, with various sensitivities and a choice of top or side connectors, which will satisfy most needs, and a range of accelerometers which have their characteristics slanted towards a particular application.

When selecting an accelerometer for a particular application the accelerometer's parameters and the environmental conditions it is to be used under need to be considered as follows:

Frequency Range: The frequency response of an accelerometer has a characteristic shape as shown in Fig.6.4. Measurements are normally confined to using the linear portion of the response curve which at the high frequency end is limited by the accelerometer's natural resonance. As a rule of thumb the upper frequency limit for measurements can be set to one-third of the accelerometer's resonance frequency so that vibration components measured at this limit will be in error by no more than + 12% ($\sim$ 1 dB). Small, low mass accelerometers can have a resonant frequency as high as 180 kHz but for the more sensitive general purpose accelerometers resonant frequencies of 30 kHz (giving an upper frequency limit of 10 kHz) are typical.

It should be noted however that an accelerometer's useful frequency range

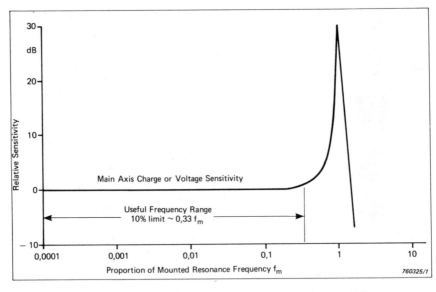

Fig.6.4. Frequency characteristic of a piezoelectric accelerometer

is significantly higher, i.e. to 1/2 or 2/3 of its resonant frequency, where for example 3 dB linearity is acceptable. This may be the case where vibration measurements are being used to monitor the internal condition of machines because repeatability is there more important than linearity.

In practice the lower measuring frequency limit is determined by two factors. The first is the low-frequency cut-off of the associated preamplifier, but this is not normally a problem as the limit is usually well below 1 Hz. The second is the effect of ambient temperature fluctuations (temperature transients) to which the accelerometer is sensitive. With modern shear type accelerometers this effect is typically 20 dB lower than for corresponding compression types which thus allows measurement down to well below 1 Hz for normal environments.

Sensitivity, Mass and Dynamic Range: Ideally, the higher the transducer sensitivity the better, but a compromise has to be made because high sensitivity normally entails a large piezoelectric assembly and consequently a relatively large, heavy unit with low resonant frequency. In normal circumstances the sensitivity is not too critical a factor as modern preamplifiers are designed to accept these low-level signals.

Accelerometer mass becomes important when measuring on light test objects. The accelerometer should load the structural member as little as possible; additional mass can significantly change the vibration levels and frequencies present at the measuring point and invalidate the measured results. An approximate indication of the change in structural response due to loading can be found using the following equations:

$$a_s = \frac{a_m(m_s + m_a)}{m_s} \quad \text{and} \quad f_s = f_m \sqrt{\frac{m_s + m_a}{m_s}} \tag{6.1}$$

where:

a_m = acceleration measured with accelerometer mounted
a_s = acceleration without accelerometer
f_m = resonance frequency measured with accelerometer mounted
f_s = resonance frequency without accelerometer
m_a = accelerometer mass
m_s = effective mass of that "part" of the structure to which the accelerometer is mounted.

As a general rule, the accelerometer mass should be no greater than one-tenth of the effective (dynamic) mass of the part of the structure to which the accelerometer is mounted.

When it is wished to measure abnormally low or high acceleration levels, the dynamic range of the accelerometer should be considered. Theoretically the output of a piezoelectric accelerometer is linear down to zero acceleration but in practice the lower dynamic limit is determined by electrical noise from

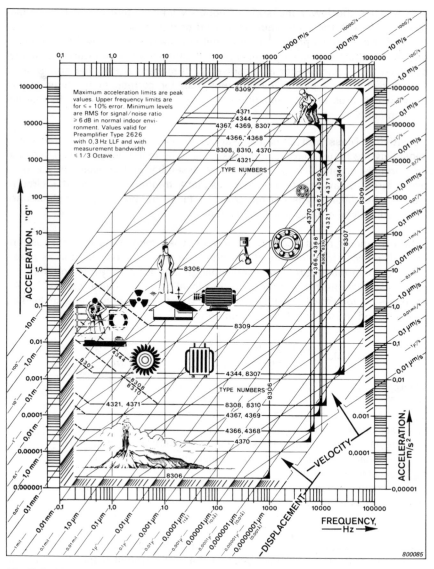

Fig.6.5. Measuring range nomogram for B & K accelerometers under the specific conditions stated

connecting cables and amplifier circuitry. This limit is normally below $0,01\,ms^{-2}$ with general purpose instruments measuring over a wide band. Significantly lower levels may be measured when using a filter for frequency analysis.

The upper dynamic limit is determined by the accelerometer's structural strength. General purpose accelerometers are linear up to 50 to $100\,kms^{-2}$ (5000 to $10000\,g$) which is well into the range of mechanical shocks. For very high shock measurements the shock accelerometer (Type 8309) shown in Fig.6.3 can be used up to $10^6\,ms^{-2}$ ($100000\,g$).

A typical example of how the various factors limit the operating range of B & K accelerometer types under specific conditions is shown in the nomogram, Fig.6.5.

Transverse Response: The transverse sensitivity of an accelerometer is its sensitivity to accelerations in a plane perpendicular to the main accelerometer axis as shown in Fig.6.6. It is normally expressed in percent of the main axis sensitivity and should be as low as possible. The transverse sensitivity varies according to which direction is considered, the direction of minimum sensitivity is marked on most B & K accelerometer types with a red paint spot. Measurement of the maximum transverse sensitivity is part of the indi-

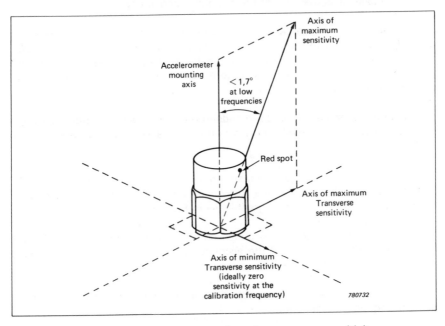

Fig.6.6. Vectorial representation of transverse sensitivity

105

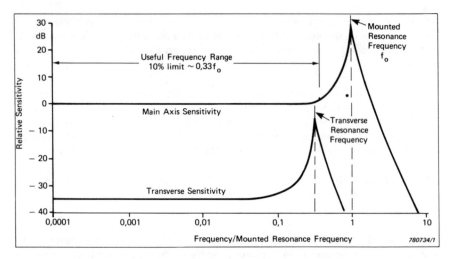

Fig.6.7. The relative response of an accelerometer to main axis and transverse axis vibration

vidual calibration procedure for many accelerometer types and is always less than 3 to 4% according to type. It should be noted that the transverse sensitivity is typically less than 1% of the main axis sensitivity.

Piezoelectric accelerometers also exhibit transverse resonance as indicated in Fig.6.7. Where high levels of high frequency transverse vibration are present at the measuring position this may result in erroneous results and in this case measurements should be made to establish the level and frequency content of transverse vibrations.

Transient Response: Shocks are sudden releases of energy often characterised by having a high level, short duration and a very wide frequency content.

The overall linearity of the measuring system can be limited at low and high frequencies by phenomena known as Zero Shift and Ringing respectively. These effects are shown graphically in Fig.6.8.

"Zero Shift" is caused both by phase non-linearities in the preamplifier and by the piezoelectric element of the accelerometer retaining charge after being subjected to very high level shocks.

"Ringing" occurs when the accelerometer resonance frequency is excited by high frequency components.

106

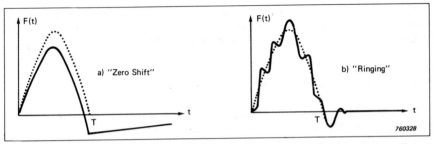

Fig.6.8. Vibration measurement system response to half sine wave pulse of length T.
a) "Zero Shift" limits the low-frequency response of the system.
b) "Ringing" limits the high frequency response of the system

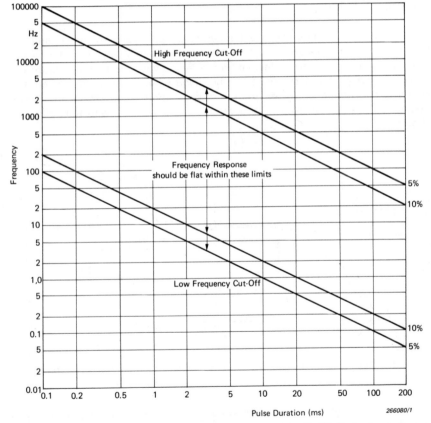

Fig.6.9. Vibration system —3 dB lower and upper limiting frequencies vs pulse duration T for acceleration measurements on transient vibrations keeping amplitude errors less than 5 and 10% respectively

107

To avoid significant measuring errors due to these effects, the frequency response of the measuring system should be limited as shown in Fig.6.9 which is based on measuring errors of less than 5% or 10%.

6.2.1. Environmental Conditions

Temperature: Typical general purpose accelerometers can tolerate temperatures up to 250°C. At higher temperatures the piezoelectric ceramic will begin to depolarise causing a permanent loss in sensitivity. Up to temperature excesses of 50°C above the specified limit the loss is gradual so that after recalibration the accelerometer is still usable. At even higher temperatures the Curie point is reached which results in complete destruction of the piezoelectric element. Special high temperature accelerometers can be used in temperatures up to 400°C.

All piezoelectric materials are temperature dependent so that changes in the ambient temperature result in changes in sensitivity. For this reason B & K accelerometers are delivered with a sensitivity versus temperature calibration curve so that corrections can be made when working in temperatures significantly higher or lower than the calibration temperature of approximately 20°C. A curve plotting the variation in sensitivity with temperature is shown in Fig.6.10.

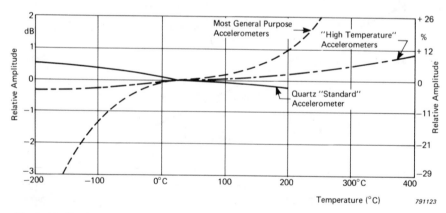

Fig.6.10. Typical charge sensitivity versus temperature characteristic for piezoelectric accelerometers

When accelerometers are to be attached to surfaces at a higher temperature than their design maximum a heat sink and mica washer can be inserted between the base and the surface to reduce heat transmission as shown in Fig.6.11.

108

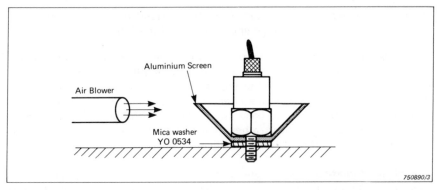

Fig.6.11. The use of a mica washer and heat sink will enable accelerometer to be used on surfaces at temperatures rather higher than the accelerometer's design maximum

Temperature Transients: Piezoelectric accelerometers also exhibit a varying output when subjected to small temperature fluctuations called temperature transients in the measuring environment. This is normally only a problem where very low level or low frequency vibrations are being measured. Modern shear type accelerometers have a very low sensitivity to temperature transients.

Cable Noise: Since piezoelectric accelerometers have a high output impedance problems can sometimes arise with noise signals induced into the connecting cable to the preamplifier. These spurious signals can result from ground loops, triboelectric noise, or electromagnetic noise.

Ground loop currents can flow in the shield of accelerometer cables because of slight differences in the electrical potential of grounding points when the accelerometer and the measuring equipment are grounded separately. The loop is broken by electrically isolating the accelerometer base from the mounting surface by means of an isolating stud (max. temperature 250°C) and mica washer.

Triboelectric noise can be generated by the accelerometer cable due to local capacity and charge changes between the conductor and shield as the cable vibrates. This problem is avoided by using a proper internally graphited accelerometer cable and fixing it to avoid cable movements as much as possible.

Electromagnetic noise can be a problem when the accelerometer cable lies in the vicinity of running electrical machinery. Double shielded cable helps to reduce this problem but in severe cases a balanced accelerometer and differential preamplifier should be used. The latter is standard practice with permanent vibration monitoring equipment on industrial machinery.

Base Strains: When an accelerometer is mounted on a surface which is undergoing dynamic deformations a spurious output will be generated as a result of strain being transmitted to the sensing element. Accelerometers have thick stiff bases to minimise this effect. Note that Delta Shear® types have a particularly low sensitivity to base strains because the piezoelectric element is mounted on a centre post rather than directly to the accelerometer base, and this does not so directly result in shear deformation of the elements.

Nuclear Radiation: Most general purpose accelerometer types may be used under gamma radiation rates of 10 k Rad/h up to an accumulated dose of 2 M Rad without significant changes in characteristics. Types intended for permanent installation on machines and equipment may also be used in heavy neutron radiation at rates of 1 M Rad/h up to accumulated doses of 100 M Rad. Special mineral insulated "hardline" cables are necessary in this case.

Magnetic Fields: The magnetic sensitivity of piezoelectric accelerometers is very low, normally less than $10\,\text{ms}^{-2}$ /T with a 50 Hz alternating field and least favourable orientation of the accelerometer.

Humidity: Most accelerometers are sealed, either by epoxy bonding or welding and are therefore impervious to moisture. However, cable connectors only offer superficial protection. For short term exposure the transducer socket and cable plug can be dipped in silicone grease before the connector is assembled. For exposure to high humidity or direct immersion the whole assembled connector should be encapsulated in an acid-free RTV silicone rubber compound. In wet environments standard Teflon insulated accelerometer cables should always be used.

Corrosive Substances: Most accelerometers are encased in stainless steel, titanium or beryllium and therefore have a high resistance to most of the corrosive substances encountered.

Acoustic Noise: The noise levels present in machinery are not normally sufficient to cause any significant error in vibration measurements. It may be expected that the acoustically induced vibration in the structure on which the accelerometer is mounted will be far greater than the airborne excitation of the accelerometer.

This concludes the list of environmental factors which need to be considered when selecting and using piezoelectric accelerometers. To illustrate the sort of figures to be expected, the full specifications of a typical general purpose accelerometer, B & K Type 4370, are tabulated in Fig.6.12.

Weight:*
54 grams

Charge Sensitivity:*
10 pC/ms^{-2} ± 2%
(~ 100 pC/g)

Typical Voltage Sensitivity:*
8,5 mV/ms^{-2}
(~ 85 mV/g)

Mounted Resonant Frequency:*
18 kHz

Frequency Range:*
5% 0,2$^+$ to 3500 Hz
10% 0,2$^+$ to 6000 Hz

Capacitance Including Cable:**
1200 pF

Max Transverse Sensitivity:***
< 4%

Piezoelectric Material:
PZ 23

Typical Temperature Response

Configuration:
Delta Shear

Typical Base Strain Sensitivity:****
(in base plane at 250 μ strain)
0,003 ms^{-2}/ μ strain
(0,0003 g/μ strain)

Typical Temperature Transient
Sensitivity:****
(3 Hz LLF)
0,08 ms^{-2}/°C (0,008 g/°C)

Typical Magnetic Sensitivity:
(50 Hz − 0,03 T)
1,2 ms^{-2}/T (0,012 g/k Gauss)

Typical Acoustic Sensitivity:
(Equiv. Acc'n. at 154 dB SPL,
2 − 100 Hz)
0,001 ms^{-2} (0,0001 g)

Minimum Leakage Resistance:
(at 20°C)
20 GΩ

Maximum Ambient Temperature:
250°C (500°F)

Maximum Positive or Negative Shock:
(along main axis)
50 kms^{-2} (5000 g)

Maximum Continuous Sinusoidal
Acceleration:
20 kms^{-2} peak (2000 g)

Maximum Acceleration with
Mounting Magnet:
500 ms^{-2} (50 g)

Base & Housing Material:
Stainless Steel AISI 316

Dimensions:

Frequency Response Curve

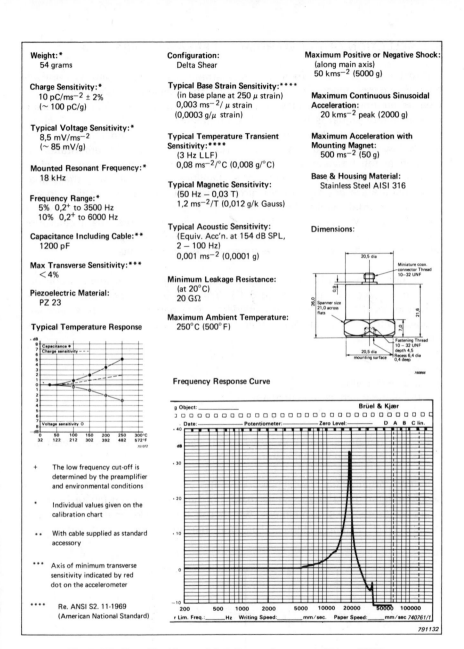

+   The low frequency cut-off is
     determined by the preamplifier
     and environmental conditions

*   Individual values given on the
     calibration chart

**   With cable supplied as standard
     accessory

*** Axis of minimum transverse
     sensitivity indicated by red
     dot on the accelerometer

**** Re. ANSI S2. 11-1969
     (American National Standard)

Fig.6.12. Specifications of B & K accelerometer Type 4370

111

6.3. SELECTION OF ACCELEROMETER PREAMPLIFIERS

Direct loading of a piezoelectric accelerometer's output, even by relatively high impedance loads can greatly reduce the accelerometer's sensitivity as well as limiting its frequency response. To eliminate this effect the accelerometer output signal is fed through a preamplifier which has a very high input impedance and a low output impedance, suitable for connection to the relatively low input impedance of measuring and analyzing instrumentation. In addition to the function of impedance conversion most preamplifiers include variable amplification and many other facilities for conditioning the signal. Preamplifiers are powered either directly from AC mains or from built-in batteries or external DC supplies. A summary of preamplifier types is shown in Fig.6.15. The type of preamplifier used depends on whether the accelerometer is considered as a voltage or charge source. Both voltage and charge sensitivities of the accelerometer are stated in the specifications.

The difference can be understood by considering the equivalent circuit diagram of an accelerometer in Fig.6.13. Within the frequency range in question, the accelerometer can be considered as a generator which is parallel - coupled with an internal capacitance C. As the charge on the capacitor is defined as

$$q = e \cdot C$$

where:
q = the electrical charge
e = the voltage across the capacitor
C = the internal capacitance

it follows that an acceleration which produces a certain voltage, e, also produces a charge q on the capacitor C.

Voltage preamplifiers, which work on the varying output voltage from the accelerometer, have been widely used, but have fallen from favour in recent years since charge preamplifiers, which see the accelerometer as a charge source, have become available. The main reason for this is that with voltage

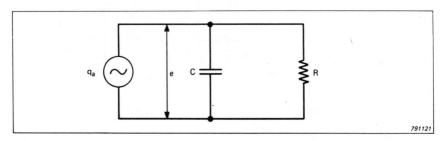

Fig.6.13. Equivalent circuit for an accelerometer

112

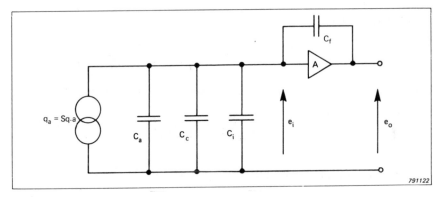

Fig.6.14. Equivalent diagram for an accelerometer plus cable plus charge amplifier

preamplifiers the sensitivity calibration of the measuring system is dependent on the capacitance of the connecting cable. Increasing the connecting cable length results in increased signal attenuation and whenever the cable length is changed the measuring system sensitivity is changed.

Charge amplifiers are now used very widely, primarily because of their simplicity of use. The influence of shunt capacitances in the accelerometer circuit is eliminated and it is not necessary to take note of the length of connected cables. All one needs to know for proper calibration is the charge sensitivity of the accelerometer.

An equivalent diagram of a charge amplifier with cable and accelerometer is shown in Fig.6.14.

A charge amplifier consists basically of an operational amplifier with high amplification, back-coupled across a condenser C_f. It can be shown that the output voltage from the amplifier can be expressed as:

$$e_o = \frac{q_a \cdot A}{C_a + C_c + C_i - C_f(A-1)} = e_i \cdot A$$

where: e_o = preamplifier output voltage
          q_a = generated charge
          A = amplification
          e_i = preamplifier input voltage
          C_a = accelerometer capacitance
          C_c = connecting cable capacitance
          C_i = preamplifier input capacitance.
          S_q = accelerometer charge sensitivity
          a = acceleration

113

From this is obtained

$$e_i = \frac{S_q \cdot a}{C_a + C_c + C_i - C_f(A-1)} = \frac{C_a}{C_a + C_c + C_i - C_f(A-1)} \cdot e_a$$

Since in this equation A is very large, the expression can be reduced to

$$e_i \approx \left| \frac{C_a}{C_f \cdot A} \right| \cdot e_a \approx \left| \frac{q_a}{C_f \cdot A} \right| \qquad (6.2)$$

which is independent of the cable capacitance C_c.

As mentioned in the introduction to this section, modern accelerometer preamplifiers are available which include many useful facilities for conditioning the signal in addition to the basic requirement of impedance conversion.

A calibrated variable gain facility is often provided to amplify the low-level accelerometer signal to a level suitable for input to tape recorders, compressor amplifiers etc. This facility is often combined with a secondary gain adjustment to normalise "awkward" transducer sensitivities so that the output sensitivity is a convenient "round" figure. For example an accelerometer sensitivity of $1,7\,pC/ms^{-2}$ can be normalised to an output sensitivity of either 1, 10, 100 or 1000 mV/ms^{-2}. This greatly simplifies the setting up, calibration and reading of a measuring system.

Some accelerometer preamplifiers include integrators to convert the acceleration proportional output from the accelerometer to either velocity or displacement proportional signals. This is convenient when the signal is to be fed to a measuring amplifier or analyzer, which are not normally equipped with integrators.

To attenuate noise and vibration signals which lie outside the frequency range of interest most preamplifiers are equipped with a range of high-pass and low-pass filters. This avoids interference from electrical noise or signals outside the linear portion of the accelerometer frequency range. Other facilities often provided are an overload indicator, reference oscillator and battery condition indicator where applicable.

By setting the upper and lower frequency limits of the preamplifier to 1 decade of frequency above and below respectively the actual range of interest, measuring errors resulting from phase distortion can be avoided. Phase distortion does not effect RMS measurements on continuous signals but can prevent the accurate measurement of peak levels and affect the usefulness of waveform measurements. For integration of shocks and transients, refer to Appendix E.

114

	2635	2626	2651	2634	2650
Preamplifier Type	 3 digit sensitivity conditioning, low noise charge amplifier	 3 digit sensitivity conditioning, low noise charge amplifier.	 3-Uni-Gain sensitivity settings. Charge amplifier. Very low frequency measurement capability	Small, robust, adjustable gain, charge amplifier. Excellent electromagnetic radiation immunity	 4 digit sensitivity conditioning, Low noise charge and voltage amplifier
Measurement Modes	Acceleration Velocity Displacement	Acceleration	Acceleration Velocity	Acceleration	Acceleration
Acceleration Sensitivity	0,1 mV to 10 V/pC (−20 to + 80 dB)	0,1 mV to 1 V/pC (−20 to + 60 dB)	0,1−1−10 mV/pC (−20 to + 20 dB)	0,9 to 10 mV/pC internally adjustable (0 to 20 dB)	0,1 mV/pC to 100 mV/pC. 100 mV/V to 100 V/V (−20 to + 40 dB)
Frequency Range	0,1 Hz to 200 kHz	0,3 Hz to 100 kHz	0,003 Hz to 200 kHz	1 Hz to 200 kHz	0,3 Hz to 200 kHz
Selectable Low Frequency Limits —	0,2; 1; 2; 10 Hz	0,3; 3; 10; 30 Hz	0,003; 0,03; 0,3; 1 Hz	———	0,3 & 3 Hz and 2 kHz
High	0,1; 1; 3; 10; 30; > 100 kHz	1; 3; 10; 30; > 100 kHz	200 kHz	———	1; 3; 10; 30; > 200 kHz
Power Supply	Internal batteries or Ext. DC	AC Mains	Ext. DC	Ext. DC	AC Mains
Other Features	Overload indicator. Test oscillator. Battery condition indicator.	Overload indicator. Direct and transformer coupled outputs.	Input signal ground floating or grounded	Normal or differential input. Can be fixed to machine frames.	Overload indicator. Test oscillator. Particularly used for comparison calibration of accelerometers

791118

Fig.6.15. Main characteristics of B & K accelerometer preamplifiers

The table in Fig.6.15 has been prepared to demonstrate the various facilities available on preamplifiers and assist in their selection.

6.4. CALIBRATION AND SYSTEM PERFORMANCE CHECKS

Each instrument produced by Brüel & Kjær has been individually checked for agreement with published specifications before leaving the factory. In the case of accelerometers the quality control procedure includes a detailed calibration of the sensitivity and response of each individual accelerometer. A typical calibration chart is shown in Fig.6.16.

The two left-hand columns give individually measured values for characteristics such as sensitivity, capacitance, transverse sensitivity etc. together with a temperature response curve and specified representative values for the accelerometer's sensitivity to various environmental effects. The frequency response curve on the right is individually plotted for each accelerometer.

Where accelerometers are stored and operated within their environmental limits, i.e. not subjected to excessive shocks, temperatures, radiation doses

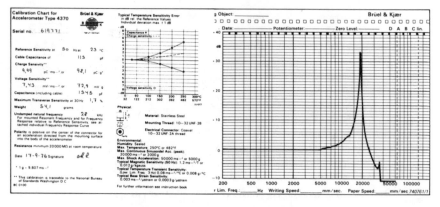

Fig.6.16. A typical accelerometer calibration chart

etc., there will be a minimal change in characteristics over a long time period; tests have shown that characteristics typically change less than 2%, even over periods of several years.

In view of this, "calibrated" readings are obtained from a measuring system merely by noting the transducer sensitivity as recorded on its calibration chart, and the gain of the measuring instrument.

However, in normal use, accelerometers are often subjected to quite violent treatment which may result in a significant change in characteristics and sometimes in permanent damage.

When dropped onto a concrete floor from hand height an accelerometer can be subjected to a shock of many thousands of *g*. It is normally wise there-

Fig.6.17. Accelerometer Calibrator Type 4291

	Acceleration ms^{-2}	Velocity mms^{-1}	Displacement μm
Peak	10	20	40
Peak-to-Peak	20	40	80
RMS	7,07	14,1	28,3

Fig.6.18. Table-vibration of Accelerometer Calibrator Type 4291 in terms of Peak and RMS acceleration, velocity and displacement

fore to make a periodic check of the sensitivity calibration, this being normally sufficient to confirm that the accelerometer is not damaged.

The most convenient means of performing a periodic calibration check is by using a calibrated vibration source as shown in Fig.6.17. This has a small built-in shaker table and generator which can be adjusted to vibrate at precisely 10 m/s^2 (1,02 g) peak. As the signal is a well defined 79,6 Hz sinusoid it can also be used for checking out systems measuring velocity and displacement, RMS or Peak. The table in Fig.6.18 shows the values obtained in these terms.

The sensitivity calibration of an accelerometer is checked by fastening it to the shaker table and noting its output when vibrated at 10 ms^{-2}. Calibration accuracy is within ± 2% when used carefully. Alternatively an accelerometer can be reserved for use as a reference. This is mounted on the shaker table with the accelerometer to be calibrated. The ratio of their respective outputs when vibrated will be proportional to their sensitivities, and as the sensitivity of the reference accelerometer is known, the unknown accelerometer's sensitivity can be accurately determined.

An equally important application for the portable calibrator is the checking of a complete measuring or analyzing set-up before the measurements are made. The measuring accelerometer is simply transferred from the measuring object to the calibrator and vibrated at a level of 10 ms^{-2}. The meter readout can be checked and if a level or tape recorder is being used, the calibration level can be recorded for future reference.

In order to check the frequency response of an accelerometer or measuring system the small calibration exciter shown in Fig.6.19 can be used. With the instrumentation set-up shown in Fig.6.20 frequency responses may be plotted from about 200 Hz up to 35 kHz. The calibrator has a built-in control accelerometer which allows the vibration level at the exciter table to be held constant over a frequency range which covers the resonant frequency of

117

Fig.6.19. Calibration Exciter Type 4290

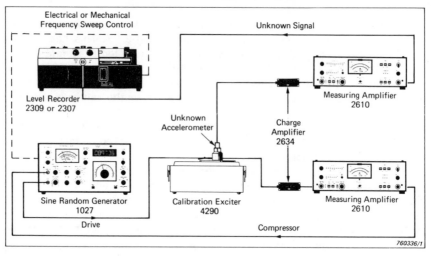

Fig.6.20. Instrumentation set-up for plotting the frequency response of accelerometers

many accelerometers. Calibration levels are rather low, that is, in the order of 1 ms^{-2} .

Some vibration testing specifications demand that transducers used on valuable test specimens are calibrated at a level equal to or higher than the test level. Since the levels these transducers will experience are often unknown, a high arbitrary confirmation level is selected, commonly $100\,g$ ($\sim 1000\,\text{ms}^{-2}$). Vibration exciters capable of exciting an accelerometer up to this level are far more powerful than the two "handy" exciters previously shown. The $380/440\,\text{N}$ ($85/100\,\text{lbf}$) force B & K exciter system includes an

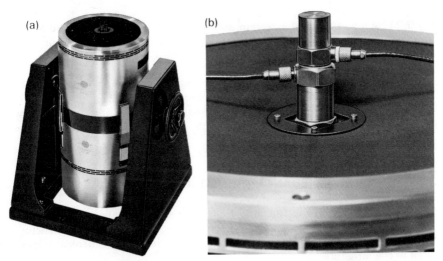

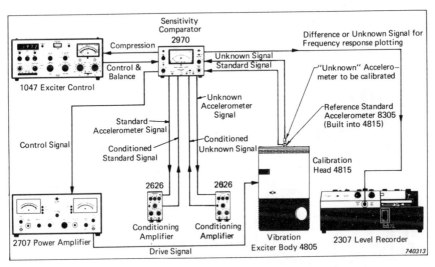

Fig.6.21.(a) A transducer calibration exciter capable of exciting accelerometers at 1000 m/s² (B & K Type 4801 T + 4815)

(b) Close-up view of the Exciter Head Type 4815 showing an accelerometer to be calibrated mounted on the Reference Standard Accelerometer Type 8305

Fig.6.22. An instrumentation arrangement for the rapid and accurate back-to-back (comparison) calibration of accelerometers

exciter head which is specially optimized to fulfil the demanding requirements of transducer calibration up to these high levels. This is shown in

Fig.6.21.(a) mounted on the system exciter body. A reference standard accelerometer is built into the exciter head for back-to-back calibration purposes as shown in Fig.6.21.(b).

An instrumentation arrangement employing the calibration head mounted on a permanent magnet exciter body is shown in Fig.6.22. The sensitivity comparator used in this arrangement is particularly valuable where many transducers are to be calibrated to a high degree of accuracy (better than ± 0,5% can be achieved).

6.5. FORCE AND IMPEDANCE TRANSDUCERS

The forces producing and resulting from mechanical vibrations are of great interest in mechanical dynamics. The force acting on a mechanical structure divided by the vibration velocity it produces defines the mechanical impedance of the structure.

Like the accelerometer, the force transducer also uses a piezoelectric element which, when compressed, produces an electrical output proportional to the force transmitted through it. For dynamic force signals the same signal conditioning and measuring instrumentation as for piezoelectric accelerometers can be used. For low frequency and semi-static forces, preamplifiers with very long time constants are necessary.

The force transducer is mounted in the force transmission path so that it is subjected to the forces to be measured. It can measure both tensile and com-

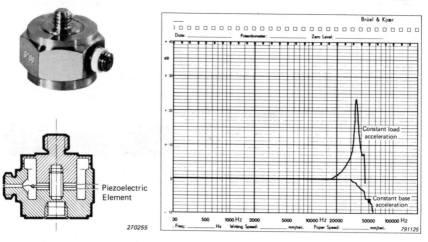

Fig.6.23. Construction and typical frequency response of Force Transducer Type 8200

pressive forces as its piezoelectric element is preloaded. A high overall stiffness ensures that it has a high resonant frequency and that when introduced into a mechanical system it has minimal disturbing effect due to deformation. A typical construction and frequency response are shown in Fig.6.23.

An impedance head contains two transducers, a force transducer which measures the force applied to a structure under investigation and an accelerometer which measures the resulting motion at the point of application. Normally the output of the accelerometer is integrated to obtain a signal proportional to velocity so that the mechanical impedance $Z = \frac{F}{V}$ can be found.

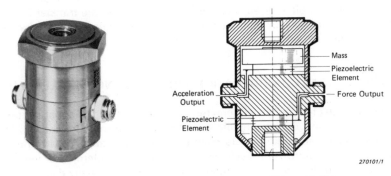

Fig.6.24. Construction of Impedance Head Type 8001

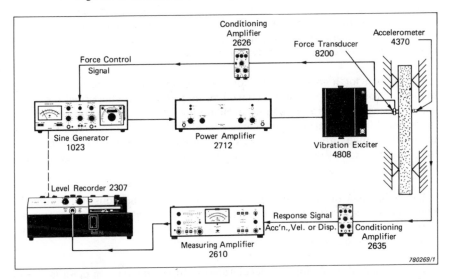

Fig.6.25. Instrumentation arrangement for measuring the impedance of an asphalt composite bar sample as a function of frequency

121

The construction of a typical impedance head is shown schematically in Fig.6.24. An important feature of the construction is that the force transducer element is located very close to the driving point to obtain a stiff, low mass coupling to the test point. It should be noted that the impedance head is dimensioned for relatively light loading and is therefore suitable for investigating a wide range of light structures, machine elements and material samples. In the medical field the impedance head can be used for measurements on soft samples and the human body.

Impedance measurements on heavier, stiff constructions are performed using a force transducer and a separate accelerometer as shown in Fig.6.25. For point impedance measurements the two transducers are mounted on opposite sides of a plate or adjacent to each other while the transfer impedance of the structure will be obtained when the two transducers are positioned remote from each other.

6.6. PRACTICAL CONSIDERATIONS IN MOUNTING ACCELEROMETERS

Having selected an accelerometer, bearing in mind the parameters discussed in section 6.2, a suitable mounting position must be chosen. The accelerometer is mounted with its main sensitivity axis aligned with the desired measuring direction. As previously mentioned the accelerometer will respond to vibration in directions other than its main axis. Sensitivity decreases as the angle between the main axis and the direction of vibration increases until at a plane normal to the main axis the transverse sensitivity is a minimum of up to 3 to 4% of the main axis sensitivity. The direction of minimum transverse sensitivity is indicated by a red spot painted on many accelerometers; in this direction the transverse sensitivity is virtually zero.

The reason for measuring vibration will normally dictate the accelerometer mounting position. It should be chosen so as to obtain a short rigid mechanical path from the vibration source avoiding gaskets etc., for example with rotating machinery, bearing housings are ideal. Valuable information can be obtained from measurements both in the axial direction and either the horizontal or vertical radial direction, whichever is expected to have the lowest stiffness.

The response of mechanical objects to forced vibrations is a complex phenomenon, so that one can expect, especially at high frequencies, to measure significantly different vibration levels and frequency spectra, even at adjacent measuring points on the same machine element.

The method of attaching the accelerometer to the measuring point is one of the most critical factors in obtaining accurate results from practical vibration measurements. Sloppy mounting results in a reduction in the mounted resonant frequency, which can severely limit the useful frequency range of the accelerometer. The ideal mounting is by a threaded stud onto a flat, smooth surface as shown in Fig.6.26 (a). A thin layer of grease applied to the mounting surface before tightening down the accelerometer will usually improve the mounting stiffness. The tapped hole in the machine part should be sufficiently deep so that the stud is not forced into the base of the accelerometer. The drawing shows a typical response curve of a general purpose accelerometer mounted with a fixed stud on a flat surface. The resonant frequency attained is almost as high as the 32 kHz mounted resonant frequency attained under calibration where the mounting surface is dead flat and smooth.

A commonly used alternative mounting method is the use of a thin layer of bees-wax for sticking the accelerometer into place. As can be seen from the response curve, Fig.6.26 (b) the resonant frequency is only slightly reduced. Because bees-wax becomes soft at higher temperatures, the method is restricted to about 40°C. With clean surfaces, bees-wax fixing is usable up to acceleration levels of about 100 m/s^2.

A mica washer and isolated stud are used as shown in Fig.6.26 (c) where the body of the accelerometer should be electrically isolated from the measuring object. This is normally to prevent ground loops as discussed elsewhere. A thin slice should be peeled from the thick mica washer supplied. This fixing method also gives good results, the resonance frequency of the test accelerometer only being reduced slightly.

Where permanent measuring points are to be established on a machine and it is not wished to drill and tap fixing holes, cementing studs can be used as shown in Fig.6.26 (d). They are attached to the measuring point by means of a hard glue; epoxy and cyanoacrylate types are recommended as soft glues can considerably reduce the usable frequency range of the accelerometer. Epoxy will be the longest lasting while cyanoacrylate is quickest and easiest to apply.

Double sided adhesive tape is a quick and easy medium for mounting accelerometers. Thin tape used on flat, smooth surfaces gives fairly good results but it can be seen from the response curve in Fig.6.26 (e) that a significant reduction in frequency range can be expected, especially with thick tape.

A permanent magnet, as shown in Fig.6.26 (f), is a simple attachment method where the measuring point is a flat ferro-magnetic surface. It also electrically isolates the accelerometer. This method reduced the resonant frequency of the test accelerometer to about 7 kHz and consequently cannot be used for measurements much above 2 kHz. The holding force of the magnet is sufficient for vibration levels up to 1000 to 2000 m/s^2 depending on the

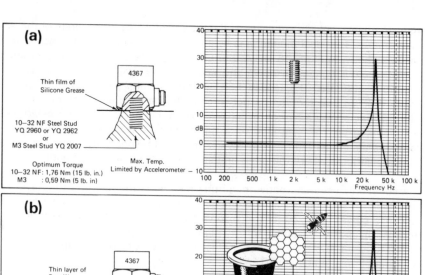

(a)

Thin film of
Silicone Grease

4367

10—32 NF Steel Stud
YQ 2960 or YQ 2962
or
M3 Steel Stud YQ 2007

Optimum Torque
10—32 NF: 1,76 Nm (15 lb. in.)
M3   : 0,59 Nm (5 lb. in)

Max. Temp.
Limited by Accelerometer

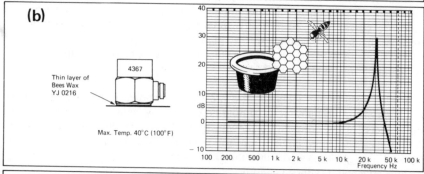

(b)

4367

Thin layer of
Bees Wax
YJ 0216

Max. Temp. 40°C (100°F)

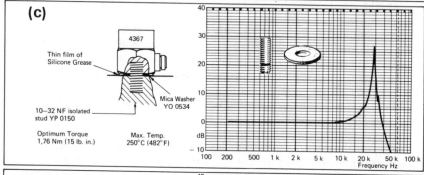

(c)

Thin film of
Silicone Grease

4367

10—32 NF isolated
stud YP 0150

Mica Washer
YO 0534

Optimum Torque
1,76 Nm (15 lb. in.)

Max. Temp.
250°C (482°F)

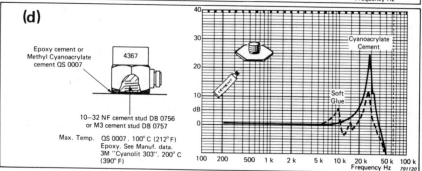

(d)

Epoxy cement or
Methyl Cyanoacrylate
cement QS 0007

4367

Cyanoacrylate
Cement

Soft
Glue

10—32 NF cement stud DB 0756
or M3 cement stud DB 0757

Max. Temp.   QS 0007 . 100°C (212°F)
Epoxy. See Manuf. data.
3M "Cyanolit 303". 200°C
(390°F)

791120

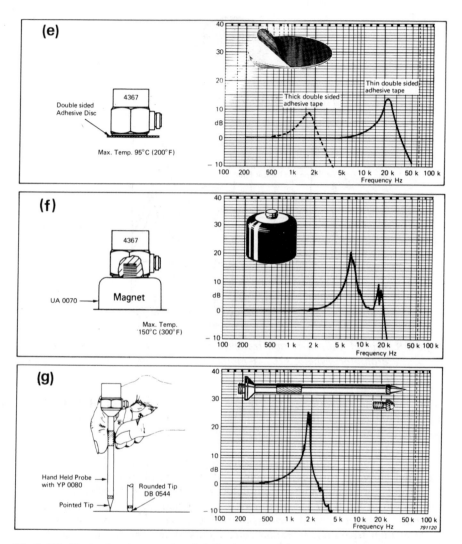

Fig.6.26. Methods of mounting B & K piezoelectric accelerometers and examples of typical frequency responses obtained

size of the accelerometer. Note that the use of the magnet does not ensure absolute repeatability of positioning.

A hand-held probe as shown in Fig.6.26 (g) with the accelerometer mounted on top is very convenient for quick-look survey work, but can give

125

Fig.6.27. Mechanical Filter UA 0559

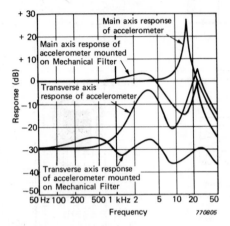

Fig.6.28. Typical main axis and transverse axis frequency response of Accelerometer Type 4370, demonstrating the effect of the Mechanical Filter UA 0559

gross measuring errors because of the low overall stiffness. Repeatable results cannot be expected. An electrical or mechanical low-pass filter should be used to limit the measuring range at about 1000 Hz.

A very useful mounting accessory is the Mechanical Filter, which is mounted between the accelerometer and the point of measurement in order to prevent the accelerometer from detecting high frequency vibration. The filter, shown in Fig.6.27 is useful where the measuring instrumentation is not equipped with a choice of low-pass filters to prevent the erroneous measurement of high frequency vibration components which can be amplified by the accelerometer's resonance. Even when using electronic integrators or low pass filters the mechanical filter will prevent overloading the input stage of the preamplifier. It protects accelerometers and amplifiers against high level, high frequency shock transients in both the accelerometer main and transverse axis directions. Curves demonstrating the effect of the filter are shown in Fig.6.28. It can be seen that the transverse and main axis resonances, which are typically 30 dB in amplitude, are substituted by a highly damped resonance response of only 3 to 4 dB amplitude.

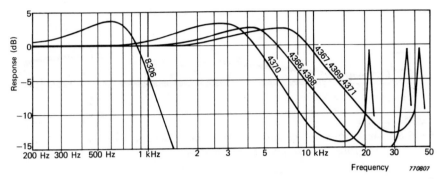

Fig.6.29. *Typical frequency response of various B & K general purpose accelerometers when mounted on the mechanical filter*

The filter is in effect a butyl-rubber buffer between the accelerometer and the vibrating surface. Its cut-off frequency depends upon the mass of the accelerometer mounted on it as can be seen from the frequency response plots in Fig.6.29. The upper cut-off frequency of any accelerometer can be further reduced by adding additional mass in accordance with Fig.6.30.

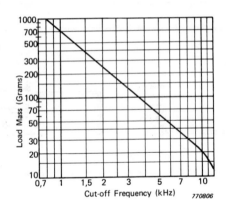

Fig.6.30. *Typical cut-off frequency (—3 dB) plotted as a function of load mass on the Mechanical Filter*

A mechanical filter should always be used when sound level meters or measuring amplifiers (without external filters or integrators) are used to measure wide-band vibration as they would otherwise include the accelerometer's resonance frequency.

After mounting the accelerometer and connecting the cable, steps should be taken to avoid problems with triboelectric noise induced into the cable as mentioned in section 6.2. The cable should be fixed to prevent relative movement as shown in Fig.6.31.

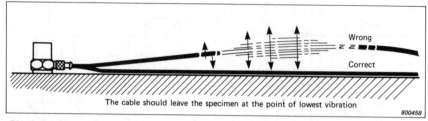

The cable should leave the specimen at the point of lowest vibration

Fig.6.31. Accelerometer cables should be fastened down to avoid cable whip and thus, interference from triboelectric noise

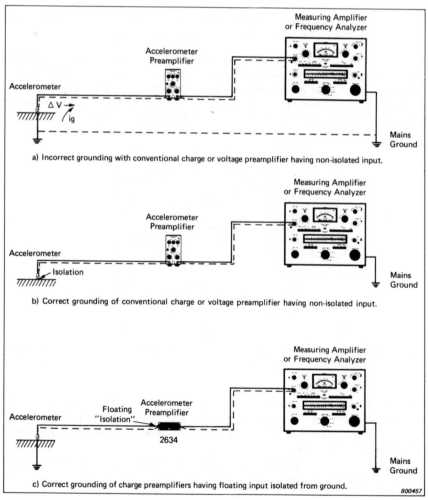

a) Incorrect grounding with conventional charge or voltage preamplifier having non-isolated input.

b) Correct grounding of conventional charge or voltage preamplifier having non-isolated input.

c) Correct grounding of charge preamplifiers having floating input isolated from ground.

Fig.6.32. The ground loop and its elimination

128

Another possible interference effect is hum picked up from the mains supply by ground loops as previously mentioned in section 6.2. Fig.6.32 (a) illustrates how a ground loop is formed. The voltage drop ΔV adds directly to the possibly weak signal from the accelerometer and can pose serious problems especially with large vibration measurement systems.

One way of eliminating ground loop hum is to ensure that the entire measurement system is grounded at one point only as indicated in Fig.6.32 (b). For this purpose it is necessary to isolate the accelerometer from the vibration test specimen using the isolated stud and washer, mechanical filter or the permanent magnet mounting discussed in section 6.6. Grounding should then be carried out by connecting the earth of the mains supply to the mains input socket ground pin of one of the measuring or analyzing instruments in the system. Correct grounding of the accelerometer and of the other instruments in the system will be effected through the screens of the coaxial cables used to interconnect the input and output sockets of the equipment concerned.

In industrial environments it is recommended that a Balanced Accelerometer be used with a preamplifier having a differential input as shown in Fig.6.32 (c). These have both poles of their piezoelectric element isolated from their housing so that noise common to both poles of the accelerometer output and preamplifier input cancels, thus greatly reducing the influence of electromagnetic radiation pick-up on measurements, and also breaking the ground loop.

6.7. PORTABLE BATTERY OPERATED INSTRUMENTS

6.7.1. The General Purpose Vibration Meter

A system for measuring shock and vibration consists basically of two parts. (1) A transducer which is mounted on the point of measurement to convert the mechanical vibrations into an electrical signal, and (2), a measuring and indicating device.

The measuring and indicating device, a vibration meter, consists of one or more instruments which amplifies and conditions the signal. Facilities provided should include switchable filters to limit the frequency range at the upper and lower ends, so as to avoid the measurement of unwanted signals, noise etc., an integrator to enable acceleration, velocity and displacement parameters to be measured, and a signal detector and indicating meter to indicate the RMS or peak value of the signal. Facilities should also be provided for connecting a switchable or tunable filter to enable frequency analysis to be performed and this will in turn require that a graphical recorder can be connected to plot a permanent record of vibration spectra. Fig.6.33 shows

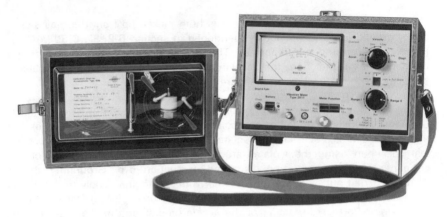

Fig.6.33. General Purpose Vibration Meter Type 2511

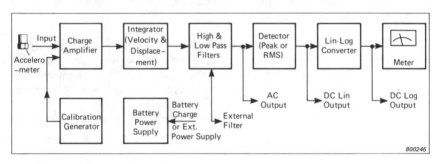

Fig.6.34. Block diagram of the General Purpose Vibration Meter

such an instrument which has the additional feature that it is powered from built-in rechargeable batteries. The block diagram in Fig.6.34 shows how the facilities mentioned are incorporated into the vibration meter shown in Fig.6.33.

As can be seen from Fig.6.35 the frequency response of the General Purpose Vibration Meter depends on whether acceleration (no integration), velocity (one stage of integration) or displacement (double integration) is chosen. The various high and low-pass filters limit the frequency range of the instrument to the range of interest and reduce the possibility of interference from unwanted low and high frequency signals, noise etc.

By adding a tunable filter the General Purpose Vibration Meter is converted into a frequency analyzer. This combination is available in a convenient carrying case complete with built-in battery chargers and is an ideal set for machine condition monitoring and the general study of mechanical vibration, both in the field and in the laboratory. With the further addition of a portable

130

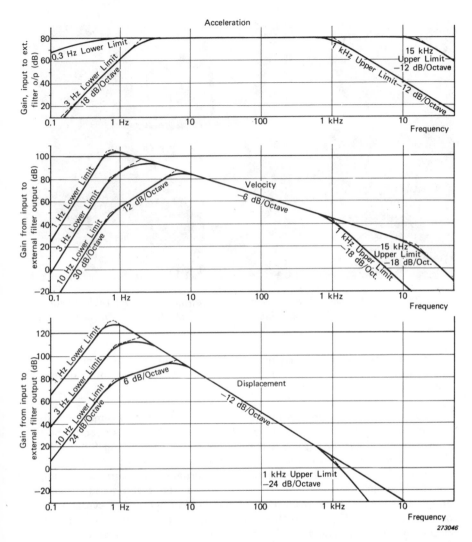

Fig.6.35. Frequency response of the General Purpose Vibration Meter Type 2511 when switched to measure acceleration, velocity and displacement respectively

level recorder, "on the spot" hard-copy frequency analyses may be obtained semi-automatically. This completely self contained system is shown in use in Fig.6.36.

The Portable Vibration Analyzer's versatility can be further increased by adding a photo-electric pickup and Trigger Unit / Phase Meter, which can also

131

Fig.6.36. The Portable Vibration Analyzer together with a Portable Level Recorder Type 2306 produces "on the spot" hard copy frequency analysis plots

be contained in the same carrying case. The set can then be used for static and dynamic balancing of machine rotors in-situ. This application is described fully in Chapter 11.

A battery-operated vibration meter dedicated to the measurement of vibratory motion with respect to its ability to cause discomfort or damage to the human body is shown in Fig.6.37. It is equipped with weighting filters for the measurement of three categories of "human" vibration; "Whole Body", "Hard-Arm", and "Motion Sickness". The instrument measures according to standards which define the measuring criteria and recommend discomfort and danger limits. These are discussed in detail in Chapter 5. Several accelerometer types may be used with the meter. Of particular interest is the Seat Accelerometer, also shown in Fig.6.37, which is placed under the buttocks of a seated person and detects vibration in three mutually perpendicular directions.

Moving back now to the tunable filter which gives the vibration meter its frequency analysis capability, the instrument contains a single bandpass filter which may be switched to either 3% or 23% (~ 1/3 octave) bandwidth and which may be tuned over the frequency range 0,2 Hz to 20 kHz in five subranges. Tuning is either manually controlled by means of the knob on the front panel or swept automatically through each frequency sub-range when used in conjunction with the Portable Graphic Level Recorder shown in

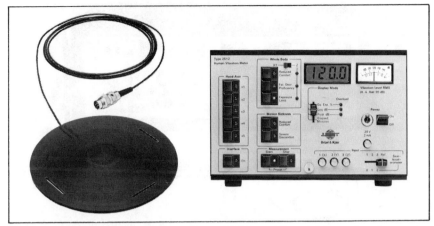

Fig.6.37. Human Vibration Meter Type 2512 and Triaxial Seat Accelerometer Type 4322

Fig.6.36. A typical 3% bandwidth analysis of gearbox vibration made using the vibration analyzer set and level recorder is shown in Fig.6.38. Selection of measurement parameters and sweep speeds is discussed in Chapter 7.

Another battery operated filter which matches the general purpose vibration meter is the tracking filter shown in Fig.6.39. In addition to being manually tunable the filter can be tuned by virtually any periodic signal for example a tachometer probe on a rotating machine. This tuning facility enables vibration signals to be analysed during machine run-up or on variable speed machinery. The filter may be switched to either 6%, 12% or 23% bandwidth and be tuned continuously over the frequency range 2 Hz to 20 kHz via the tachometer input. When tuned manually this range is covered with two sub-ranges. A typical analysis arrangement using the tracking filter is shown in Fig.6.40.

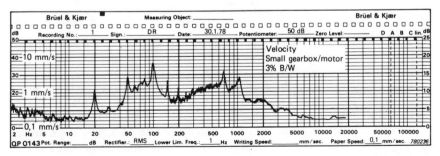

Fig.6.38. Typical frequency analysis made using battery operated portable instruments

133

Fig.6.39. Tracking Filter Type 1623 combines with Vibration Meter Type 2511 to form a versatile tracking analyzer

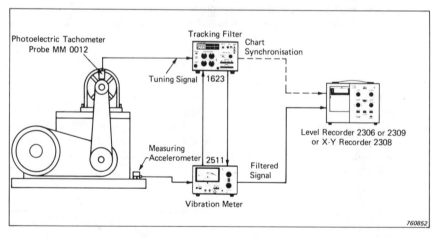

Fig.6.40. Typical portable instrumentation set-up for order and frequency analysis

An additional feature of this filter is that it can be tuned to any ratio combination of the tuning (tachometer) signal frequency between 1/99 and 99/1. This enables order analysis to be performed, that is, the vibration level attributable to the various harmonics and sub-harmonics of a machine's fundamental rotation frequency are measured as a function of rotation speed.

The tracking filter also provides synchronisation signals for the portable le-

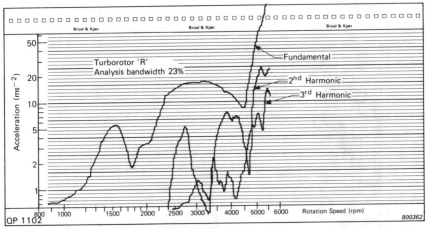

Fig.6.41. An order analysis plotted on the X-Y Recorder Type 2308 using the instruments shown in Fig.6.40

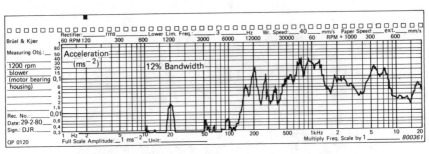

Fig.6.42. Frequency spectrum plotted on the Portable Level Recorder Type 2306 using the instruments shown in Fig.6.40.

vel recorder or X-Y recorder (mains operated) enabling vibration level versus machine speed plots to be made automatically. Typical recordings are shown in Figs.6.41 and 6.42.

6.7.2. The Sound Level Meter (SLM) as a Vibration Meter

While considering portable vibration meters it should be mentioned that some sound level meters can also be used for vibration measurements. A typical example is shown in Fig.6.43. While the SLM is not by any means an ideal general purpose vibration meter it may be economically attractive to the user who needs a precision sound level meter and has the occasional need to measure vibration.

Fig.6.43. Precision Sound Level Meter Type 2209 fitted with integrator adaptor ZR 0020, 1/3 Octave Filter Set Type 1616 and an accelerometer

Fig.6.44. Integrator Type ZR 0020 complete with a Mechanical Filter UA 0559 and slide rule for converting dB scale readings to vibration units. Note that SLM Type 2209 has interchangeable meter scales allowing direct reading in mechanical vibration units

Several B & K sound level meters, as shown in the table in Fig.6.45, may be used for acceleration measurements by merely adding an accelerometer pickup. With the further addition of the Integrator ZR 0020, (Fig.6.44) which

Sound Level Meter Type		 2203	 2209	 2210	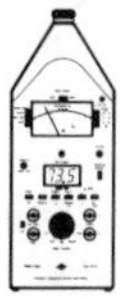 2218
Frequency Range with Integrator ZR 0020 (± 0,5 dB)	Acc.	10 Hz to 20 kHz	3 Hz to 30 kHz	31,5 Hz to 12,5 kHz	
	Vel.	25 Hz to 5 kHz	25 Hz to 5 kHz	31,5 Hz to 2 kHz	
	Disp.	50 Hz to 2 kHz	50 Hz to 2 kHz	50 Hz to 2 kHz	
Detector Modes		RMS	RMS, Impulse Peak Hold Impulse Hold	RMS Impulse Peak All with or without max. Hold	RMS Impulse Peak Hold
Averaging Times		"Fast" "Slow"	"Fast", "Slow", "Impulse"		
Provision for Connecting External Filters		Yes			
Outputs		AC Lin	AC Lin DC Lin	AC Lin, DC Log	
Vibration Meter Scales		Conversion from dB Necessary	Yes	Conversion from dB Necessary	

791115

Fig.6.45. Sound Level Meters which may be used for vibration measurement and analysis

fits on the meter in place of the microphone, velocity and displacement measurements can be made.

The main limitations associated with using SLM's for vibration measurement are in frequency range, and in dynamic range when using the integrator for velocity and displacement measurements. SLM's also have a voltage preamplifier input which means that the measuring sensitivity is dependent on the length of cable between pickup and meter. When using SLM's for wide band vibration measurements it is important to limit the high frequency response of the instrument to the linear portion of the accelerometer response curve. This is most simply achieved by using the previously-mentioned mechanical filter UA 0559 together with the accelerometer.

Fitting a band-pass filter to the sound level meter facilitates frequency analysis. Octave and third-octave filter sets are available which fasten directly to the body of the SLM's as shown in Fig.6.43. Narrow-band and tracking analysis can also be performed with SLM's using the filters previously mentioned in connection with the General Purpose Vibration Meter. These systems can all be synchronised with the Portable Level Recorder so that hard copy frequency analysis plots of sound and vibration can be made.

For convenience in field use the SLM's are available in carrying cases containing the accessories necessary for sound and vibration measurements.

6.7.3. The Tape Recorder in Vibration Work

It may often be more convenient to record vibration signals on magnetic tape for later analysis in the laboratory rather than making on-the-spot frequency analyses in the field. This is especially the case when it is wished to analyse transient vibration, shocks and continuous signals on sophisticated mains-operated laboratory-type instrumentation. In large machine condition monitoring programmes it is often most rational to go from machine to machine with a battery-operated tape recorder, taking a short sample from the many measuring points involved, then making the analysis back in the laboratory.

By replaying a tape at higher speed, very low frequency signals can be brought into the frequency range of ordinary frequency analyzers and analysis time can also be reduced.

Two recording principles are in common use, direct recording (DR) and frequency modulation (FM). Their relative merits are shown in Fig.6.46.

FM recording techniques are normally employed in order to obtain the linearity and low frequency response necessary for many vibration measurement purposes.

A Tape Recorder of instrumentation quality, which is designed with both field and laboratory use in mind, is shown in Fig.6.47. It has four FM recording channels as standard but one or more channels may be converted to direct recording by exchanging certain plug-in circuit cards (full DR specifications only obtainable in a 2 channel version with special heads). For versatility, the built-in rechargeable battery cassette may be exchanged for a power

	DR	FM
Dynamic Range (narrow band - typical)	70 dB	60 dB
Lower Frequency Limit	2,5 Hz*	DC
Upper Frequency Limit (typical)	50 kHz	10 kHz
Amplitude Stability	acceptable	excellent
Phase Linearity	poor	good
Preservation of Recorded Information	acceptable	good

*Playback speed 10x recording speed   790719

Fig.6.46. Comparison of DR and FM recording techniques

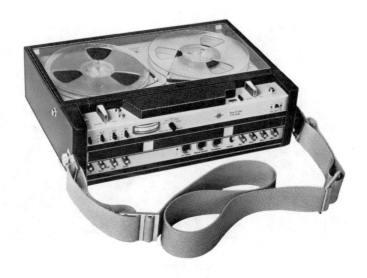

Fig.6.47. Portable FM Tape Recorder Type 7003

supply adaptor enabling operation directly from the AC mains, or alternatively, the power supply may be connected by cable for simultaneous charging and operation.

Since the tape recorder is likely to be the most limiting factor in determining the dynamic range of the system, it is wise to choose the parameter for recording (acceleration or velocity) which has the flattest spectrum, regardless of which is to be used for final evaluation. Conversion between the parameters is of course straight forward once a narrow band spectral analysis has been carried out.

It is necessary and convenient to precede each input channel of the tape recorder with a signal amplification and conditioning device. If one of the sound level meters previously shown to be suitable for vibration measurements is available, this may be used to feed one of the four recorder channels.

An ideal input preamplifier for the level recorder is the battery operated instrument shown in Fig.6.50. This is a general purpose accelerometer preamplifier which includes comprehensive signal conditioning facilities. Accelerometer sensitivity is dialled into the three digit sensitivity adjustment network so that a rounded calibrated output, adjustable in 10 dB steps, can be obtained. This feature greatly simplifies the calibration of the tape recorder or measuring/analyzing instruments following it. Amplification is adjustable up to 80 dB, which enables the 1 V full scale level for the tape recorder to be achieved, even with small signals. Integrators are included so that acceleration, velocity and displacement measurements can be performed. A wide

Fig.6.48. The Portable tape recorder being used to simultaneously record vibration in the vertical and two horizontal planes on the pillar of a railway bridge for subsequent analysis in the laboratory. The separate carrying case (KA 2000) contains three Preamplifiers Type 2635 and a Portable Calibrator Type 4291, all of which are battery operated

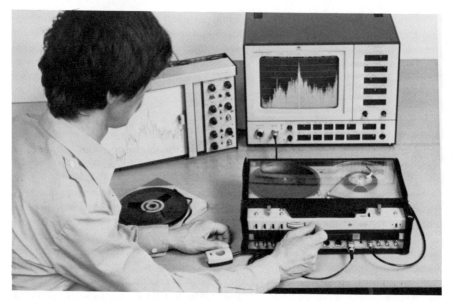

Fig.6.49. Back in the laboratory taped signals are examined, here using the Narrow Band Analyzer Type 2031 and X-Y Recorder Type 2308

choice of high and low-pass filters can be selected so that unwanted signals, noise, etc. can be prevented from influencing the measurements.

For the application shown in Fig.6.48 three preamplifiers were used to feed three channels of the recorder, the fourth channel was used for verbal comments via the microphone / loudspeaker included with the recorder. The portable calibrator also shown in Fig.6.48 provides a reference vibration source for checking out the whole measuring chain and allows a $10\,ms^{-2}$ (~1 g) reference vibration level to be recorded on the tape. The preamplifiers and calibrator are mounted in a convenient carrying case.

Fig.6.50. Battery operated Charge Amplifier Type 2635

6.7.4. Stroboscopic Motion Analysis

The ability to visually freeze or slow-down rotating and reciprocating machine parts is highly desirable in mechanical development and trouble-shooting work. This is possible using the stroboscopic motion analyzers shown in Fig.6.51 and 6.52. Illuminated by a high intensity lamp flashing in synchronisation with rotary or vibratory mechanical motion, structural supports, clearance between moving parts, eccentricity of rotation and the engagement of meshing gear teeth can be observed in detail. The flash frequency may be controlled from a built-in generator or alternatively from an external trigger source such as a vibration exciter controller, magnetic pickup or photoelectric tachometer probe. The mains operated instrument shown in Fig.6.51 has a frequency offset facility which allows the test object to be examined in apparent slow motion (0,3 Hz to 5,7 Hz) and also phase control allowing an object to be examined in any part of its cycle. In addition to the basic stroboscope facility, the small battery operated unit shown in Fig.6.52 has a tachometer display indicating the trigger or flash frequency.

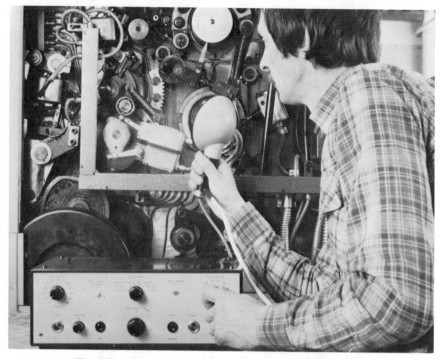

Fig.6.51. Stroboscopic Motion Analyzer Type 4911

Fig.6.52. Portable Stroboscope Type 4912

6.7.5. Waveform Studies

Without dispute, the frequency analysis of vibration signals is the singularly most useful tool for revealing the background to mechanical vibration problems. However the usefulness of waveform analysis, that is the plotting of signal amplitude versus time, should not be forgotten.

An oscilloscope is generally the simplest method of displaying a vibration waveform but in the trace fundamental frequency components are often buried in noise and the method is therefore of limited practical use.

With the help of a waveform retriever it is possible to plot out the amplitude of vibration signals as a function of time, with all non-harmonically related components and noise filtered out, but with a selected number of harmonic components retained. This facilitates the examination of the dynamic behaviour of machine parts through each phase of their cycle and the identification of irregularities caused by, for example, faulty gear teeth and aerodynamic anomalies.

The waveform retriever shown in Fig.6.53 requires a periodic reference signal to trigger the sampling circuitry which looks at the signal waveform at a progressively later point in each cycle, i.e. like the stroboscope in "slow motion" mode. With mechanical systems the time reference can be conveniently provided by Photo-electric Tachometer Probe which gives a trigger pulse for each revolution of a shaft, for example. The waveform is fed out at a much lower frequency to a level recorder or X-Y recorder. Lowpass filters remove non-synchronous variations over a selectable effective number of cycles.

As the waveform retriever is battery operated and completely portable, a battery operated level recorder will normally be the most convenient plotting device and allow waveform plots to be made on-the-spot, out in the field. A typical battery operated system is shown in Fig.6.54. Note that the waveform retriever is a two channel device so that differences in vibration phase and amplitude between two different locations may be examined.

Fig.6.53. Waveform Retriever Type 6302

143

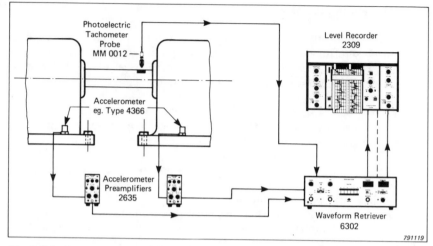

Fig.6.54. Battery operated instrumentation set-up for recording the time history of periodic waveforms

Averaged orbit plots can be drawn by feeding the outputs from X and Y axis transducers via the waveform retriever to an X-Y recorder.

6.7.6. Monitoring for Mechanical Bumps and Shocks

Mechanical shock is a severe environmental hazard during the transportation of many items of machinery, equipment and more or less fragile products. A specially designed instrument for continuously monitoring and recording the level of excessive shocks is shown in Fig.6.55. It is a self-contained, fully electronic apparatus that measures the maximum velocity and acceleration together with the time of occurrence of shocks which exceed a preset threshold level and records them on a reel of paper tape.

Shocks are picked up by a piezoelectric accelerometer which can be mounted inside the sturdy recorder case or remotely on a critical part of the transported item. It monitors simultaneously in three mutually perpendicular directions so that shocks occurring in any random direction are resolved into three vectors. These are combined in the instrument to represent the magnitude of the applied shock.

Built-in rechargeable batteries power the instrument for approximately 18 days, for longer journeys an external battery pack can be connected. By connecting a very high sensitivity accelerometer to the recorder its sensitivity can be increased by a factor of 1000 making it suitable for recording ground tremors and building shocks due to, for example, rock blasting or heavy traffic. The photograph in Fig.6.56 shows the bump recorder in use.

144

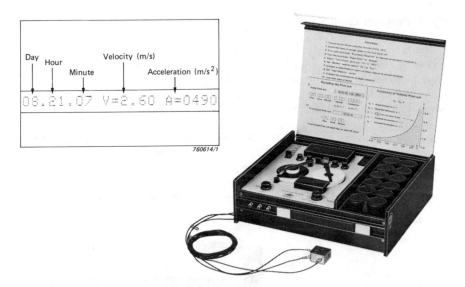

Day
Hour
Minute
Velocity (m/s)
Acceleration (m/s²)

08.21.07 V=2.60 A=0490

760614/1

Fig.6.55. Bump Recorder Type 2503 together with a typical bump readout printed on a 6 mm wide paper strip

Bump Recorder 2503

800659

Fig.6.56. Bump Recorder Type 2503 packed in its reusable protective container, mounted on a machine tool. The triaxial accelerometer pickup is mounted on the headstock of the machine

145

6.7.7. Portable Level Recorders

Where more than a few vibration measurements are made, or frequency and waveform analysis are performed, it is a severe drawback to have to manually plot results on a record sheet. A level recorder facilitates the automatic recording of time and frequency spectra on a precalibrated paper chart, of which there are numerous examples shown in this book.

Battery operated level recorders are available in both single and two channel versions as shown in Fig.6.57. They are equipped with an RMS rectifier and can record AC signals in the frequency range 1,6 Hz to 20 kHz normally on a logarithmic frequency scale or linear time axis. DC signals may be recorded on both linear and logarithmic amplitude scales.

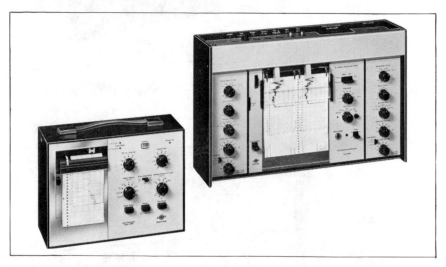

Fig.6.57. Portable battery operated Level Recorders Types 2306 (single channel) and 2309 (two channel)

Recording chart paper is stored on a roll in the recorder and is fed out at between 0,01 and 30 mm/s according to which of the eight paper speed settings are chosen. For frequency analysis work the paper feed is semi- or fully automatically synchronised with the sweep of the filters previously mentioned.

The two-channel recorder is particularly convenient where it is required to plot two varying parameters with respect to a common parameter, for example, time, frequency or rpm. Typical examples that can be mentioned are the plotting of excitation force and response vibration as a function of frequency

146

or the vibration level at two different locations on a machine as a function of rotation speed.

6.8. LABORATORY ORIENTED MAINS-OPERATED INSTRUMENTA-TION

The instruments described in the previous section are powered from internal batteries and can therefore be run independently of AC mains power. Most of them can, however, be run from the mains in laboratory situations via one of the battery chargers or power supplies available for this purpose.

Although battery-powered instruments are already showing a high degree of sophistication we still must look to mains powered instrumentation for the most powerful measuring and analyzing systems. Research and development work in the laboratory and the analysis of tape recorded data is still the domain of mains operated instrumentation.

The first stages of the vibration measuring chain, the transducer and preamplifier discussed in 6.1 and 6.2 apply to both battery and mains-operated measuring and analyzing instrumentation. From there on there is a wide choice of mains-operated filtering, detection and recording instrumentation available.

The measuring amplifier is a central instrument here, it is used alone as a precision signal detector and level indicator and together with a filter set, to perform frequency analysis. A measuring amplifier and filter-set are often combined into a signal instrument called a frequency analyzer or spectrometer.

6.8.1. Measuring Amplifiers

The choice of measuring amplifier will mainly depend on whether it should be able to be additionally operated from a DC supply, whether peak indication

Fig.6.58. A typical measuring amplifier, B & K Type 2610

Instrument Type	 2425	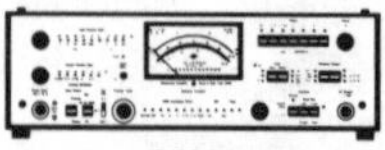 2636	 2610
Frequency Range	0,5 Hz to 500 kHz	1 Hz to 200 kHz	2 Hz to 200 kHz
Detector Modes	RMS Average + Peak — Peak Max. Peak and Hold	RMS Impulse Peak Max. Hold on all modes	RMS Peak Max. Hold on both modes
Averaging Times	Fast, Slow	Fast, Slow 0,1s to 100 s	Fast, Slow 20 s
Accepts Ext. Filters	No	Yes	Yes
Output	AC & DC Lin.	AC & DC Lin. & DC Log IEC Interface	AC & DC Log.
Vibration Meter Scale	No	Yes	Yes
Power Supply	AC Mains Ext. DC	AC Mains	AC Mains

791114

Fig.6.59. Main data for measuring amplifiers suitable for vibration measurement

in addition to RMS is required and whether long time constants are required, as is often the case when analyzing with narrow-band filters. A typical measuring amplifier suitable for vibration measurement is shown in Fig.6.58. The main data of this and similar instruments is shown in Fig.6.59.

6.8.2. Separate Filters

Add-on filters for measuring amplifiers facilitate frequency analysis; both constant bandwidth and constant percentage bandwidth types are available as shown in Fig.6.60.

The Heterodyne Slave Filter Type 2020 is tuned in the frequency range 10 Hz to 20 kHz to the difference frequency of two high frequency signals. Tuning signals are obtained from one of the B & K Generators Types 1023

148

Fig.6.60. Heterodyne Slave Filter Type 2020 (constant bandwidth) and Third-Octave Bandpass Filter Type 1618 (constant percentage bandwidth)

and 1027, the Heterodyne Analyzer Type 2010 or the Tracking Frequency Multiplier Type 1901. The filter is widely used for analysis on a linear frequency scale which is best suited to constant bandwidth filters, and is particularly valuable for analyzing dynamic system response in conditions of high noise and distortion and for tracking analysis when tuned from the tracking frequency multiplier.

For analysis in standard octave and third-octave contiguous bands, filter sets such as that shown in Fig.6.60 are used. Third-octave and octave bandwidth analysis is of limited value in the general study of mechanical vibration where narrower bandwidth resolution is normally required. Third-octave analysis can be of value however where it is required to correlate vibration spectra with noise spectra and also where simple spectrum comparison is needed for machine health monitoring and quality control purposes.

Main data for add-on filters is shown together with the data for dedicated analyzers in Fig.6.62.

6.8.3. Frequency Analyzers

Most convenient for performing frequency analysis of vibration signals in the laboratory are the range of analyzers shown in Fig.6.61. Two types of analyzers are represented, serial analyzers and real-time analyzers. The serial analyzers may be synchronised with, and read out to, level or X-Y recorders. Real-time frequency analyzers provide analysis in all frequency bands simultaneously giving a virtually instantaneous graphical display of frequency spectra on a large built-in screen. These spectra can, of course, also be read out to a graphic recorder.

Looking at the analyzers in turn, the first analyzer shown in Fig.6.61 allows a continuous analysis to be made by sweeping through the desired frequency range. A *constant percentage* filter bandwidth as narrow as 1% al-

Frequency Analyzer Type 2120

Heterodyne Analyzer
Type 2010

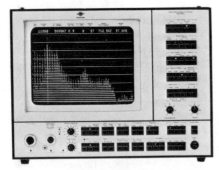

Narrow Band
Spectrum Analyzer
Type 2031

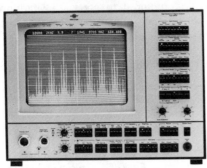

High Resolution Signal Analyzer
Type 2033

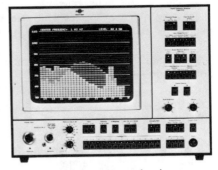

Digital Frequency Analyzer
Type 2131

Fig.6.61. Mains-operated frequency analyzers used for the analysis of mechanical vibration

lows very fine resolution analyses to be made facilitating the detailed examination of vibration phenomena.

A narrow *constant* bandwidth analysis may often be required in development, diagnostic and experimental work. This is especially the case with vibration problems associated with rotating machines such as gearboxes where a fine constant bandwidth is needed to identify multiple harmonics and sidebands due to modulation which occur at constant frequency intervals.

The Heterodyne Analyzer shown in Fig.6.61 facilitates constant bandwidth analysis with bandwidths between 3,16 Hz and 1000 Hz and has a frequency range from 2 Hz to 200 kHz. Both linear and logarithmic frequency sweeps may be selected.

	Filters for use with measuring amplifiers			Frequency Analyzers				
	2020	1617	1618	2120	2010	2031	2033	2131
Classi-fication	Continuous sweep. Constant bandwidth	Stepped octave and third-octave. Constant percentage bandwidth.		Continuous sweep. Constant percentage bandwidth	Continuous sweep. Constant bandwidth	Constant-bandwidth Real time		Octave and third-octave Real-time
Bandwidth	3,16 Hz 10 Hz 31,6 Hz 100 Hz	1/1 Octave 1/3 Octave		1% 3% 10% 1/3 Oct. (~23%)	3,16 Hz 10 Hz 31,6 Hz 100 Hz 316 Hz 1000 Hz	0,25% of selected freq. range ie. from 0,025 Hz to 50 Hz	As 2031 plus x 10 zoom (0,025% BW) (ie. 0,0025 Hz to 5 Hz)	1/1 Octave 1/3 Octave
Centre Frequency Range	10 Hz to 20 kHz	2 Hz to 160 kHz	2 Hz to 20 kHz	2 Hz to 20 kHz	2 Hz to 200 kHz	0—10 Hz to 0—20 kHz in 11 ranges	As 2031 plus x10 zoom	1,6 Hz to 20 kHz
Power Supply	AC Mains			AC Mains and Ext. DC	AC Mains			791116

Fig.6.62. Main data for mains-operated filters and frequency analyzers

In addition to its analyzer function this instrument is equipped with a signal generator which can be tuned over the same frequency range as the analyzer. The output level of the generator can be controlled automatically via its built-in compressor amplifier so as to allow the excitation level of, for example, vibration test objects to be kept constant during a frequency sweep. The analyzer side of the instrument can be used at the same time to filter and measure dynamic response signals. A typical application example is shown in Fig.6.63.

The Analysis Bandwidth (B) and averaging time (T_A) of the instrument may be manually selected or automatically changed during a frequency sweep in accordance with four preprogrammed sequences built-in. The significance of selecting optimum values of B and T_A to obtain a short analysis time and a given accuracy is dealt with in detail in the following chapter. The four pro-

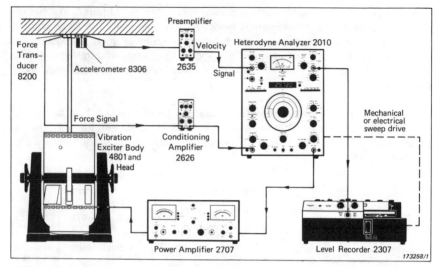

Fig.6.63. Arrangement for measuring the mechanical impedance of a structure

grammes available are as follows: (1) T_A constant, B variable; suitable for log frequency sweep to give approximately constant percentage bandwidth. In conjunction with a built-in bandwidth compensation network, power spectral density and energy spectral density measurements can be made. (2) B constant, T_A variable; approximates optimum conditions for constant bandwidth analysis on a logarithmic frequency scale. (3) and (4) Two programmes giving an approximately constant (selectable) BT_A product but using different change-over frequencies. These programmes give approximately constant statistical confidence over the entire frequency range.

6.8.4. Real-Time Analyzers

The outstanding advantage of real-time frequency analyzers is that they provide analysis in all frequency bands over their entire analysis range simultaneously. Furthermore, they give a virtually instantaneous graphical display of analyzed spectra on a large built-in screen which is continuously updated. Typical examples are shown in Fig.6.64. Dynamic and spectral changes such as occur when increasing vibration test level or machine speed can thus be seen as they actually happen, which is of particular benefit in vibration test and prototype development work. Also, the time saved in not having to wait for a level or X-Y recorder readout is considerable, making real-time analyzers an absolute must for quick look investigative work such as called for in production line testing and fault finding with products.

152

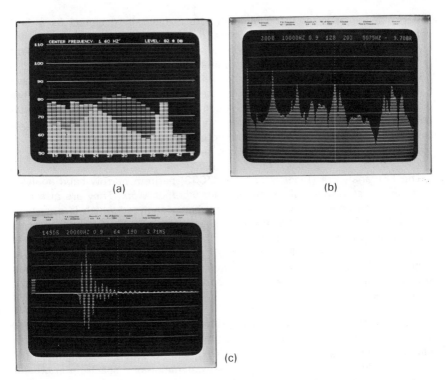

Fig.6.64. Typical real-time analyzer displays. (a) a 1/3 Octave spectrum alternating with a reference spectrum held in the 2131's memory. (b) a narrow-band spectrum displayed on the 2031's screen. (c) a time function on the 2031's screen

Real-time analyzers are also particularly well suited for analysis of short duration signals, such as transient vibration and shock. Readout and display of analyzed transient and shock spectra takes place practically at the very instant of capture, which with serial frequency analyzing instrumentation is just not possible, as these signals must first be recorded for repetitive playback as a pseudo-periodic signal before analysis may be attempted. In addition, real-time analyzers can store analyzed spectra, or spectra entered digitally for alternate display with later incoming data. This facilitates quick, easy comparison of spectra as is necessary in machine condition monitoring programs as discussed in Chapter 8.

Three real-time analyzers are shown in Fig.6.61. Type 2131 is fundamentally different from the other two analyzers in that it generates a constant percentage, 1/3 or 1/1 octave bandwidth spectrum and is based on recursive digital filtering while the other types based on the FFT procedure, produce constant bandwidth spectra on a linear frequency scale.

153

Because the analyzer using digital filters is basically designed as a 1/3 octave (~23%) analyzer its main applications for vibration measurements are for production testing and quality control work as well as efficient permanent monitoring of machine condition. It should be noted however, that with the additional use of an external controller it is possible to generate 1/12 octave bandwidth (~6%) frequency spectra by making four passes and changing the digital filter coefficients each time. A complete 1/12 octave analysis cannot be made in real time but the method is still fast in comparison with stepped or sweeping filter analysis. The method can be used on non-stationary (e.g. transient) signals provided that they can be repeated exactly four times.

The FFT analyzers (Types 2031 and 2033) perform narrow band analysis and are therefore particularly suitable for vibration work. They are also able to display the time function of the signal being analysed which is a particularly valuable facility in the analysis of transient signals. One can thus be sure of analysing valid data. The fact that the FFT analyzers are equipped with two memories enables two spectra to be compared with the difference displayed. For example, in the evaluation of vibration isolators, the excitation spectrum can be compared with the response spectrum and the transmissibility of the isolators displayed.

The High Resolution Signal Analyzer Type 2033 is an expanded version of Type 2031 featuring an extended (× 10) transient recorder size, a linear amplitude display in addition to the log display, and probably most significantly, a zoom facility. The zoom facility allows examination of a spectrum in greater detail by expanding part of the frequency scale by a factor of 10. Multiple zooms can be made on the same data, effectively allowing a 4000 line spectrum to be built up from ten contiguous sets of 400 channels, the maximum which can be displayed on the screen at any one time. The extra sample storage capacity of the Type 2033 allows it to record much longer time signals so that longer events, for example one or more complete cycles of an engine, may be examined in detail, even in high frequency ranges, where the normal record length would be shorter than the cycle time.

Together with a tracking frequency multiplier, the high resolution FFT analyzer is valuable for studying machine vibration under variable speed conditions. The tracking frequency multiplier monitors the machine speed via a suitable pick-up such as the magnetic transducer MM 0002 as shown in Fig.6.65 and controls the external sampling source for the analyzer. In normal analysis, if the speed of the machine varies, the position of speed related components of the signal under analysis will change on the display screen. However when using the tracking multiplier, machine speed changes result in a proportional change in the analyzer sampling frequency so that speed related components stay in the same channels on the screen. This allows the relationship between the amplitudes of the various shaft speed related components or "orders" to be studied.

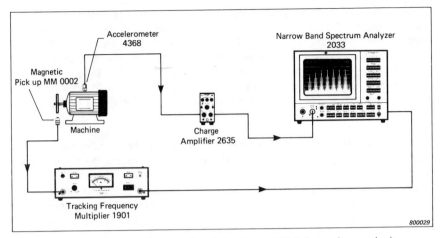

Fig.6.65. *Use of the Narrow Band Analyzer 2031 for order analysis*

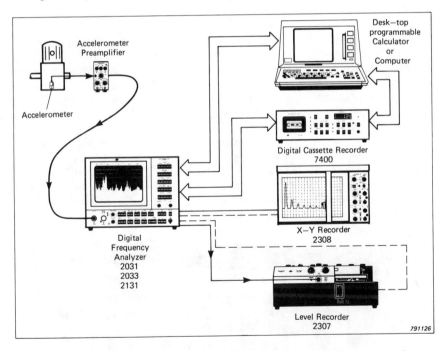

Fig.6.66. *Spectra analyzed by a real-time frequency analyzer may be recorded or processed further by a calculator or computer*

Using an external sampling frequency means that there is a danger of encountering aliasing of high frequency components if these lie above half the

155

sampling frequency. It is at all times possible, however, to select an optimal internal low-pass filter, based on the current machine speed, so that at least 60% of the total spectrum (i.e. 240 lines) would always be valid. Using "zoom" and concentrating on the first 10% of the baseband spectrum it is even possible to obtain 400-line order analyses without the influence of aliasing over a very wide speed range, but the spectrum update time is then a minimum of 1 s, and the procedure can only be used for slowly changing signals.

Data analyzed by the three real-time analyzers can be transferred to X-Y or level recorders, or via the built-in IEC interface to digital data peripherals such as tape recorder, tape punch, printer or desk-top calculator. The interfacing of a real-time analyzer to a suitably programmed calculator or computer thus facilitates the rapid automatic processing of analysed data. Some output options are shown in Fig.6.66.

6.8.5. Digital Data Recording

Where it is required to store data in digital form, a cassette tape recorder such as that shown in Fig.6.67 may be employed. The recorder shown is a two-track device used for the storage and reconstruction when.desired, of digital data originating from instruments having IEC/IEEE or B & K low-power interface. For vibration work its use will primarily be directed to the recording of spectra from the real-time analyzers previously shown. About 100 narrow band spectra or several hundred 1/3 octave spectra can be contained on each data cassette. Stored data can be rapidly recalled from the cassette for display on the analyzer screen and compared with new spectra. New and standard data may be displayed "simultaneously" on the analyzer display screen using the "alternate" function. The recorder can be remotely controlled from a desk-top calculator or computer via the IEC interface for use in automatic monitoring and analysis systems.

Fig.6.67. Two-track Digital Cassette Tape Recorder Type 7400

In connection with the High Resolution Signal Analyzer it is possible to transfer time records consisting of 10 K samples (or 1 K) to and from the recorder. From one such record it is possible to generate a large number of zoomed and non-zoomed spectra, including an average spectrum over the whole record.

6.8.6. Graphical Recorders (Mains Operated)

The battery operated single and two channel level recorders discussed in section 6.6 are indeed widely used for plotting spectra from mains-operated instrumentation. However, where a mains supply is available two other alternatives may be chosen as shown in Fig.6.68.

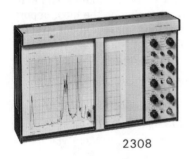 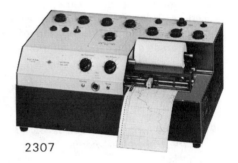

2308 2307

Fig.6.68. X-Y Recorder Type 2308 and Level Recorder Type 2307

The Level Recorder shown in Fig.6.68 is a comprehensive instrument with a wide range of useful facilities. It is equipped with rectifiers which facilitate the recording of the RMS, peak and average values of AC signals from 2 Hz to 200 kHz. In the DC mode signals from 0 to 6,4 Hz can be plotted. Six range-potentiometers, two linear and four logarithmic, allow the recorder resolution to be changed as desired. All B & K filter sets and analyzers, including the real-time instruments, can be synchronised with the recorder chart movement so that spectra can be plotted automatically on pre-printed calibrated paper suitable for immediate documentation. Numerous examples are shown throughout this book.

The X-Y recorder is designed for the linear DC recording of slow and rapidly changing voltages, signal frequency analyses, waveforms or any graphical plot requiring two fully controllable axes. The sensitivity of each input can be adjusted continuously and independently so that the plot size can be arranged to completely fill the 185 × 270 mm writing area. A sweep generator is built in, which can control the X or Y sweep of the carriage and some frequency generators and analyzers. Automatic frequency analysis and response

157

plots may be made on frequency graduated recording paper in conjunction with these instruments.

6.9. A SUMMARY

A careful study of the preceding sections of this chapter should enable the vibration engineer to select and utilize the measuring equipment necessary to perform thorough and meaningful vibration measurements in most of the situations occurring in practice. Further details of the frequency analysis of continuous and transient signals are given in the next chapter (Chapter 7). A further study of that chapter may thus be required before measurements are made. On the other hand, whether the vibrations consist of steady (stationary) vibrations or shocks it may be useful at this stage to outline a summary procedure. This summary is meant as an aid in remembering the most important factors in the setting up and use of a vibration measurement system, rather than as a detailed "turning-of-the-knobs" type of procedure.

1. *Determine carefully where to place the vibration transducer, and its possible mass-loading effects* (Section 6.2).

2. *Estimate what types and levels of vibrations that are likely to be present at the transducer mounting point* (periodic vibrations, random vibrations, shocks).

3. *Select the most suitable vibration transducer (accelerometer) considering items 1 and 2 above as well as environmental factors* (temperature, humidity etc.). See section 6.2.

4. *Determine what type of measurement would be most appropriate for the problem at hand.* (Overall measurement of acceleration, velocity or displacement, waveform recording, magnetic tape recording, frequency analysis).

5. *Select the most suitable electronic equipment,* considering frequency and phase characteristics, dynamic range, and convenience of operation. See sections 6.1, 6.7 and 6.8.

6. *Check and calibrate the overall system including accelerometer and connecting cables,* see section 6.4.

7. *Make a sketch of the instrumentation system* with all type numbers and serial numbers included.

8. *Select the appropriate accelerometer mounting method,* considering vibra-

tion levels, frequency range, electrical insulation problems and ground loops. See section 6.6.

9. *Mount the accelerometer onto the structure, carry out the measurements and record the result.*

10. *Note down the setting of the various instrument control knobs.*

It is good policy always to *check the "back-ground noise" level* of a vibration measurement system. This can be done by mounting the accelerometers on a non-vibrating object and measuring the "apparent" vibration level of this arrangement.

To obtain reasonably good accuracy in the actual vibration measurements the "apparent" vibrations should be less than one third of the measured vibrations. Or said in other words: The noise "floor" of the installation should be at least 10 dB below the vibration levels to be measured.

6.10. BIBLIOGRAPHY

B & K PUBLICATIONS:
(Miscellaneous)   Accelerometer Calibration for accurate Vibration Measurements. Publication BR 0173

Piezoelectric Accelerometers and Vibration Preamplifiers — Theory and Application Handbook. Publication 033-0205

OLESEN, H.P.:   Measurement of the Dynamic Properties of Materials and Structures. B & K Application Note 17—180

7. FREQUENCY ANALYSIS OF VIBRATION AND SHOCK

7.1. INTRODUCTION

The traditional way of performing a frequency analysis is to pass the signal through a system consisting of filter, detector and recorder (or display) as illustrated in Fig.7.1. The time taken to obtain a result for each frequency (bandwidth) will be determined by the delays involved in each of the three elements, and these will thus be discussed in the following. The discussion applies to both analogue filters, and also to the more recent digital filters, which behave in a very similar manner to their analogue counterparts.

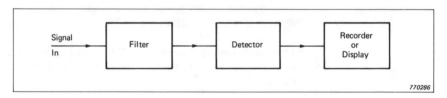

Fig.7.1. Block diagram of basic analyzer system

The other digital frequency analysis technique in common use, viz. FFT analysis, involves a quite different approach, a direct numerical evaluation of estimates of the Fourier Transform, and this will thus be discussed separately.

7.1.1. Response Properties of Filters, Detectors and Recorders

The response time T_R of a filter of bandwidth B is of the order of $1/B$ as illustrated in Fig.7.2, and thus the delay introduced by the filter is also of this order. This relationship can be expressed in the form

$$BT_R \approx 1 \qquad (7.1)$$

which is most applicable to constant bandwidth filters,

160

or
$$b\hat{n}_R \approx 1 \qquad\qquad (7.2)$$

where b is the relative bandwidth $(= B/f_o)$, n_R is the number of periods of frequency f_o in time T_R $(= f_o T_R)$ and f_o is the centre frequency of the filter. This form is more applicable to constant percentage bandwidth filters.

Thus the response time of a 10 Hz bandwidth filter is approx. 100 ms while the response time of a 1% bandwidth filter is approx. 100 periods.

Fig.7.2 also illustrates that the "effective" length of the impulse (T_E) is also approximately $1/B$, while to integrate all of the energy contained in the filter impulse response it is necessary to integrate over at least $3\,T_R$.

The detector is used to measure the mean power in the filter output, and consists of a squaring section to obtain the instantaneous power, followed by an averaging section to smooth out fluctuations and find the mean square value over a specified averaging time T_A.

There is no effective delay in the squaring section, but errors can occur if a true squaring is not achieved. In some instruments the parabola corresponding to squaring is approximated by piecewise linear sections, and the result will only be valid for crest factors up to a specified value, e.g. 5. So-called LMS (log mean square) detectors achieve true squaring by logarithmic conver-

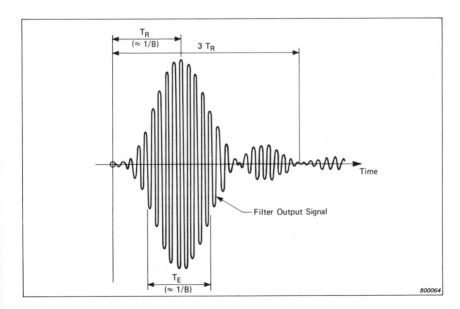

Fig. 7.2. Typical filter impulse response

161

sion followed by amplification by a factor of 2, and are not likely to have crest factor limitations within their dynamic range. In both digital filter and FFT instruments, squaring is performed numerically and is thus virtually perfect within the dynamic range limitations.

Since there is a continuous output from the filter, the ideal averaging would be a running linear average over the previous T_A seconds. This is very difficult to achieve, however, and recourse is normally made to 2 alternatives.

(a) **Linear averaging** with uniform weighting over given time periods of length T_A, where the result is only available at the end of each period, and is usually held until something is done with the result. This means that a result is not available at all times, and that new data may be lost while a result is being held.

(b) **Running exponential averaging**, where a result is available at all times and represents approximately the previous T_A seconds, but where the maximum weighting is on the most recent input and there is an exponentially decaying weighting backwards in time.

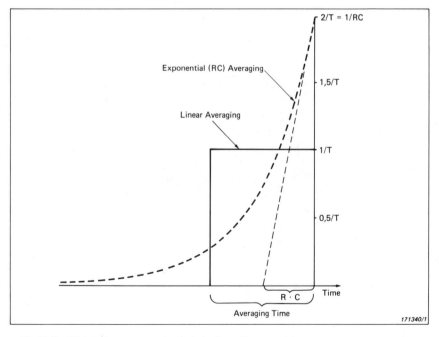

Fig. 7.3. Weighting curves for equivalent linear and exponential averaging

Fig.7.3 illustrates the two weighting functions (effectively the averager impulse response functions reversed in time) scaled so as tó give equivalent averaging on stationary signals. This is found to be the case when $T_A = 2RC$ (where RC is the time constant of the exponential decay) and where the peak output of the exponential circuit is twice that of the linear circuit (i.e. + 3 dB).

The delay introduced by the detector is of the order of the averaging time, but with exponential averaging the most severe limitation is that the maximum rate of fall is 8,7 dB per averaging time and this must be set in relation to the steepness of filter characteristic which may have to be recorded in a swept frequency analysis.

The influence of a graphic recorder depends on whether AC or DC recording is used. For DC recording (of the DC output from an analogue detector) a sufficiently high writing speed can always be chosen so that the limitation comes from the detector and not the recorder. For AC recording, however, where the AC signal directly from the filter is squared and averaged in the recorder, the writing speed may be the limiting factor. The writing speed W is first chosen so as to give the required averaging time (see later, Fig.7.10) and then the analysis speed may be chosen so as not to limit the ability of the pen to follow the maximum slope of a filter characteristic.

7.1.2. Digital Filters

A (recursive) digital filter is a calculation device which receives a sequence of digital values at its input, operates on each sample in a defined manner, and outputs a sample for each input. The digital operations carried out, viz. addition, multiplication and delays, mean that the relationship between input and output samples can be described by a difference equation, whose properties can be made very similar to a differential equation which might describe an analogue filter. Fig.7.4 shows a typical 2-pole section used in a 1/3-octave digital filter analyzer (3 of these are cascaded to give 6-pole filtration).

There are two ways of changing the properties of a given digital filter circuit such as that shown in Fig.7.4:

(a) For given coefficients (e.g. H_0, B_1, B_2 in Fig.7.4) the filter characteristic is only defined with respect to the sampling frequency. Thus, halving the sampling frequency will halve any cut-off frequencies, centre frequencies and bandwidths, and thus maintain constant percentage characteristics one octave lower in frequency. This is one reason why digital filters are so well adapted to constant percentage bandwidth analysis on a logarithmic (i.e. octave-based) frequency scale.

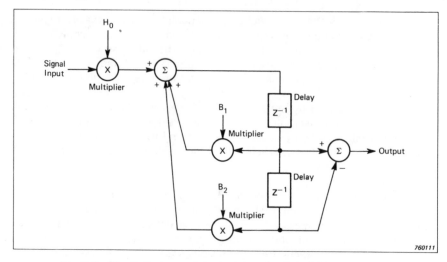

Fig. 7.4. Block diagram of typical 2-pole digital filter section

(b) For a given sampling frequency the characteristics can be changed by changing the coefficients used in the calculations.

Thus, the three 1/3-octave characteristics within each octave are generated by changing coefficients, while the various octaves are covered by repetitively halving the sampling frequency. Every time the sampling frequency is halved, it means that only half the number of samples must be processed in a given time, and it will be seen that the total number of samples for all octaves lower than the highest is (1/2 + 1/4 + 1/8 + ...) which in the limit is the same as the number in the highest octave. This means that by being able to calculate twice as fast as is necessary for the upper octave alone, it is possible to cover any number of lower octaves in real-time, and this is the other reason why digital filters are so well adapted to real-time constant percentage bandwidth analysis over a wide frequency range.

7.1.3. FFT Analysis

The FFT algorithm is an extremely efficient way of calculating the so-called Discrete Fourier Transform (DFT) which is a discrete, finite approximation to the Fourier Transform given in Chapter 2. The actual equation for the forward transform is:

$$G(k) = \frac{1}{N} \sum_{n=0}^{N-1} g(n) e^{-j\frac{2\pi kn}{N}} \qquad (7.3)$$

164

and for the inverse transform is

$$g(n) = \sum_{k=0}^{N-1} G(k) e^{j\frac{2\pi kn}{N}} \qquad (7.4)$$

where $G(k)$ represents the spectrum values at the N discrete frequencies $k \, \Delta f$, and $g(n)$ represents samples of the time function at the N discrete time points $n\Delta t$.

Whereas the Fourier transform equations are infinite integrals of continuous functions, the above equations are finite sums, but otherwise they will be seen to have similar properties. The function being transformed is multiplied by a rotating unit vector $e^{\pm j\frac{2\pi kn}{N}}$ which rotates (in discrete jumps for each increment of the time parameter n) at a speed proportional to the frequency parameter k.

There are three "pitfalls" introduced by the finite, discrete nature of the DFT.

(a) **Aliasing** caused by sampling of the time signal, and meaning that high frequencies after sampling can appear as lower ones (as with a stroboscope). This is eliminated by lowpass filtering the signal before sampling to ensure that it contains no frequencies above half the sampling frequency. (This is also necessary with digital filtering).

(b) **Time window effect,** resulting from the finite length of the record. Because the resulting spectrum is calculated at discrete frequencies separated by $1/T$, where T is the record length, the time record is treated implicitly by the analyzer as one period of a periodic signal of period T. The time record can be considered to be first multiplied by a "time window function" of length T and the resulting segment then joined into a loop. If the time window is rectangular (or "flat") and the original signal was longer than T, an unknown discontinuity can arise at the loop junction, which gives rise to spurious components not present in the original signal. Actually, the multiplication in time corresponds to a convolution in frequency with the Fourier transform of the time window, which thus acquires the role of a filter characteristic. The solution is to use other smooth window functions having zero value and slope at the ends of the record in order to eliminate the discontinuity. One common choice is the so-called *Hanning* window (one period of a cosine squared function) whose filter characteristic is compared with a flat weighting in Fig.7.5. It is seen that the sidelobes of the Hanning characteristic fall off much more rapidly, and thus the overall characteristic is better, even though the bandwidth is increased by 50%.

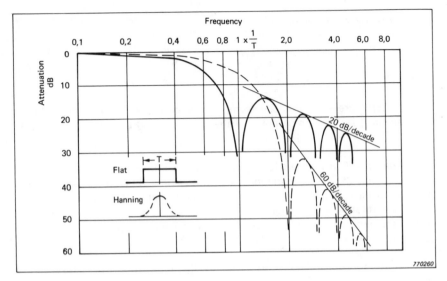

Fig. 7.5. Comparison of Flat and Hanning window functions

Flat weighting is used in the case of a transient function which fits into the record length T. The value at each end will then in any case be zero, and no discontinuity will arise from joining the segment into a loop. It would in fact be detrimental to use a smoothly shaped window function to analyze a short transient, because it would give a different weighting to different sections and thus modify the result. This is not a problem with stationary signals whose properties do not vary along the record.

(c) **Picket fence effect**, resulting from the discrete sampling of the spectrum in the frequency domain. It is as though the spectrum is viewed through the slits in a picket fence, and thus for example peak values are not necessarily seen. The possible error resulting from this depends on the overlapping of adjacent filter characteristics as shown in Fig. 7.6, and is not a unique feature of FFT analysis. It occurs whenever discrete filters are used such as in typical 1/3-octave analysis. It is eased by having a greater overlap of adjacent filters, and with Hanning weighting for example, it is a maximum of 1,4 dB (compared with 3,9 dB for flat weighting). The error can be compensated for where it is known that there is only one frequency component which falls between two spectral lines (e.g. with a calibration signal). One special case of the picket fence effect is where the spectrum samples fall at the zeros between the sidelobes mentioned in (b), and the time window effect becomes invisible (Fig. 7.7). This corresponds with an exact integer number of periods in the record length T, but seldom occurs in practice because the frequencies in question must

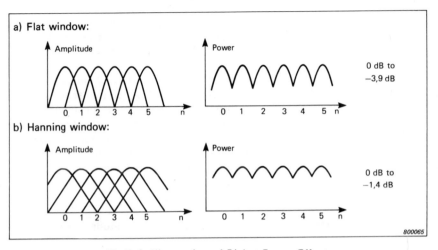

Fig. 7.6. Illustration of Picket Fence Effect

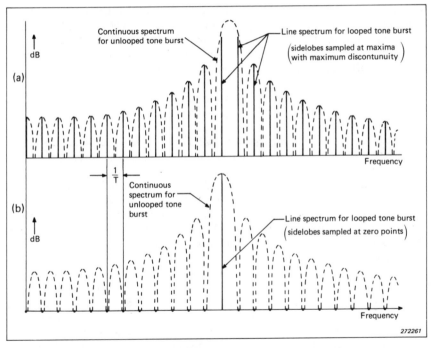

Fig. 7.7. Effect of spectrum sampling on sidelobe effect

be accurate to 1 in 10^6 or so. With an integer number of periods in the record length, of course, a periodic repetition does not give any discontinuity, and this is another explanation of the lack of sidelobes.

At this stage it can be seen that the FFT process gives very different results to digital filtering. The uniform spacing (Δf or $1/T$) of the spectral lines means that the frequency scale is intrinsically linear. Also, the filter characteristic is the same for all lines and is thus constant bandwidth. Another major difference is that a complete time record (of N samples) must first be collected before it can be transformed, whereas with digital filtering each sample is processed fully before the next one arrives, and the time signal does not need to be stored.

7.1.4. Choice of Bandwidth, Frequency Scale and Amplitude Scale

In general it is found that analysis time is governed by expressions of the type $BT \geqslant K$, a constant, (see for example the section on filter response time) where T is the time required for each measurement with bandwidth B. Thus, it is imperative to choose the maximum bandwidth which is consistent with obtaining an adequate resolution, because not only is the analysis time per bandwidth proportional to $1/B$ but so is the number of bandwidths required to cover a given frequency range, altogether a squared effect.

It is not possible to give generally valid rules for selection of bandwidth, but the following discussion gives some guidelines:

For *stationary deterministic* and in particular *periodic* signals containing equally spaced discrete frequency components, the aim is to separate adjacent components, and this can best be done using a constant bandwidth on a linear frequency scale. The bandwidth should for example be chosen as 1/3 of the minimum expected spacing (e.g. the lowest shaft speed, or its half-order if this is to be expected) (Fig.7.8.a). This assumes a fairly good filter characteristic (e.g. Shape Factor* 5) and the bandwidth should be smaller if the shape factor is poorer, or if separation is required over more than 50 dB.

For *stationary random* or *transient* signals, the shape of the spectrum will most likely be determined by resonances in the transmission path between the source and the pickup, and the bandwidth should be chosen as, say, 1/3 of the width of the narrowest peak (Fig.7.8.b). For constant damping these will tend to have a "constant Q" or constant percentage bandwidth character, and thus constant percentage bandwidth on a logarithmic frequency

---

* The **Shape Factor** of a filter is the ratio of the width of the characteristic at -60 dB to that at -3 dB (its 3 dB bandwidth).

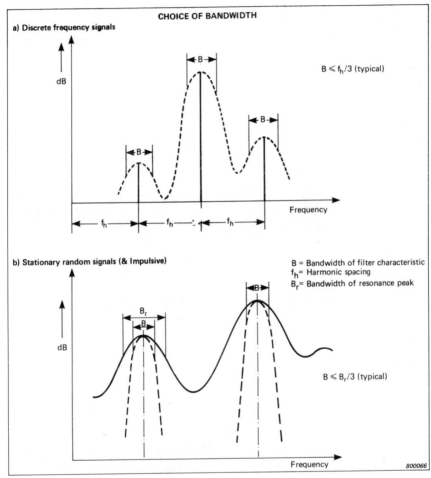

Fig. 7.8. Choice of filter bandwidth

scale would often be most appropriate. Sometimes it is necessary for practical reasons to choose constant bandwidth in order to achieve a sufficiently small percentage bandwidth in part of the spectrum, since 1% is about the minimum constant percentage bandwidth available in practice and 6% (1/12-octave) the usual minimum for digital filters.

As already mentioned, a linear frequency scale is normally used together with constant bandwidth, and logarithmic frequency scale together with constant percentage bandwidth, as each combination gives uniform resolution along the scale. A logarithmic scale may be chosen in order to cover a wide frequency range, and then constant percentage bandwidth is virtually obliga-

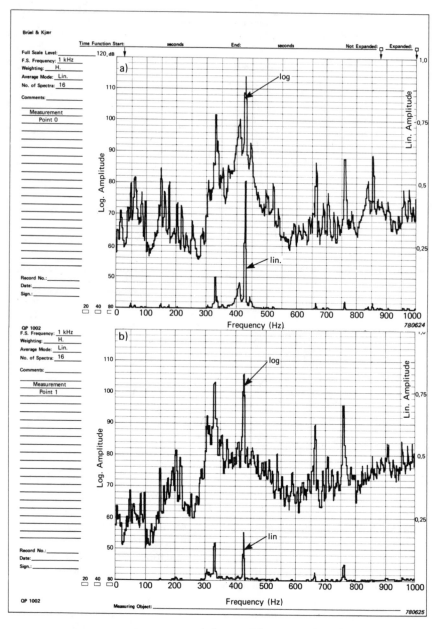

Fig. 7.9. Influence of linear and logarithmic amplitude scales

tory. A logarithmic frequency scale may, however, occasionally be chosen in conjunction with constant bandwidth (though over a limited frequency range) in order to demonstrate a relationship which is linear on log-log scales (e.g. conversions between acceleration, velocity and displacement, see Fig.6.1).

The amplitude scale of a frequency analysis should almost always be logarithmic for a number of reasons. In fact it is only when the parameter being measured is directly of interest (e.g. strain) that there is any point in having a linear scale. Normally, the vibrations measured are an indirect expression of internal forces, and then the logarithmic scaling makes the results less sensitive to the influence of the more or less random transmission path by which the signal has reached the measurement point. Fig.7.9 illustrates this for two measurement points on the same gearbox (both being equally representative of the internal condition). The logarithmic representations of the two spectra are quite similar, while the linear representations are not only different, but hide a number of components which could be important.

7.2. SERIAL ANALYSIS OF STATIONARY SIGNALS

Although serial analyzers have been superseded by real-time analyzers for problems requiring a detailed analysis, it is still the most common technique used in portable battery operated equipment (see Section 6.7) and this section will thus concentrate on that application. The graph of Fig.7.10 can be used more generally, however, and for more detail reference can be made to the B & K book, "Frequency Analysis" for the selection of analysis parameters.

The normal procedure to be followed is to choose a suitable averaging time based on the signal type and analysis bandwidth. From this an equivalent writing speed may be chosen, and finally a paper speed based on the bandwidth or writing speed. Fig.7.10 contains the required information.

7.2.1. Choice of Averaging Time

For analysis of *stationary deterministic* signals, where the filter bandwidth is such that only one discrete frequency component is in the filter at a time, the only requirement of the averaging is that it reduces the ripple of the detector output to an acceptable level. This will be the case if the averaging time contains at least 3 periods of the lowest frequency to be analyzed (see line for $f\,T_A = 3$ in Fig.7.10). At higher frequencies where the (constant percentage bandwidth) filter will most likely contain several frequency components at once it is best to then treat the signal as random.

For *stationary random* signals the averaging time should be chosen so as

171

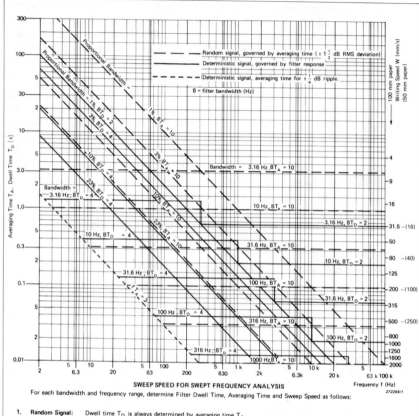

SWEEP SPEED FOR SWEPT FREQUENCY ANALYSIS

272264/1

For each bandwidth and frequency range, determine Filter Dwell Time, Averaging Time and Sweep Speed as follows:

1. **Random Signal:** Dwell time T_D is always determined by averaging time T_A.

 From the graph read off T_A from the appropriate line for $BT_A = 10$ (horizontal lines for constant bandwidth, sloping lines for constant proportional bandwidth). This value will correspond to $\pm 1\frac{1}{2}$ dB RMS error. For a higher BT_A product and consequent reduced error, increase the value of T_A proportionally. Calculate $T_D = 2\,T_A$.

 For DC recording calculate sweep speed $S = \frac{B}{T_D}$.

 For AC recording, T_A is determined by recorder writing speed W and this can be read directly from the right-hand scale. Sweep speed can then be calculated from $S = \frac{BW}{50}$ (applicable to 50 dB potentiometer and 100 mm paper).

2. **Deterministic Signal** (periodic or quasi-periodic): Read T_D based on filter response time from appropriate line for $BT_D = 4$ (or 2 where bandwidth $\leqslant 1\%$). Read also minimum averaging time T_A based on $\pm 1/4$ dB ripple from line $fT_A = 3$ (independent of bandwidth).

 For DC recording calculate sweep speed based on filter response as $S = \frac{B}{T_D}$.

 For AC recording read off writing speed W corresponding to T_A and calculate sweep speed based on recorder response as $S = \frac{BW}{50}$. The governing sweep speed is the lesser of this and the value as calculated for DC recording.

 In all cases where sweep speed is governed by filter response time, increase T_A to the highest value which does not affect sweep speed. (i.e. $T_D/4$ for DC recording)

Note (1) Averaging times will normally be constant over at least a half decade, whereas filter response times change automatically with frequency.

Note (2) S will be in Hz/s for B in Hz, but will be directly in mm/s for B expressed as equivalent recorder paper length in mm.

(3) Above applies to 100 mm paper width. For 50 mm paper substitute 2W for W.

272264/1

Fig. 7.10. Sweep speed for swept frequency analysis

172

to achieve an acceptable accuracy of the result. The relative standard deviation of the error (in RMS values) is given by the formula.

$$\epsilon = \frac{1}{2\sqrt{BT_A}} \qquad (7.5)$$

Table 7.1 gives values of ϵ (in dB) for various values of the product BT_A.

BT_A	10	20	30	40	50	80	120
ϵ (dB)	1,5	1,0	0,8	0,7	0,6	0,5	0,4

Table 7.1. Standard error ϵ vs BT_A product

Fig. 7.10 can be used to select values of T_A for various bandwidths and centre frequencies for a BT_A product of 10. This value of T_A can then be modified proportionally for other BT_A products.

Where AC recording is used, as will normally be the case with a portable analysis set because the dynamic range of the meter DC output is usually < 50 dB, the averaging time is selected indirectly by selection of the pen writing speed. This equivalence is indicated in Fig. 7.10 where the values for 50 mm paper width can be applied to the battery operated portable Level Recorders Types 2306 and 2309.

7.2.2. Choice of Analysis Speed

The speed at which the filter can be swept through the analysis range is limited by one of the 3 factors:

(a) **Filter Response Time** — This will only be the limitation for deterministic signals where a small averaging time is required and where the recorder writing speed does not dominate. The time taken to sweep one bandwidth (T_D) is made greater than 4 filter response times (i.e. $BT_D \geqslant 4$) in order that the frequency error (delay) of the recorded spectrum will be less than one-quarter bandwidth.

(b) **Averaging Time** — This will only be the limitation for DC recording and is thus not normally the limiting factor with portable analyzers.

(c) **Recorder Writing Speed** — This will always be the limitation for AC recording of analyses of random signals, and may also dominate over filter response time for deterministic (discrete frequency) signals.

For analysis with a typical portable set having bandwidths 3% and 23%, a logarithmic frequency axis with 50 mm per decade, and 50 mm paper width representing 50 dB, the options are much more limited. Assuming, as for most machine vibration signals, that the lowest frequency components (e.g. from shaft rotation) are stable and deterministic, Table 7.2 has been drawn up to allow the selection of both pen writing speed and recorder paper speed as a function of the lowest frequency to be analyzed.

Lowest Frequency (Hz)		2 − 5	5 − 15	15 − 50	50 − 150	> 150
23% Bandwidth	W(mm/s)	16	16	40	100	100
	P(mm/s)	0,3	1	3	10	10
3% Bandwidth	W(mm/s)	16	16	40	100	100
	P(mm/s)	0,03	0,1	0,3	1	3

800716

Table 7.2. Writing Speed (W) and Paper Speed (P) vs. minimum valid frequency for discrete frequency signals using Portable Analyzer Type 3513 and Level Recorder Type 2306 (AC Recording)

At the changeover frequencies 20 Hz, 200 Hz and 2 kHz it would be possible to adjust the parameters to achieve higher sweep speeds if this is indicated in the table. However, because at higher frequencies there is a chance that several harmonics will be included in the bandwidth (from the 5th harmonic with 23% bandwidth, and 34th harmonic with 3% bandwidth) it is recommended that the increase in paper speed be no more than one step (factor 3) with 23% bandwidth and 2 steps (factor 10) with 3% bandwidth. (The total analysis time is in any case dominated by the lower frequencies.) The writing speed appropriate to the new paper speed can be seen from the table. If the signal contains random components (e.g. from turbulence, cavitation) then it should be checked in Table 7.3 whether any speedup is possible.

Lowest Frequency (Hz)		50 − 150	150 − 500	500 − 1,5 k	> 1,5 k
23% Bandwidth	W(mm/s)	16	40	100	100
	P(mm/s)	1	3	10	10
3% Bandwidth	W(mm/s)	—	16	40	100
	P(mm/s)	—	0,3	1	3

800717

Table 7.3. Writing Speed (W) and Paper Speed (P) vs. minimum valid frequency for random signals using Portable Analyzer Type 3513 and Level Recorder Type 2306 (AC Recording)

It will be seen that with the AC recording assumed, the minimum valid frequencies for random components are relatively high. In order to make valid analyses at lower frequencies it would be necessary to use the 1 s or 10 s averaging time of the Vibration Meter Type 2511 and DC recording. Note that in this case the dynamic range is limited to 40 dB. Sweep speeds can be determined using the general procedure of Fig. 7.10, with the modification that dwell time T_D can be made equal to T_A (instead of $2T_A$) taking into account the filter characteristic of the portable equipment.

7.3. REAL-TIME ANALYSIS OF STATIONARY AND TRANSIENT SIGNALS

At one time it was common for even detailed laboratory analysis to be carried out by serial analysis techniques as described in Section 7.2. The rapidly decreasing cost of digital circuitry, however, has meant that digitally based Real-Time Analyzers (RTA's) are now no more expensive than an advanced serial analysis system, and produce results in a very much shorter time (often in real-time* as the name implies). The real-time feature is also used to advantage for trouble-shooting applications in the field, because of the very rapid response to changing conditions, and this has opened up a number of applications which were previously not possible or extremely difficult.

As regards the analysis of transients, the real-time analyzer approach is even more advantageous. Impulse analysis by serial analysis techniques is possible (and described in detail in the B & K book "Frequency Analysis") but requires the use of an additional recorder (digital or tape recorder) from which the transient can be repeatedly played back, and this makes the system even more costly, while (in particular with a tape recorder) still requiring a considerably longer analysis time than the real-time approach.

Of the two real-time techniques discussed in Section 7.1, by far the most important for vibration analysis is the FFT method, and therefore this section concentrates mainly on this type of analyzer. The primary advantage of FFT analysis lies in its constant bandwidth, linear frequency scale nature, as many diagnostic problems rely on being able to identify families of equally spaced components such as harmonics, sidebands and inter-harmonics. Fig. 7.11 is a typical example illustrating the latter case.

The digital filter analyzer finds its main application in the analysis of rapidly changing intrinsically broad-band signals, primarily in the field of acoustics. It

---

* In frequency analysis, real-time operation means that the entire input signal is analyzed, in all frequency bands (of interest) all of the time, even though there may be a time delay between input and output.

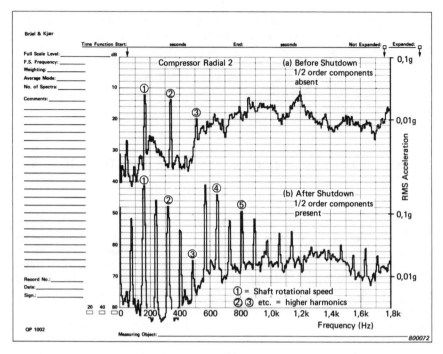

Fig. 7.11. Inter-harmonic components resulting from insufficiently tight assembly of journal bearing components

does have the advantage of covering a wide frequency range with a relatively small number of filters, and is thus often the most efficient and economical technique to use in machine monitoring and quality control applications. Other applications include the analysis of shocks and transients, and where the vibration measurements are to be compared with sound spectra, typically presented in 1/3-octaves.

7.3.1. FFT Analysis of Stationary Signals

A typical FFT analyzer has a transform size (N in Eqn. (7.3)) of 1024 data samples, and in theory gives 1024 frequency values. However, since the data values are real, the second half of the calculated spectrum (representing the negative frequencies less than the Nyquist frequency* because of the implicit periodicity of the spectrum) is determined by the first half (the corresponding positive frequencies). For this reason, only the 512 positive fre-

---
* Half the sampling frequency.

quency values are calculated, although because each frequency component is complex, this represents the same amount of data (and occupies the same memory space) as the original 1024 real-valued time samples. Not all of the 512 values can be used; to eliminate the problem of aliasing (Section 7.1.3) a low-pass filter is applied with a cut-off frequency less than the Nyquist frequency to allow for its finite slope. For the B & K analyzers it is typical to place the filter cut-off so that the first 400 lines are valid, and are displayed, while the last 112 lines are affected by the filter and are not operated on further (when the complex spectrum is converted to a power spectrum etc.).

Thus, the frequency *resolution (Δf)* is always 1/400 of the selected *full-scale frequency ($f_{f.s.}$)*, and the automatically-selected sampling frequency is 2,56 times the full-scale frequency $f_{f.s.}$. When using *flat* weighting, the filter characteristic is a *sinx/x* function with bandwidth equal to the resolution Δf. As mentioned in Section 7.1.3, the spectrum obtained is that of a *periodic* signal of period T (= NΔt) and the line spacing Δf is thus *1/T*.

Thus,
$$B = \Delta f = \frac{1}{T} \qquad (7.6)$$

From Eqn. (7.6) it can be seen that each spectrum calculated by an FFT analyzer has a *BT* product of 1. Even where for example *Hanning* weighting is used, and the bandwidth is increased by 50%

i.e.
$$B = 1{,}5 \, \Delta f = \frac{1{,}5}{T} \qquad (7.7)$$

the effective record length T_E is reduced correspondingly (by removal of information towards the ends of the record) so that the BT_E product is still unity (i.e. for statistical purposes the effective length is *2T/3*).

The above relationships mean that there is a simple inverse relationship between frequency range and record length,

viz.
$$T = \frac{1}{\Delta f} = \frac{400}{f_{f.s.}} \qquad (7.8)$$

Table 7.4 indicates the record lengths vs. frequency range for a 400-line analyzer.

$f_{f.s.}$ (Hz)	20 k	10 k	5 k	2 k	1 k	500	200	100	50	20	10
T	20 ms	40 ms	80 ms	200 ms	400 ms	800 ms	2 s	4 s	8 s	20 s	40 s

Table 7.4. Record length vs. Frequency Range for 400-line Analyzer

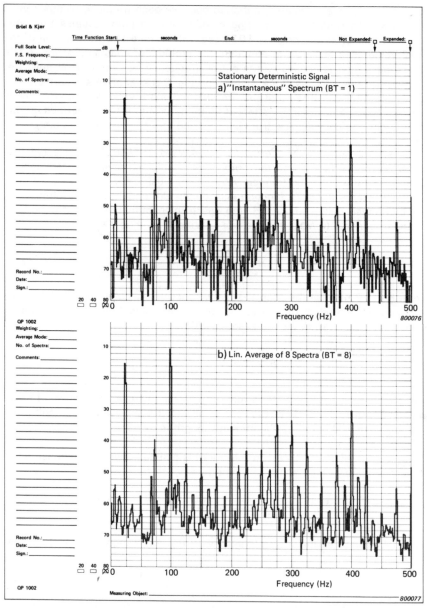

Fig.7.12. Effect of averaging with a stationary deterministic signal

In the analysis of *stationary deterministic* signals it is theoretically not necessary to employ spectrum averaging, as each "instantaneous" spectrum

178

(with BT product = 1) should fully describe all stable, discrete frequency components. In practice, an average over, say, 8 spectra would normally be used to average out minor fluctuations. Fig.7.12 illustrates a typical case, where the "instantaneous" spectrum gives virtually the same result as an average over 8 spectra for the discrete harmonic components, but the averaged spectrum has smoothed out the low level noise (presumably coming from tape recording) at around — 60 dB.

In the analysis of *stationary random* signals, it is necessary to average over a number of spectra to reduce the standard error ϵ to an acceptable level. Since each individual spectrum carries a BT product of 1 (whether or not Hanning weighting is used), the number of independent spectra averaged gives directly the total BT_A product to be inserted in Equation (7.5). There is one small point to be noted here. When Hanning weighting is used, the effective record length is reduced to a little over one-half the actual, and in some analyzers use is made of this to shorten the overall averaging time (in particular at low frequencies) by a 50% overlapping of consecutive time records. Because of the small redundancy which still occurs, the effective number of independent records is in that case 95% of the actual, but because of the square root in Eqn. (7.5) this will be seen to be a very minor effect. In practice, in any case, it is not always necessary to decide in advance how much averaging is to be done, as a linear average over a large number (e.g. 2048) can be started and then stopped manually when the fluctuations have reached an acceptable level.

Fig.7.13 illustrates the effect of averaging on a typical stationary random signal, with averages over 1, 8 and 128 spectra. This practical example helps in interpreting the meaning of the standard error ϵ given in Eqn.(7.5). Statistically, there is a 68% probability that the fluctuations will be within $\pm\epsilon$, 95,5% probability that they will be within $\pm 2\epsilon$ and 99,7% probability that they will be within $\pm 3\epsilon$. Thus, as illustrated in Fig.7.13, the peak excursions almost always lie between $\pm 2\epsilon$ and $\pm 3\epsilon$.

For stationary random signals, it may be desired to express the results as a Power Spectral Density (PSD). Because of the constant bandwidth, this involves only a modification by a scaling factor which is uniform for the whole spectrum. First, the scale must be converted from dB into the equivalent power spectrum (amplitude squared) units. The normal internal scaling of the analyzer is in dB re $1\,\mu V$ so that $120\,dB$ represents $1\,V^2$, but conversions can be made to other units (e.g. g^2, $(ms^{-2})^2$, $(ms^{-1})^2$) making use of the conversion factor from engineering units to volts. It should be kept in mind that for these "power" units, each decade corresponds to 10 dB. Finally, the power units are to be divided by the bandwidth to convert them to power spectral density. The bandwidth can be obtained either from Equation (7.6) or (7.7) for flat or Hanning weighting respectively. Equation (7.8) or Table 7.4

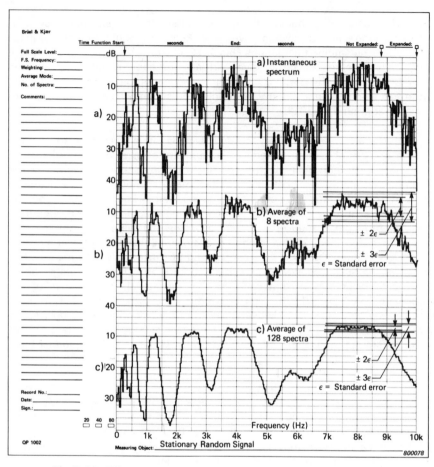

Fig. 7.13. Effect of averaging with a stationary random signal

can be used for both. Since the scaling of B & K's analyzers is adjusted to give the same (peak) level for discrete frequency components, the spectrum level of broadband components will be 1,76 dB higher when Hanning weighting is used and this is cancelled out when dividing by the 50% greater bandwidth $(10 \log_{10}(1,5) = 1,76$ dB$)$. It should be noted that conversion to PSD is only valid where the spectrum peaks are broader than the analyzer bandwidth, and thus any peaks as narrow as the filter characteristic (bandwidth 1,5 lines) should be suspected as invalid.

One more point to be taken into account is the question of stationarity. The vibration signals from high-speed machines will normally be stationary, even over time periods comparable with the analyzer record length, provided the

180

machine speed and load remain constant. The same applies to stationary random signals such as arise from fluid flow (turbulence, cavitation) provided the physical conditions remain constant. The vibration signals from slow-speed rotating and reciprocating machines have another character, however. Even though they may be considered stationary over time periods including several machine cycles, the signal within each cycle may be quite non-stationary, often consisting of a series of different impulsive events.

Where the analyzer is operating within its real-time frequency range, there is no problem, as the entire incoming signal is analyzed. Above the highest real-time frequency, however, some of the incoming signal is lost, and if the record length T (Table 7.4) is shorter than the machine cycle time, then the sections analyzed will not necessarily be representative. For example, a machine with a basic speed of 600 c.p.m. (i.e. 1200 r.p.m. for a 4-stroke engine) has a basic cycle time of 100 ms, and this is to be compared with the 10 ms effective length of record (for Hanning weighting) when the signal is analyzed in the 20 kHz range. If the analyzer has a 10 K memory length (200 ms in 20 kHz range) the best way to solve the problem is to record the full 10 K and perform a "scan" analysis to obtain the averaged 400-line spectrum over this record length, this being equivalent to a real-time analysis. This can be repeated as many times as desired to obtain an average over a suitable number of cycles. Even though data is lost in between the successive recordings, this does not matter because each recording includes several machine cycles. If the analyzer only has a 1 K memory size, it is still possible to do something similar if use is made of a tachometer signal (once per cycle) as external trigger, and variable "Records-After-Trigger" settings to move the section of cycle analyzed throughout the entire cycle (Fig. 7.14). With this setup it is also possible to obtain a separate analysis for each part of the cycle, rather than averaging them all together, and this is discussed further in section 7.4, in the discussion on non-stationary signals.

Finally, it is worthwhile discussing the use of frequency "zoom", which gives the possibility of obtaining a finer resolution than that given by the 400-line baseband spectrum. It may be best to illustrate the use of "zoom" by taking a typical example where it is often required in practice, viz. the analysis of gearbox vibrations. These are characterized by the presence of sidebands, spaced around the toothmeshing frequency and its harmonics and due to modulation by lower frequencies, typically the shaft rotational speeds. The sideband *spacing* is equal to the modulating frequency, whether it is a question of amplitude modulation, frequency modulation, or a combination of both. It is often desired to measure these sideband spacings so as to trace the source of modulation in a gearbox, since this often indicates faults. To obtain an idea of the required resolution, take the case of a 50-tooth gearwheel modulated at its own rotating speed. A baseband spectrum covering 80 harmonics of the rotational speed would thus include the toothmeshing fre-

181

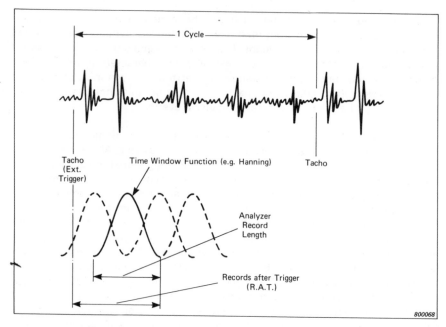

Fig.7.14. Analysis of a reciprocating machine cycle

quency (50th harmonic) well within its range. The sideband spacing would be equal to the shaft speed, and thus harmonics 49 and 51 would represent modulation by this frequency, 48 and 52 modulation by the 2nd harmonic and so on. In a 400-line spectrum, the sidebands would be separated by 5 lines and this should be adequate to identify them. If it were desired to include higher harmonics of the toothmeshing frequency, however, or gears with larger numbers of teeth, it can be seen that the 400-line resolution would not be adequate. A zoom factor of 10 on the other hand, gives the equivalent resolution of a 4000 line spectrum, and would thus cover the vast majority of practical cases. There is a limit in the other direction as to how much zoom is practicable, since for a 4000-line spectrum to be useful the frequencies involved must be stable to 1 in 4000.

Fig.7.15 illustrates these points. In Fig.7.15 a) is shown a baseband spectrum with full-scale frequency 2 kHz. The toothmeshing frequency is 333 Hz and the first four harmonics of this can be seen, although in many cases adjacent sidebands are higher. The dominant sideband spacing is 25 Hz (the 3rd harmonic of the input pinion speed) and was due to a slight "triangularity" of this gear. Fig.7.15.b) shows a zoomed spectrum centred around the third toothmeshing harmonic. The greatly increased resolution means that in addition to the 25 Hz sideband spacing, an 8,3 Hz spacing (corresponding to the

182

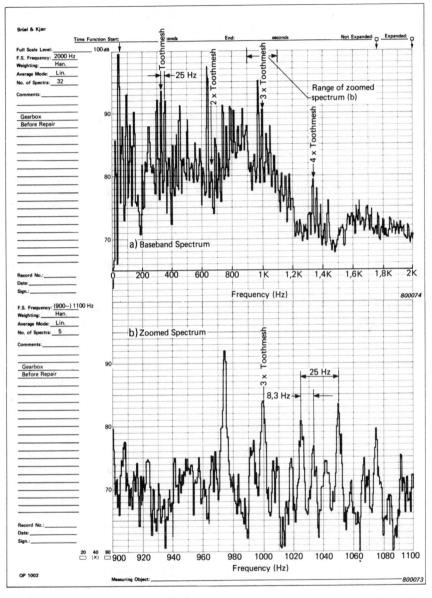

Fig. 7.15. Comparison of baseband and zoomed spectra for a gearbox vibration signal

pinion speed) is also now apparent. On the other hand, because of speed fluctuations, the major peaks have spread over a number of lines, and thus a higher zoom factor would not give any benefit.

7.3.2. Digital Filter Analysis of Stationary Signals

As mentioned previously, this type of analysis is more applicable to acoustics than vibration studies, and therefore the discussion will be kept fairly brief.

For 1/3-octave analysis, it is really only necessary to choose between exponential and linear averaging and to decide on a suitable averaging time. The 1/3-octave digital filter analyzer Type 2131 is real-time over its full frequency range up to 20 kHz, and thus gives correct results even when the signal is impulsive and non-stationary in the short-term.

Exponential averaging would tend to be used only in setting up a measurement, as its primary application is to non-stationary signals. Normally, a linear average over a certain averaging time T_A would derive the maximum information from a certain length of signal (e.g. a tape recording) and is therefore the best to use. The analyzer Type 2131 does have a "constant confidence" mode, where there is uniform BT_A product across the whole spectrum, and for which exponential averaging is necessary. The only advantage, however, is the uniformity of accuracy of the result; it is in any case necessary to wait about twice the averaging time, T_A, for the lowest frequency considered, before a valid result can be obtained, whereas a linear average over T_A would have the same accuracy at the lowest frequency, and increasingly better accuracy at higher frequencies.

In order to choose a suitable averaging time, use can be made of Fig.7.16, which indicates the values of BT_A product corresponding to various centre frequencies and averaging times. For discrete frequency components the BT_A product must be at least 1, and for random signals the suggested minimum value is 10. Thus, with the shortest available averaging time (31 ms) the lowest valid frequency band for a deterministic component is 160 Hz, and for random components is 1600 Hz.

It is also possible to make 1/12-octave (6% bandwidth) analyses using either a desktop calculator or special controller to control the analyzer. This makes it possible to select other filter coefficients than those used for 1/3-octave analysis, but as only 3 filters per octave can be calculated in one pass, it is necessary to make 4 passes, each time calculating a different set of three 1/12-octaves in each octave. The controller finally arranges the intermediate results in the correct order, and can transfer (overlapping) sets of 42 conti-

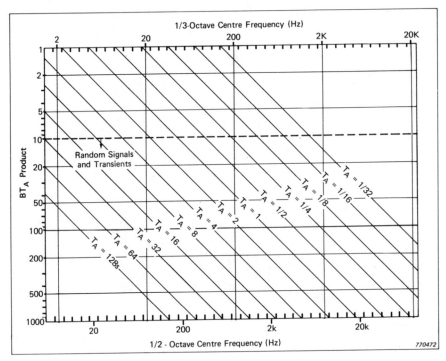

Fig.7.16. BT_A product vs. averaging time for the Digital Filter Analyzer Type 2131

guous spectrum values into the analyzer for display on the screen. Fig.7.17 compares a 1/12-octave spectrum obtained in this way with the equivalent 1/3-octave spectrum. Note that even though the method is not "real-time", because not all the spectrum is calculated at one time, the entire time signal is processed for each pass, and therefore any short-term non-stationarity will not have any adverse effect on the results.

The appropriate scale of Fig.7.16 can also be used in this case for selection of a suitable averaging time.

7.3.3. Impulse Analysis by FFT and Digital Filter Techniques

When it comes to the analysis of shocks and transients (single impulses) it is no longer so clear whether constant bandwidth (FFT) or constant percentage bandwidth (digital filters) is preferable. It depends partly on the properties of the signal itself, and partly on the application to which the results will be applied. Table 7.5 compares the main features of the two approaches.

185

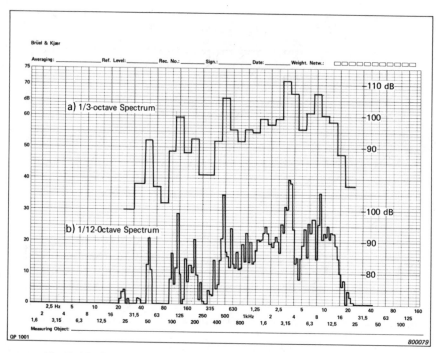

Fig.7.17. Comparison of 1/3-octave and 1/12-octave spectra

FFT	Digital Filter
Constant bandwidth	Constant percentage bandwidth (Constant Q)
Signal processed blockwise	Signal processed sample-for-sample
Length limited by record length	Length limited by averaging time
Linear frequency scale	Logarithmic frequency scale
Restricted frequency range	Wide frequency range

Table 7.5. Choice of method for impulse analysis

Taking first the case of FFT analysis, there is no problem provided the entire transient fits into the transform size T without losing any high frequency components. Fig.7.18 shows a typical transient and its frequency spectrum up to 20 kHz. There is evidently no appreciable energy above 20 kHz, and the transient is shorter than the 20 ms record length in this range. "Flat" weighting must be used in this case.

The only question is that of scaling the results. This is best done in terms of "Energy Spectral Density" (ESD) since this will be the same virtually inde-

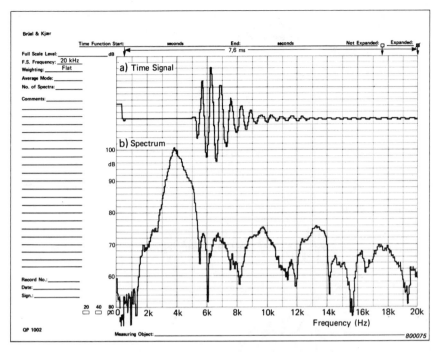

Brüel & Kjær

Time Function Start: _____ seconds   End: _____ seconds   Not Expanded: ☐ Expanded: ☒

Full Scale Level: _____ dB |←——————— 7,6 ms ———————→|

F.S. Frequency: __20 kHz__

Weighting: __Flat__   a) Time Signal

Average Mode: _____

No. of Spectra: _____

Comments: _____

100 b) Spectrum

dB

90

80

70

Record No.: _____

Date: _____   60

Sign.: _____

20 40 80

☐ ☐ ☒ 0   2k   4k   6k   8k   10k   12k   14k   16k   18k   20k

QP 1002   Frequency (Hz)

Measuring Object: _____   800075

Fig.7.18. Time signal and spectrum of a transient

pendent of the analysis parameters (for example changing to frequency range 10 kHz would give the same results for the frequencies up to 10 kHz). Since as mentioned previously, the FFT calculation assumes the signal to be a periodic repetition of the memory contents, the resulting power spectrum values (obtained as described in Section 7.3.1 for stationary random signals) must be multiplied by the record length T (Table 7.4) to convert them to energy (contained in one record length). Finally, the values of energy (per bandwidth) must be divided by the bandwidth (Eqn. (7.6)) to convert them to energy spectral density. In this case the conversion would always be valid; provided the transient fits into record length T, its own intrinsic bandwidth must always be $>1/T$.

Problems arise when the transient is longer than the 1 K record length T, although there are two ways in which the analysis can still be made with an analyzer with 10 K memory length, provided the transient can be contained in this 10 times longer memory:

(1) **Zoom FFT.** Using zoom (and flat weighting) it is possible to obtain the complete 4000-line spectrum of the 10 K transient in 10 passes, each time calculating 400 lines (Fig.7.19 a). The 10 times smaller bandwidth

187

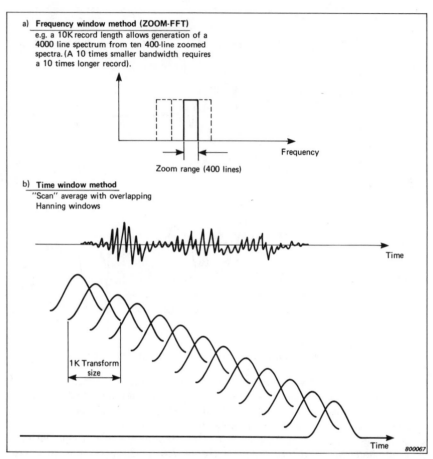

a) **Frequency window method (ZOOM-FFT)**
e.g. a 10K record length allows generation of a
4000 line spectrum from ten 400-line zoomed
spectra. (A 10 times smaller bandwidth requires
a 10 times longer record).

Frequency

Zoom range (400 lines)

b) **Time window method**
"Scan" average with overlapping
Hanning windows

Time

1K Transform
size

Time *800067*

Fig. 7.19. Two methods of analyzing a long transient with an FFT analyzer

(for the same full-scale frequency) must be taken into account when converting to ESD, and incidentally results in a 10 dB loss of dynamic range.

(2) **Moving windows.** It is also possible to obtain the averaged 400-line
spectrum over the entire record, by performing a "scan" analysis, i.e.
moving a Hanning window in overlapping steps along the record
(Fig. 7.19 b). Note that the equivalent record length (for conversion from
power to energy) is 9,25 K because of the effects of the Hanning weighting at each end (even though there can be a uniform weighting along
most of the record) (Fig. 7.20). The transient should ideally be placed in
the centre 8,5 K of the record to avoid end effects. There is no advantage
in overlapping more than 75% (step length 0,25 K) and in fact this would
reduce the length of the uniformly weighted portion.

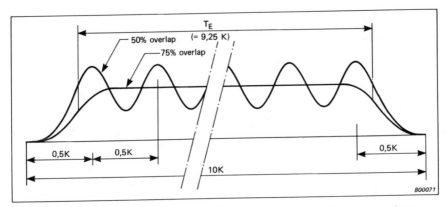

Fig.7.20. Overall weighting in a "Scan" analysis for different overlaps

Note also that the bandwidth is determined by the Hanning weighting and is thus given by Eqn. (7.7). In this case it is not certain that the conversion to ESD is valid, and thus any peaks having the appearance of the filter characteristic (a bandwidth of 1,5 lines) should be suspect. The method does, however, have the advantage of not losing dynamic range as with the zoom method.

Considering now impulse analysis by digital filter techniques, the approach is quite different. It is known that the output of a filter contains that part of the energy applied to the input which falls within the filter passband, but it is necessary to sum over the entire filter output. As mentioned in connection with Fig.7.2 this should be at least 3 times the filter impulse response time (i.e. $3T_R$) plus the length of the original impulse (T_I). Fig.7.21 traces the path of a typical impulsive signal (an N-wave) through the complete analysis system of filter, squarer and averager for both a narrow-band filter (i.e. low frequency, for constant percentage bandwidth) and a broad-band filter (high frequency).

For the narrow-band filter, $T_R \gg T_I$ and the filter output resembles its impulse response. For the broad-band filter, $T_R \ll T_I$ and the filter output consists of two short bursts of length $\approx T_R$ and separated by T_I. Thus, the averaging time must everywhere be given by

$$T_A > T_I + 3T_R \tag{7.9}$$

and will thus be determined by the lowest frequency to be analyzed. The ideal solution would be running linear integration (with T_A chosen from Eqn. (7.9)) followed by a "Max. Hold" circuit. The output of such a running linear averager is shown in Fig.7.21, and it is seen that during the time the entire filter output is contained in the averaging time T_A, the averager output gives the correct result, and this would be held by the "Max. Hold" circuit. As men-

189

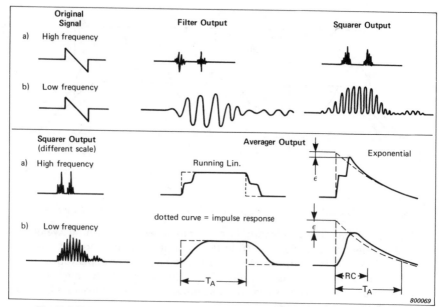

Fig.7.21. Passage of a transient through filter, squarer and averager

tioned in Section 7.1.1., however, this is not possible, and it is necessary to choose between fixed linear averaging and running exponential averaging.

The problem with fixed linear averaging is that it must be started just before the arrival of the impulse and thus cannot be triggered from the signal itself (unless use is made of a delay-line before the analyzer). It is, however, possible to record the signal first and then insert a trigger signal (for example on another channel of a tape recorder).

It may be found necessary to make the total analysis in two passes, in order to extract all information from a given signal. Fig.7.22 shows for example the analysis of a 220 ms N-wave (Sonic Boom) with averaging time T_A = 0,5 s. This is only valid down to 50 Hz ($T_I + 3T_R$ = 0,48 s) but on the other hand includes frequencies up to 5 kHz. Fig.7.23 (a) shows an analysis of the same signal with T_A = 8 s so as to include all frequencies down to 1,6 Hz ($T_I + 3T_R$ = 8,3 s). Because of the 12 dB loss of dynamic range with this longer averaging time, all the frequency components above 500 Hz have been lost. This result (with scaling adjusted by 12 dB) is given as a dotted line in Fig.7.22 and shows that the two results are identical over the mutually valid range. Fig.7.23 (c) shows a 1/12-octave analysis obtained by 4 passes of the same signal, with T_A = 8 s. This gives a 6 dB loss of dynamic range and is only valid down to 6,3 Hz ($T_I + 3T_R$ = 8,5 s) but in the frequencies from 6,3 — 250 Hz it gives more detail of the spectrum than the 1/3-octave analysis.

190

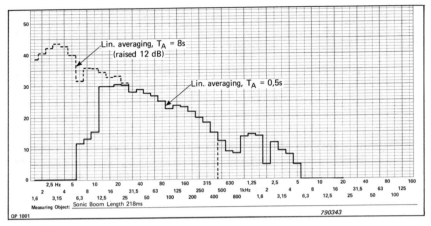

Fig.7.22. 1/3-octave transient analysis with different averaging times

Where 1/3-octave analysis is to be carried out in real-time on randomly occurring impulses it is possible to use exponential averaging followed by
"Max. Hold", but there is now the added complication that the averager
"leaks" energy at a (max.) rate of 8,7 dB per averaging time, and thus the total impulse length must be short with respect to T_A. If the ratio $T_A/T_E > 10$
where T_E is the effective total length of the filter output signal, the detector
output resembles its impulse response and the error will be $< 0,5$ dB
(ϵ in Fig.7.21). For this purpose, T_E can be obtained from

$$T_E = T_I + T_R \qquad (7.10)$$

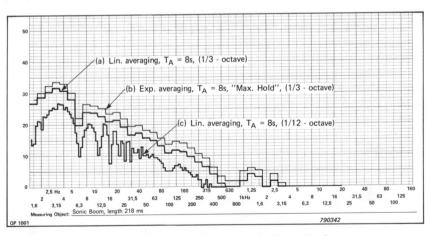

Fig.7.23. Comparison of analysis methods

This means that even where $T_R >> T_I$, T_A must always be such that $T_A > 10T_R$ or in other words $BT_A > 10$. The frequencies for which this applies can be obtained from Fig.7.16 as for stationary random signals.

Note that as illustrated in Figs.7.3 and 7.21 the peak output of an exponential averager is 3 dB higher than from the equivalent linear averager and thus the equivalent averaging time to be used in converting from power to energy is $T_A / 2$.

Fig.7.23 (b) shows an analysis made with $T_A = 8$ s, exponential averaging, and "Max. Hold", and this confirms that the result is approx. 3 dB higher than for linear averaging over most of its range, but the difference reduces down to 2,5 dB at 8 Hz, the lowest valid frequency ($T_I + T_R = 0,76$ s).

7.4. ANALYSIS OF NON-STATIONARY SIGNALS

The type of analysis considered in this section is the use of a moving time window to see how the short-term frequency spectrum varies with time (Fig.7.24). It is assumed that the window length can be chosen so that the individual windowed sections are quasi-stationary, without being so short that the attainable resolution is too coarse.

Two main application areas are envisaged:

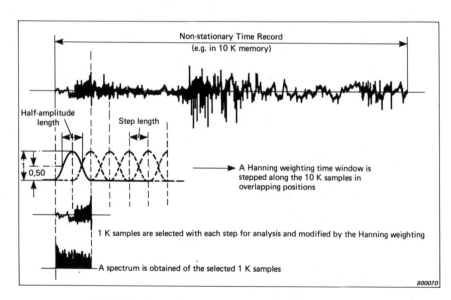

Fig.7.24. Analysis along a non-stationary record

192

(a) Analysis along a single record, such as a machine run-up or run-down.

(b) Cyclic signals, such as obtained from low-speed reciprocating machines, where the signal within each cycle consists of a series of impulsive events, but where the results for each window position can be averaged over a number of similar cycles. (Fig.7.14).

Many considerations are common to both cases, since case (a) can be considered a special case of (b) with an average over one cycle only. Consequently, it is primarily case (b) which will be discussed in detail, though any special considerations applicable to case (a) will be discussed where appropriate.

7.4.1. Choice of Analysis Parameters

In order to minimise the amount of data to be handled, the time window should be chosen as long as possible, though not so long that the signal changes appreciably within the window length. In case (b) above the window length should be chosen so as to separate the individual impulses, but ideally should be appreciably longer than the individual events so that the weighting function does not distort their spectrum when they are located in the centre of the window. This choice also optimises the frequency range and resolution of the results, because the bandwidth is approximately the reciprocal of the effective window length (Eqns. (7.6), (7.7)). The bandwidth also sets the minimum frequency for which meaningful results can be obtained. With an FFT analyzer the window length is determined by the Full-scale Frequency (Table 7.4) and in some cases the latter will have to be chosen higher than necessary in order to obtain a sufficiently short window, but in that situation the upper frequencies outside the desired range can simply be discarded. In rare cases, it may be necessary to accept a lower full-scale frequency than desired in order to obtain a sufficiently long window.

The type of window function is not very critical; for an FFT analyzer, the natural choice would be the internal Hanning window, while for a digital filter analyzer a premultiplication of the signal by a gaussian-shaped window is suggested (Fig.7.25).

The step length with which the window is displaced should be chosen as a suitable proportion of the window length with regard to the following factors:

(1) Choosing the "half amplitude length" (Fig.7.24) of the window (= half the total length for a Hanning function) would give virtually uncorrelated results and reduce the amount of data to a minimum, but could give an error of up to 6 dB for extremely localised transients between two win-

193

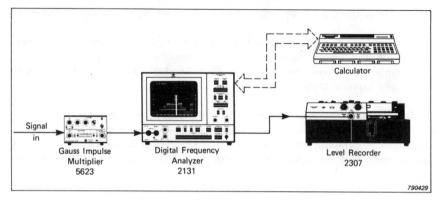

Fig.7.25. Analysis set-up with digital filter analyzer

dow positions (c.f. the "picket fence effect" in the frequency domain). This choice would often be made for condition monitoring applications where the aim is to detect changes with time and where the amount of data to be compared is to be minimised.

(2) A reduction of the steps means that successive spectra are correlated, but this helps in visualising the spectrum changes, for example in 3-dimensional landscape representations (e.g. Fig.7.26). Steps of between 20% and 50% of the "half-amplitude length" have been found suitable.

The number of spectra to be averaged in each window position should be chosen so as to obtain stable repeatable results, and depends greatly on the variability of the signal from one cycle to another. It can best be found by trial and error, by storing one result and comparing with others, obtained with the same parameters.

7.4.2. Example

In order to illustrate the general procedure, the example will be taken of vibration signals (velocity) measured on the cylinder head of a 4-cylinder, 4-stroke diesel engine running at 1500 r.p.m. (750 cpm or 80 ms cycle time). The measurement and recording system were linear up to 10 kHz, but the signals contained information up to 20 kHz. The signals were recorded at 15 i.p.s. on an FM recorder, in parallel with a once-per-cycle tacho signal obtained with a photo-electric pickup from the camshaft. The analyses were made with the FFT analyzer Type 2031.

Viewing the time signal on the screen of the analyzer it could be determined that individual impulses had a length of $\approx$ 2 ms, and for this reason it was desirable to have a window length as short as 8 ms (i.e. half-amplitude length 4 ms with Hanning weighting). This could not be achieved directly, as the shortest window length available (in 20 kHz range) is 20 ms (Table 7.4), but by slowing down the tape recorder 10:1 on playback it was possible to achieve the desired parameters in the 5 kHz range (T = 80 ms). This meant that the effective full-scale frequency was now 50 kHz, but only the first 160 lines (< 20 kHz) were utilised in displaying the results. The total cycle time of 80 ms could be covered by varying the "Records-After-Trigger" setting (Fig.7.14) between 0,0 and 9,8 memory lengths with increments of 0,2 (i.e. effectively 1,6 ms steps or 40% of the half-amplitude length). An average over 64 cycles was found to be necessary, partly because of a slight "jitter" of the tacho pulses which could have been eliminated by a more elaborate set-up.

Fig.7.26 shows a 3-dimensional representation of the results as a frequency-time landscape. The measurements were performed automatically using a desktop calculator to control the analyzer, store the results, and later

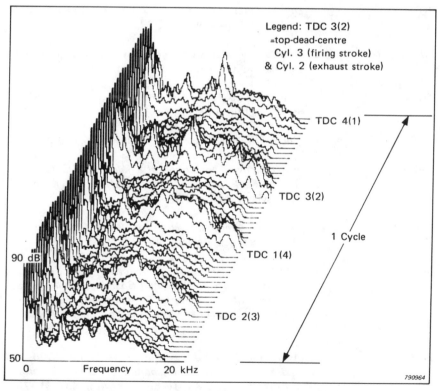

Fig.7.26. Frequency-time representation of diesel engine cycle

195

plot them on a digital plotter. The results as plotted have a linear frequency scale, but the calculator could be used to convert them to constant percentage bandwidth on a logarithmic frequency scale.

7.5. BIBLIOGRAPHY

BENDAT, J.S. and PIERSOL, A.G.:
Random Data: Analysis and Measurement Procedures. Wiley, N.Y., 1971

RANDALL, R.B.:
Frequency Analysis. B & K Publication. Sept. 1977

RANDALL, R.B. and THRANE, N.:
Impulse Analysis using a Real-time Digital Filter Analyzer. B & K Technical Review No.4, 1979

RANDALL, R.B. and UPTON, R.:
Digital Filters and FFT Technique in Real-Time Analysis. B & K Technical Review No.1, 1978

ROTH, O.:
Digital Filters in Acoustic Analysis Systems. B & K Technical Review No.1, 1977

THRANE, N.:
Analysis of Impulsive Signals by use of Digital Techniques. SEECO 79, Soc. Env. Eng., England

THRANE, N.:
The Discrete Fourier Transform and FFT Analysers. B & K Technical Review No.1, 1979

THRANE, N.:
Zoom-FFT. B & K Technical Review No.2, 1980

UPTON, R.:
An Objective Comparison of Analog and Digital Methods of Real-Time Frequency Analysis. B & K Technical Review, No.1, 1977

WAHRMANN, C.G. and BROCH, J.T.:
On the Averaging Time of RMS Measurements. B & K Technical Review, Nos.2 & 3, 1975

WELCH, P.D.:
The Use of Fast Fourier Transform for the Estimation of Power Spectra: A Method Based on Time Averaging Over Short, Modified Periodograms. IEEE Trans. Audio Electroacoust. Vol. AU-15, pp.70-73, June 1967

ZAVERI, K.:
Averaging Time of Level Recorder Type 2306 and "Fast" and "Slow" Response of Level Recorders 2305/06/07. B & K Technical Review No.2, 1975

8. VIBRATION MEASUREMENTS FOR MACHINE HEALTH MONITORING

8.1. BASIC CONSIDERATIONS

All machines vibrate. In the process of channelling energy into the job to be performed forces are generated which will excite the individual parts of the machine directly or via the structure. Some of the parts in the transmission path are accessible from the outside so that we can easily measure the vibration resulting from the excitation forces.

As long as the process is constant or only varying within certain limits the vibration measured will be practically constant. Furthermore, it is found for most machines that the vibration frequency spectrum has a characteristic shape when the machine is in good condition. When faults begin to develop in the machine some of the dynamic processes in the machine are changed and some of the forces acting on parts - or the mechanical properties of the parts themselves - are changed, thereby influencing the vibration spectrum. This is the basis for using vibration measurements and analysis in machine health monitoring.

Unfortunately it is possible with a few wrong choices of parameters and procedures to end up with systems unable to give reliable results. It is hoped the following comments will clear up these matters.

8.2. THE RELATIONSHIP FORCE - VIBRATION

As already mentioned, machine vibration is usually measured at points accessible on the outside of the machine. How does this relate to what is going on inside?

In Fig.8.1 a rotor is exerting a varying force on the bearings of a machine. As rotor forces are mostly transmitted through bearings, this is a preferred location for measurements. These forces result in both a relative vibration of the rotor to the bearing housing and an absolute vibration of the whole bear-

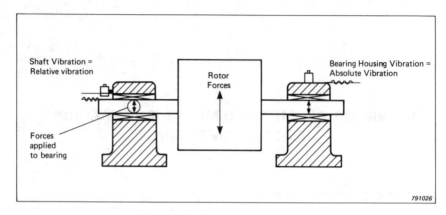

Fig.8.1. Basic rotor-stator system

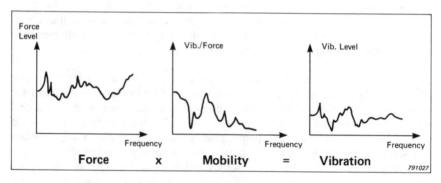

Fig.8.2. The relationship Force-Vibration

ing housing. In both cases the vibration is the product of force x mobility (= the willingness to be set in motion), see Fig.8.2. It can be seen that to get a stable vibration reading, the force spectrum and the associated mobility must be stable, and luckily this is the case with most machines. When the force doubles the vibration measured doubles.

For the relative motion of the rotor journal in its bearing, the mobility is dominated by the oil film properties, whereas for the absolute bearing housing vibration the mobility is made up of components from both oil film and bearing support mobilities. The mobility can change considerably from machine to machine so it is often recommended that one measures it in order to correlate the actual vibration level with the internal forces.

In a journal bearing the forces are transmitted through an oil wedge pumped in by the high relative speed of the journal to the bearing shell. As the mobility of the oil film is normally rather high, it is possible to get a good

198

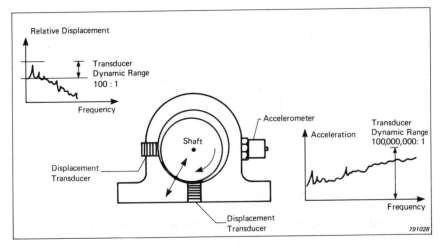

Fig.8.3. Alternative methods for measurements on journal bearings

measurement of the relative vibration between journal and bearing: the so-called Shaft Vibration. Due to the limitations in dynamic range of relative displacement transducers (typically 100:1) one seldom obtains much information above 3 x the running speed, but for phenomena manifesting themselves within that range relative displacement measurements are finding a widespread use (see Bibliography VDI 2059, API 670). See Fig.8.3.

The absolute vibration as measured on the bearing housing is often 2-4 times smaller due to the lower mobility of the bearing housing, but because of the much larger dynamic range of the accelerometers typically used here (100,000,000:1) and the possibility of selecting any of the parameters: absolute acceleration, velocity, or displacement, one is able to follow the vibration spectrum and any changes in it up to very high frequencies.

It is sometimes argued that because of instability, compliance and resonances in oil films it is impossible to use bearing vibration measurements on many journal bearings. If these problems were important the oil film mobility as seen by the journal would not be stable and the relative measurements would suffer even more, but in fact experience shows that both types of measurement can be made with good repeatability.

Note that any vibratory forces not actually being absorbed in exciting the rotor must be transmitted to the bearing housing. Should bearing loading be increased, the oil film gets thinner (and stiffer) so that the relative vibration decreases. The decreased rotor motion means that more force is transmitted to the bearing housing, whose vibration thus increases (as overall mobility, dominated by bearing supports, remains practically constant). As higher loading

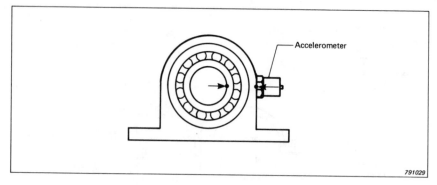

Fig.8.4. Rolling element bearing

would tend to accelerate bearing failure, the bearing housing vibration here gives the right tendency.

In a rolling element bearing the oil film is extremely thin as there is no relative velocity between the surfaces at the points of contact. The rolling elements are stiff so the inner mobility and outer mobility are virtually the same. Relative vibration between shaft and housing is usually negligible even for large vibration forces, so here the bearing housing vibration is quite dominant. Accelerometers will clearly give the largest dynamic range and frequency range (Fig.8.3).

8.3. FREQUENCY RANGE - DYNAMIC RANGE - PARAMETERS

One of the most important requirements of vibration instrumentation for maintenance is that it is able to register the entire vibration spectrum in a sufficiently wide frequency range that all important components are included. This includes frequencies associated with unbalance, misalignment, ball-passing, gear-meshing, blade-passing, blade resonances, bearing element radial resonances; often a frequency range requirement of 10 - 10,000 Hz or more. It is often found that the higher frequencies contain information on faults developing well before they influence the actual ability of the machine to do its job, whereas the lower frequencies show the faults when they have occurred. To be able to predict breakdown, the higher frequencies therefore become very important.

The vibration level of most machines usually varies with frequency. The range in which the instrumentation must be able to present the values with an acceptable accuracy (the dynamic range) must include all values within the frequency range (Fig.8.5).

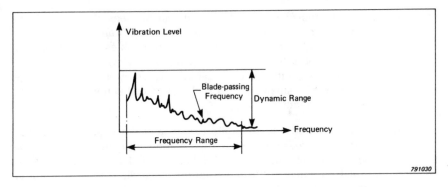

Fig.8.5. Frequency and dynamic range requirements

It is not enough that only the highest peaks are measured, for some of the important indicators may have a low level. For example, the force signal from the blade-passing frequency in a turbine has to be transmitted through the heavy rotor, through the bearing and bearing housing to the accelerometer and in this transmission the signal is attenuated by a large factor. However, should the forces acting in this area double, the attenuation remains largely the same and the measured vibration doubles. This change by a given factor represents a change by a corresponding number of decibels (e.g. a doubling would give 6 dB) and this is one of the reasons why a logarithmic amplitude (or decibel) axis should always be used when representing vibration levels for machine monitoring. This is also reflected in the fact that all common vibration criteria are expressed on logarithmic amplitude axes, meaning that equal changes in vibration severity represent changes by a certain number of dB.

In Fig.8.6 a vibration spectrum is shown using two different parameters out of the three usually used to describe vibration: Displacement, Velocity and Acceleration. They describe the same machine condition, so if a line is

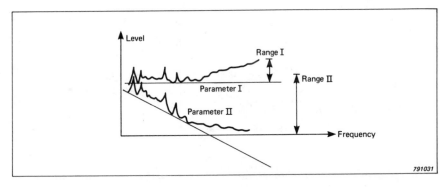

Fig.8.6. A vibration spectrum described with 2 different parameters

201

drawn through the bottom of each spectrum it can be seen that the relative heights of the peaks are the same. If the vibration force at any frequency doubles then the magnitude of the vibration component doubles, in both parameters, so both are useable for maintenance purposes. However, Parameter I happens to give a horizontally aligned spectrum whereby the dynamic range requirements become the smallest. This is therefore called the "Best Parameter" for such measurements.

It can be further noted that no single component in the spectrum of Parameter I needs to increase by more than Range I to give a measurable change in the overall vibration level. For Parameter II the change of some components must be equal to the much larger Range II. Therefore if one attempts to use overall vibration levels for indication of machine condition, rather than frequency analysis, it is imperative that one uses the Best Parameter for such measurements.

For many machines the Best Parameter is velocity and this is one reason why many standards (e.g. VDI 2056) specify this parameter. Standards such as VDI 2059 relying on relative displacement measurement put main emphasis on unbalance and misalignment and are forced to disregard large parts of the spectrum.

In Fig.8.7 are shown results from a machine with a fault developing in one component. Following the machine with 5 periodic measurements it can be seen that the overall level measured suddenly jumps up at the last measurement. Does this indicate that the machine is in the middle of a breakdown or can it be operated for another period before the vibration level reaches the limit? This cannot be determined from the overall levels. If we instead follow the development of the affected frequency component over the 5 periodic measurements we can extrapolate with reasonable accuracy and find out when the vibration level will reach the limit, thereby predicting the time be-

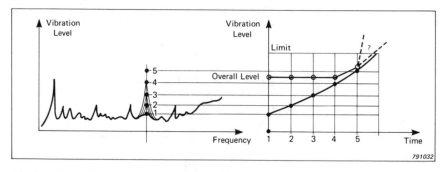

Fig.8.7. Development of a machine fault as seen by overall measurements and by analysis

fore maintenance is necessary. Without this periodic spectrum analysis the prediction capability is seriously impaired.

The presentation of the data in a measuring system greatly affects its usefulness and the following is a further explanation of why logarithmic amplitude axes are preferable to linear (see also Appendix F).

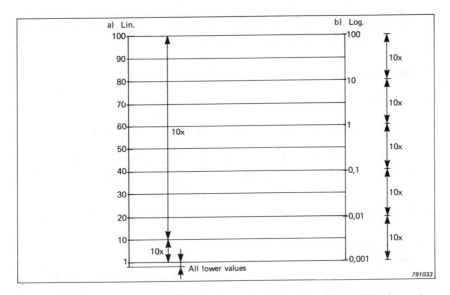

Fig.8.8. Presentation range of an instrument in linear and logarithmic mode

Fig.8.8 illustrates an instrument having a scale with an accuracy and resolution of 1% of Full Scale, so that there are 100 known different values possible. Fig.8.8.(a) gives a linear presentation 0 - 100% of Full Scale. Accepting a maximum error in the results of 10% of the reading, the scale can be used down to 10% of full scale as 1 step in 10 gives 10% accuracy. This means that a dynamic range of 10:1 (20 dB) is covered on this scale. Very often this is not enough to cover the vibration spectrum of a machine even if the Best Parameter is used. Another point is that constant factor changes give different deflection in different parts of the scale. A factor 10 is 90 steps in the upper end and less than 1 step in the lower end.

Assuming the same instrument but letting each of the 100 steps represent an 11% (1 dB) change from the previous step (Fig.8.8.(b)), then 20 steps down gives a factor 10, 20 more another factor 10, and so on. The 100 steps will in this way cover a range of 100,000:1 (100 dB) with the desired accuracy. This dynamic range ensures that all parts of the spectrum are within range, and it can be seen that constant factors represent a constant number of steps on the scale. This greatly eases the work of the maintenance engineer as he can quickly locate the components with the highest changes in force levels even if the mobility involved is very small.

8.4. USE OF VIBRATION MEASUREMENTS FOR MAINTENANCE

Vibration measurements should only be used where they will give a definite advantage or cost saving so the maintenance engineer should base the decision on their use on a careful evaluation:

1. Does it suit the maintenance system and machines in use?

2. Can the measurements be performed with personnel already available?

3. How few instruments are needed to give the most economical system?

4. Can the use of vibration measurements reduce operation costs or maintenance costs to give a definite improvement in plant economy?

8.4.1. Maintenance Systems

A. Run-to-Break Maintenance
In industries running many inexpensive machines and having all important processes duplicated, machines are usually run until they break down. Loss of production is insignificant and the spare machines can take over in the usuallly brief repair period. There is little advantage in knowing when machines will break down, so vibration measurements are just used to check the quality of the repair.

In some industries (e.g. chemical plants) the product often has such a high value that there is a tendency to sometimes let even large unduplicated machines run to break. In this case it is valuable to know what is going wrong and when the final breakdown can be expected. This information can be obtained by analyzing spectrum trends from regular measurements. However, the consequential damage resulting from such breakdowns often greatly increases both the cost of repair and the production loss during the extended shut-down period. Using the condition monitoring techniques described in Section 8.4.1.C these extra costs can be considerably reduced, while the periods between shutdowns can still be kept to the maximum.

B. Time Based Preventive Maintenance
Where important machines are not fully duplicated, or where safety of personnel is involved, maintenance work is often performed at fixed time intervals such as every 3000 operating hours. The intervals are often determined

statistically as the period in which no more than 2% of the machines will fail from being in new or fully serviced condition. By having 98% of the machines statistically surviving the maintenance periods, the machines are believed to have been "prevented" from failure.

However, it has been found for many machines (See Reference, Kent & Cross) that if they are run for another interval of the same length *without* any maintenance between the intervals the number of machines failing in the second interval will be less, or no higher, than in the first and less than if maintenance had been performed between the intervals. There is therefore a marked tendency to replace the fixed interval servicing or renovation of machines with fixed interval measurements of each individual machine's condition and only when the measurements indicate that the particular machine needs it, will service be performed before breakdown.

C. On-Condition Maintenance

When vibration measurements and analysis are performed systematically and intelligently (termed condition monitoring) they will not only allow determination of present machine condition but also permit (by following trends for individual components in the spectrum) prediction of when such components most likely will have reached unacceptable levels. This is called Predictive Maintenance and allows a long term planning of work to be done. For example it permits the engineer to purchase the necessary spare parts ahead of time and thereby avoid a permanent large spare part stock. Furthermore, the maintenance personnel can be actually trained for the type of repair coming up so that they can effect it in a minimum of time with a maximum of reliability. Used together, Condition Monitoring plus Predictive Maintenance permits efficient On-Condition Maintenance with a minimum of maintenance cost and a minimum of unscheduled production stops.

8.4.2. Maintenance Staff

When vibration measurements are introduced into a maintenance system it is most common to use personnel already in the system. This is possible because the skills required are easily learned and developed from experience, and good instruction material is available.

Two types of personnel are usually employed. One is the operator who will perform the actual measurements following a fixed measurement procedure. In a fully developed scheme he has only to record the vibration signals with preset instruments and turn over the data in the form of taped signals or graphs of spectra to the maintenance engineer at the end of the day for later analysis or evaluation. The maintenance engineer is responsible for preparing the measurement procedure and often performs analysis and evaluation himself, particularly during the development period.

The measurement procedure should include which points on the machines should be measured in what sequence, the manner in which the instruments should be used and the desired running conditions of the machines. The points on the machines should be prepared for easy attachment of the vibration transducer and marked with a reference number. The engineer should instruct the operator in the purpose and the execution of the programme. It is advisable to gain experience by measuring many times on a small number of machines. This will also reveal the repeatability of the procedure.

The engineer should also gather technical details to help him later diagnose any faults detected. These are details such as rotational speeds, bearing geometry, numbers of rolling elements, gear teeth, turbine blades etc. This information can be set up in a diagnostic reference sheet for each machine. He will also compile available information on acceptable vibration limits (relative or absolute) from manufacturers and other organisations.

8.4.3. Instruments for On-Condition Maintenance

Looking over the instrument systems in use today we find that they can be grouped in 3 classes:

Class 3: is a vibration meter making a simple overall vibration reading in a single frequency band (Fig.8.9). Most of the standardized vibration measurements fall into this category. The readings may allow detection of major faults that have already developed but will not allow diagnosis (what went wrong) or reliable trend prediction.

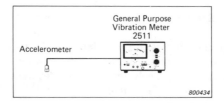

Fig.8.9. Typical instrument for simple overall measurements

Class 2: uses two levels of instrumentation. First, the Class 3 instruments are used until they indicate that levels have exceeded the standardized maximum levels or have changed drastically. Then an analyzer is brought into action to analyze the current spectrum which is then compared with a reference spectrum taken at the same point when the machine was known to be

206

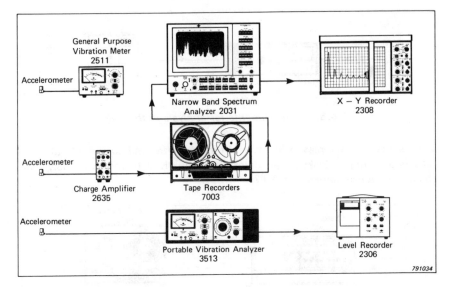

Fig.8.10. Instruments for simple overall measurements followed by analysis when changes have been indicated

in good condition (Fig.8.10). This procedure will reveal what changes have taken place but the analyzer is only brought into play, either directly or via a tape recorder, when the simple wide band measurements show a change, and as we have previously seen this may be very late - or too late in some cases.

Regarding trends, it is seen that this procedure gives only 2 points on the trend curves, which is too little to give the shape. Predictive capability has been lost by a too sparing use of the analyzer.

Class I: means full analysis and comparison with reference spectra each time. This gives full information on the condition of a machine together with the best predictive capability. The cost per measurement need not be higher than for the other classes thanks to the new efficient instrumentation available today. Narrow band analyzers able to provide a hard copy of measured spectra are found in two versions. One is a portable battery operated serial analyzer with all facilities, which plots out a vibration spectrum in any parameter (acceleration, velocity, displacement) on the spot for each measuring point (Fig.8.11). Comparisons may be done visually using a transparent reference spectrum.

When large numbers of machines are to be monitored the operator uses a tape recorder to record a short sample of the vibration signal at each measuring point. Typically, 4 samples can be recorded in less than a minute. The

207

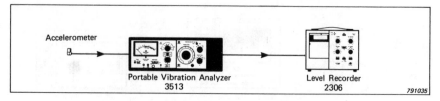

Fig.8.11. Instruments for analysis in the field

taped signal is later played into a real-time analyzer and compared automatically (e.g. using a desktop calculator) or manually with the previously established reference values (Fig.8.12).

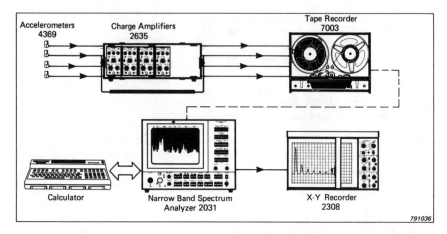

Fig.8.12. Instruments for rapid analysis of signals from a large number of machines

This approach benefits from the speed and sophistication of laboratory type instruments, gives improved detection and diagnosis, and reduces the cost per measurement.

The measurements described until now have all been periodic. The usual mean operating time between failures dictates the measurement intervals. At least 6 measurements should be planned for this period to give reasonable prediction capabilities.

8.4.4. Permanent Monitoring

Permanent monitoring is a system whereby a set of instruments is continuously checking machine condition at a limited number of measuring points.

208

In the basic system, a single vibration monitor continuously measures the best parameter in a single frequency range or a parallel set of 3 frequency bands. If limits are exceeded alarm relays can activate shutdown, or give a warning indication (Figs.8.13 and 8.14).

The continuous measurement will usually begin to show high levels hours

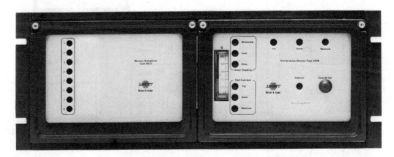

Fig.8.13. Multi-purpose Monitor Type 2505 and Multiplexer Type 5833

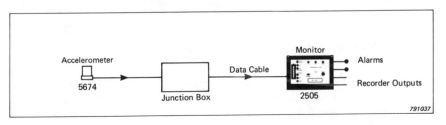

Fig.8.14. Basic monitor system

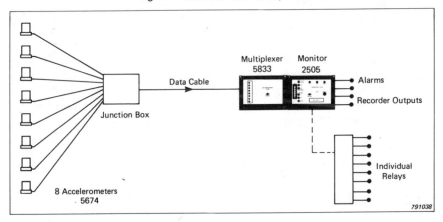

Fig.8.15. Multi-channel basic monitor system

209

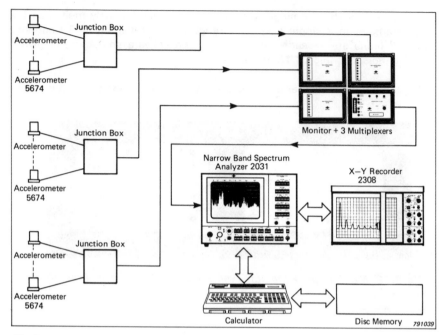

Fig.8.16. Multi-channel basic monitor system with fully automatic spectrum monitoring added

before actual failure, and most machines cannot be stopped immediately anyway, so it is often possible to let a single monitor scan over many channels via a multiplexer (Fig.8.15). When all the measurement channels come from one machine group, only one shutdown relay is required. This greatly reduces cost but the system is quite flexible as individual shutdown levels can be set for each channel. But the limitation of one or a few frequency bands remains.

For full spectrum monitoring a spectrum analyzer plus a calculator is added to the output of the monitor (Fig.8.16). In such a system individual limits can be set for each measuring point, and if the analyzer is to be used for other purposes, the monitor still protects the machines in the meantime using the simple pass-band measurement.

Monitors including multiplexers with preamplifiers are in general no more expensive than the equivalent number of preamplifiers.

8.4.5. Cost Effectiveness

Equipment for vibration measurement should only be bought if it can be expected to yield a clear profit, so the question often arises as to how the economic gain can be assessed.

In a report made in 1975 for the British Department of Industry (see Bibl.), later revised with 1978 values, M.J. Neale & Associates evaluated the benefits from introducing On-Condition Monitoring into British industry. They found that if just 2000 factories employed these techniques instead of what they were doing in 1975 a minimum annual saving of £180 million could be expected with operating plus investment costs of £30 million - ensuring a net profit of £150 million or 500% return. This saving corresponds to roughly 3% of the total annual investment in Britain for machines and equipment.

The savings arise mainly from the higher availability factor of the machines, giving fewer production losses.

8.5. BIBLIOGRAPHY

API 670:	*"Non-contacting Vibration and Axial Position Monitoring System"*. June 1976. American Petroleum Institute, Washington
DOWNHAM, E. & WOODS, R.:	*"The Rationale of Monitoring Vibration on Rotating Machinery in Continuously Operating Process Plant"*. ASME Paper No. 71-Vibr.-96 Journal of Engineering for Industry (B & K Reprint No. 19—023)
I.S.V.R.:	*"Workshop in On-Condition Maintenance"*, Southampton University, 5 - 6 January, 1972
KENT, L.D. & CROSS, E.J.:	*"The Philosophy of Maintenance"*, 18.IATA PPC-Sub Committee meeting, Copenhagen Oct. 19, 1973
NEALE, M.J. & WOODLY, B.J.:	*"Condition Monitoring Methods and Economics"*, Symposium organised by Society of Environmental Engineers, Imperial College, London, September 1975. B & K reprint no.16—054
NEALE, M.J. & Associates:	*"A Guide to the Condition Monitoring of Machinery"*. HMSO, London, 1979
VDI 2056:	*"Beurteilungsmaßstäbe für mechanische Schwingungen von Maschinen"*, October 1964. Beuth-Vertrieb, Berlin
VDI 2059:	*"Wellenschwingungsmessungen zur Überwachung von Turbomaschinen"*, November 1972. Beuth-Vertrieb, Berlin

9. ACOUSTIC EMISSION

9.1. INTRODUCTION

Minute imperfections in loaded structures and materials, which could lead to ultimate failure, can be revealed by several non-destructive testing (NDT) methods in common use. Typical examples are microscopic and X-ray inspection, strain measurements and flaw detection by dye penetrants, eddy currents and ultrasonic transmission or reflection.

These methods are common in one respect; they reveal imperfections without differentiation between irrelevant "passive" irregularities which have no influence on the ability of the structure to perform its intended task, and "active" developing faults which, if left, could seriously threaten the integrity of the structure. Results obtained from these tests require a high level of judgement in determining their significance. Furthermore, for critical structures, tests have to be made regularly and extensively to ensure that new faults, for example caused by corrosion, overloading and wear, have not occurred.

Acoustic Emission (AE) is a relatively new NDT technique which differs from the above-mentioned techniques in that it is able to detect *when* a flaw or a crack occurs and *where* it occurs i.e. it detects "active" flaws. Once the existence of a flaw has been established by AE its nature can be investigated by the other methods. For critical structures, AE measuring instrumentation can listen continuously to warn of faults immediately they occur.

9.2. DEFINITION

AE (sometimes called Stress Wave Emission SWE) can be defined as:

The elastic wave generated by the release of energy internally stored in a structure.

Although this definition includes many kinds of waves, (e.g. earthquakes and microseismic phenomena) AE-systems are designed to handle only a small part of the full spectrum. Mechanical shocks and clicks are not included, although AE-systems are used in some cases to detect loose parts in microelectronic devices.

9.3. AE SOURCES

AE "Sources" which can be described as processes emitting elastic waves, can be basically classified in 4 different groups:

1. Dislocation movements
2. Phase transformations
3. Friction mechanisms
4. Crack formation and extension.

The signals emitted may be broadly divided into two types i) continuous emission (resembling white noise) and ii) burst-type emission, mostly detected as single decaying sinusoids due to resonances in the structure and the transducer. The two types of signals are shown in Fig.9.1. A clear distinction between the two types cannot be made however, as there is no logical transition point.

Fig.9.1. Continuous and Burst Type signals

For comparison purposes the relative amplitudes of the emitted signals from the different mechanisms are shown below:

Dislocation movements	1 - 10
Phase transformations	5 - 1000
Crack formation	20 - 1000

The energy released by a single dislocation movement (displacement of a particular type of line imperfection through the crystal lattice) is normally too small to be detected by AE equipment. However, many dislocations often combine to form an avalanche of movements giving rise to a continuous AE-signal which can be detected. A typical phase transformation source is martensite formation in carbon steel; a single burst signal can be detected for every grain transformed.

Crack formation occurs at surface notches or at points inside a material where local stresses exceed the fracture stress. Crack formation results in the creation of new surfaces, strain energy is released and this is partly transformed into AE signals. The AE signals generated by crack formation are of the burst type and are often emitted at a very high rate.

Friction also occurs in cracks, and the sudden sliding mechanism releases burst type signals. Crack formation and friction burst signals are very useful for detecting and localizing cracks.

9.4. PROPAGATION

AE-sources behave in a manner similar to a radio antenna with a specific radiation pattern for the different wave types (shear-waves and compression-waves); however the position and properties of AE sources are only known in special rare cases.

If the source emits a spherical wave packet, it will only be propagated as such in an infinite isotropic, homogeneous, ideally elastic medium. In real structures the propagation will be affected by surfaces which create reflections and formation of surface waves (Rayleigh or Lamb). Inhomogeneities (e.g. welds) may also create reflections and distort wavefronts.

An important example is waves propagating in a plate, especially on large structures like pressure vessels where source location techniques are used. These waves are subject to dispersion as shown in Fig.9.2. a_n and s_n denote the antisymmetric and symmetric waves of the n'th order.

It can be seen that the dispersion relationships are complicated, making it difficult to predict the exact group velocity involved. Furthermore, dispersion changes the waveform which introduces ambiguities when time differences have to be measured for localization.

The above mentioned factors make it extremely difficult to study the source mechanisms except under conditions especially designed for the purpose. However, research is still being carried out in this field, and this will further enhance the usefulness of the AE technique.

It should be noted, that in most of the present applications it is not necessary to have a detailed knowledge of the source mechanisms and the propagation. These applications include, for example, the determination of the typical

214

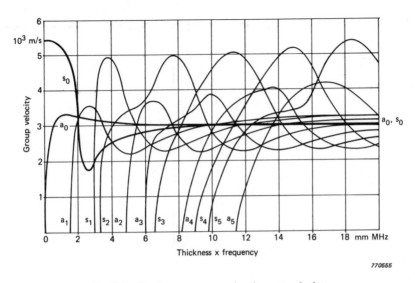

Fig.9.2. Surface wave modes in a steel plate

AE pattern from a specimen prior to fracture so that future activity on similar objects can be evaluated, and fault localization on large steel structures where a certain amount of ambiguity can be tolerated.

9.5. AE TRANSDUCER PRINCIPLES AND CALIBRATION

When the emitted stress waves reach the transducer position via a propagation path as shown in Fig.9.3 (a to e) the stress-strain condition is converted into an electrical signal which can be treated by electronic means.

Piezoelectric (PZ) transducers are by far the most widely used. They are mostly undamped, having very high sensitivities at resonance. A simple piezoelectric disc with electrodes mounted on its faces, perpendicular to the polarization direction is often used for AE and ultrasonic transducers. For a plane infinite disc adjoining a structure and coupling (damping) material, the response to an incoming plane wave with normal incidence can be calculated. It must be stressed that this is a typical situation for ultrasonic applications, but **not** for AE signals which are in most cases mainly surface waves, (Rayleigh or Lamb).

Ultrasonic transducer calibration methods are therefore not suitable for AE purposes. This is illustrated in Fig.9.4. A PZ-disc, 1,9 mm thick and 9 mm in diameter is mounted directly on a steel structure. The thickness mode can be calculated to be 1 MHz, but a *surface wave* of 1 MHz ($\lambda = 3$ mm) will not

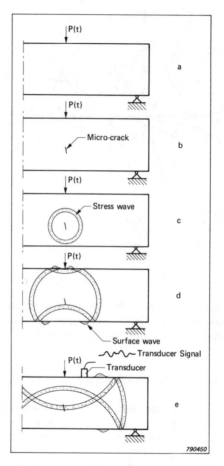

Fig.9.3. Propagation of a stress wave in a specimen

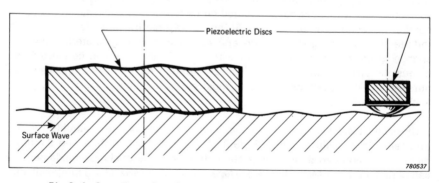

Fig.9.4. Coupling of surface waves to two different transducers

give any output as seen from the symmetric deformation shown in the figure, whereas a wave corresponding to $\lambda/2 = 9\,mm$, ($f = 167\,kHz$) will couple strongly.

To overcome this problem the disc can be made small; however the capacitance of the disc is then reduced considerably resulting in a much lower sensitivity when loaded with external capacitances from cable etc. If a large wear plate is used for coupling to the structure, it is difficult to ensure coupling at the point opposite the piezoelectric disc. If a small plate is used tilting may become a problem.

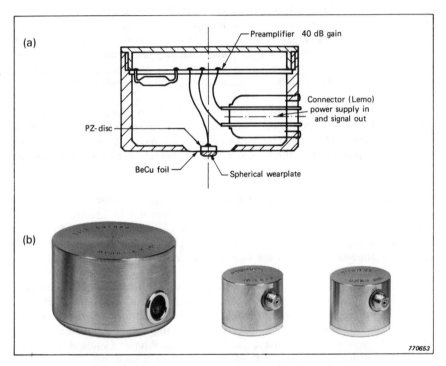

Fig.9.5. (a) Constructional details of Broad-band AE Transducer Type 8312
(b) Broad-band Transducer Type 8312 together with Resonance Transducers Types 8313 and 8314

The transducer construction shown in Fig.9.5 (a) overcomes these problems and therefore can be used over a broad range of frequencies. The integral preamplifier ensures a small capacitive loading, the membrane suspension gives an appropriate coupling force and the slightly spherical wear plate ensures adequate coupling regardless of tilting. This transducer, together with two others, which are of the simple resonance type and intended to detect AE over a narrow frequency band around their resonance, are shown in the photograph in Fig.9.5 (b).

Some precautions should be taken in the mounting of transducers to ensure good results. The surface on which the transducer has to be mounted must be flat and clean to permit effective coupling. Scale and rust must be removed e.g. by grinding. Even though the surface may be flat and clean only a few points will be in intimate contact with the wearplate.

By using a drop of oil, grease or highly viscous "goop" (e.g. Dow Chemicals 276-V9), the voids are filled out enabling the stress waves to be transmitted to the transducer. If a permanent installation is desired, various adhesives may be used. Transducers coupled with fluids must be kept in place by elastic bands, adhesive tape, springs or fixtures as may be practical. The transmission of plane waves through the coupling layer can be calculated in the same manner as the frequency response. In general, it is desirable to make the coupling layer as thin as possible to get maximum sensitivity.

Several methods have been proposed for calibration. Many of these are inspired by the AE phenomenon itself and use transient pulses generated by breaking pencil leads, glass capillaries or by spark impact. Others use continuous sources like gas jets (broad band random signal) or transducers used as transmitters.

If these "sources" have a sufficiently broad frequency spectrum and if the transmitting structure permits transmission of the whole spectrum without distortion, they may be used for sensitivity comparison and relative frequency response determination of AE transducers. If an absolute calibration is desired a detailed knowledge of the source and structure is necessary.

Basic research is undertaken at several institutes to find suitable calibration methods but no generally acceptable method has yet been proposed. Most commercial transducers available today are calibrated in the same way as ultrasonic transducers in a face to face configuration where no surface waves are generated at all. These calibrations are of limited value if the transfer function from surface waves to electrical signals is required.

A different method proposed by Hatano & Mori (see Bibliography) is used at Brüel & Kjær. This method is based on the reciprocity principle which is well known in network theory, and also used for calibration of microphones, hydrophones and vibration transducers.

Fig.9.6 shows the set-up used for the reciprocity calibration. A warbled tone signal is applied to a transmitting transducer which excites Rayleigh waves in the medium. These surface waves are detected by the receiving transducer normally positioned 200 mm from the transmitter. The output sig-

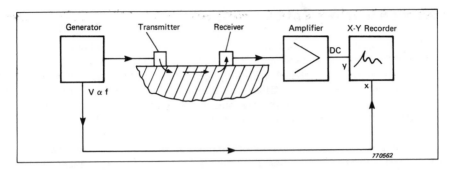

Fig.9.6. Set-up for Reciprocity Calibration

nal is amplified and a DC voltage proportional to the RMS value of the signal is supplied to the Y input of an X-Y recorder. A voltage proportional to the centre-frequency of the warbled tone signal is fed to the X-input of the X-Y recorder. The current to the transmitting transducer is measured using the same set-up.

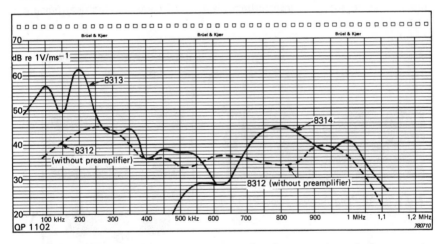

Fig.9.7. Typical frequency response curves for the acoustic emission transducers Types 8312, 8313 and 8314

Absolute calibration is achieved using three transducers, one of which can function either as a transmitter or receiver. Three consecutive measurements are made, as described, with a specific interchange of transducers between each measurement. Typical calibration results are shown in Fig.9.7.

219

9.6. SIGNAL AMPLIFICATION

The transducer is followed by a preamplifier - amplifier combination giving up to 100 dB total amplification. The preamplifier stage, which has a low output impedance and can therefore feed long cables, may be built into the transducer as shown in Fig.9.5. Otherwise a separate preamplifier, as shown in Fig.9.8, is placed near to the transducer. Preamplifier gain is fixed (e.g. 40 dB) and the preamplifier may also be fitted with bandpass filters.

For meaningful comparison of preamplifiers, their noise level should be measured and compared when the input is loaded by the transducer impedance. If suitable modern electronic components are used, the noise level will be determined by the thermal noise of the piezoelectric disc. Because of noise the minimum detectable AE amplitude for a transducer in the 200 kHz range is in the order of 10^{-14} m at room temperature.

The signal from the preamplifier is fed into a conditioning amplifier with adjustable gain, e.g. from 0 to 60 dB in 1 dB steps. Fig.9.9 shows an amplifier which is especially suitable for AE work and which has selectable frequency filters so as to suppress interference from low frequency electrical noise and mechanical vibration.

Fig.9.8. AE Preamplifier Type 2637

Fig.9.9. Conditioning Amplifier Type 2638

9.7. DATA ANALYSIS AND PRESENTATION

A variety of methods are available for analysis and presentation of the amplified AE signal. These are summarised in Fig.9.10. Some guidelines about the choice of the most suitable measuring principle can be given as follows:

220

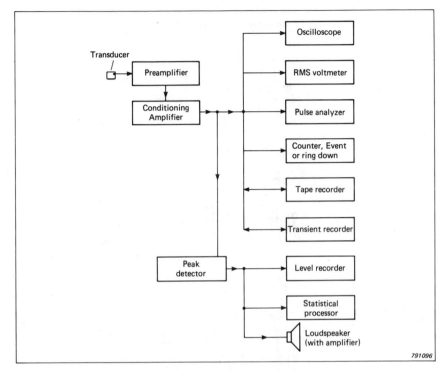

Fig.9.10. Methods of AE data analysis and presentation

The oscilloscope is always very useful to get an immediate impression of AE activity.

For continuous emission the RMS value is most suitable and physically also most meaningful.

For burst type signals an indication of total damage or rate of damage occurring is indicated by ring down counting or pulse area measurements. Three alternatives are shown schematically in Fig.9.11.

A high frequency pulse analyzer measuring the time a threshold is exceeded will give the approximate pulse area of an AE signal (Fig.9.11 (a)). The approximation can be improved by the combination of several thresholds. The principle is illustrated in Fig.9.11 (b). Both of these analysis methods can be carried out with the AE pulse analyzer shown in Fig.9.12.

Ring-down counting, illustrated in Fig.9.11 (c), is another way of assessing pulse area. The method is very approximate as it takes no account of time but the instrumentation is simple and widely used.

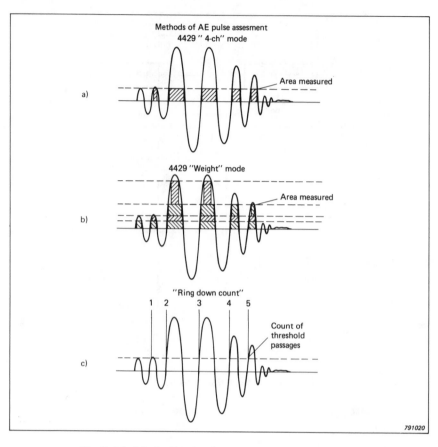

Fig.9.11. Methods of pulse magnitude assessment

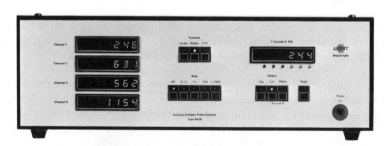

Fig.9.12. Acoustic Emission Pulse Analyzer Type 4429

A linearity comparison between actual pulse area and the analyzer "count" is shown in Fig.9.13. The curves are typical and may depend upon the shape

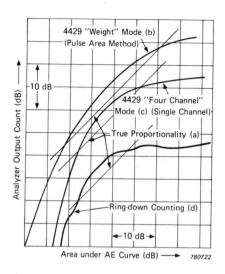

Fig.9.13. Relationship between area under the AE curve and output count for various methods of quantising AE activity. The curves are separated for clarity

of the AE signal. For the AE pulse analyzed the ring-down count method (d) is approximately linear over a 15 dB range and the one-threshold time-based method (c), over a 20 dB range. By using 4 thresholds (b), the linearity range of the time-based method can be improved to 30 dB.

The tape recorder, which is normally a modified videorecorder or special instrumentation recorder, is useful for storing AE signals for later analysis, or when analysis of multiple channels is desired. However, the dynamic range is often very limited (~ 30 dB).

The transient recorder is useful when single pulses have to be analysed. The stored signal can be played back at different rates either to an oscilloscope, or a level recorder and it can be frequency analysed. Dynamic range and memory size are limited (e.g. 8 bits resolution ~ 48 dB and 1 - 2 K words).

A peak detector with a short rise time (0,5 μs) and a comparatively slow decay time permits interconnection with level recorders and similar equipment. In this way a level recorder can give a time picture of the peaks of AE activity which is useful to assess trends. The conditioning amplifier shown in Fig.9.9 is equipped with a suitable peak detector. An example of an AE activity versus time plot made using this set-up is shown in the upper half of Fig.9.18.

A statistical processor is used to count the number of events falling within different amplitude windows. A loudspeaker connected via the peak detector converts the AE bursts to audible "cracks".

9.8. ACOUSTIC EMISSION SOURCE LOCATION

Multichannel systems are used for AE source location, for example on large pressure vessels. With suitable control, location systems can discriminate between signals coming from a certain area of interest and signals arriving from other areas.

With two transducers a source location can be determined in one dimension. With three transducers the source location can be calculated in two dimensions. Usually an extra channel is added enabling the system to automatically ignore inconsistent data.

The time difference between the arrival time of the signal at two transducers determines a hyperbola in a plane if the propagation velocity is known. The intersection of hyberbolas obtained from other transducer pairs defines the location of the source. This is shown schematically in Fig.9.14.

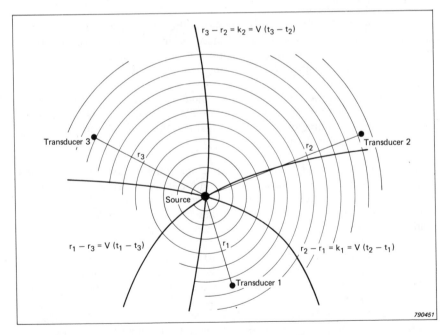

Fig.9.14. System for localization of AE sources

9.9. FIELDS OF APPLICATION

The study of plastic deformation and crack formation and extension are two of the frequently reported application areas of AE measurement. Fig.9.15 shows sketches of two typical results from plastic deformation of test pieces.

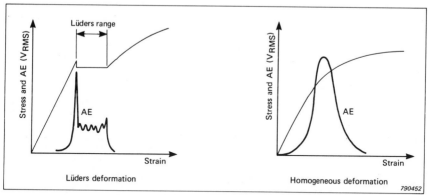

Fig.9.15. Stress and Acoustic Emission activity as a function of strain for two types of plastic deformation

The decrease in stress at the start of the Lüders range is due to the formation of slip-bands (Lüders bands) associated with high AE activity. This continues until the end of the Lüders range when work-hardening starts and the AE activitiy decreases. During homogeneous deformation dislocations occur throughout the test piece until they are finally trapped and the AE activity decreases.

On account of the AE-activity associated with crack formation this was one of the first areas of application for AE techniques. If the AE-activity increases significantly before failure it can be used as a direct warning. Fig.9.16 shows results obtained from a fatigue test on a notched specimen, where the increase in AE activity long before failure is quite noticeable. Metallurgists and scientists working with fracture mechanics have adopted AE as a valuable tool for estimating certain fracture-toughness parameters.

Because AE signals are generated by most materials when deformed, and may be detected over the entire surface of a structure, AE analysis has a large number of applications limited only by the detection possibilities.

In industrial applications the AE techniques are used for testing and monitoring of structures. The purpose of AE analysis in these application areas is to detect, locate and evaluate flaws, fractures and other faults. While the evaluation is still a difficult area where other NDT methods are normally

225

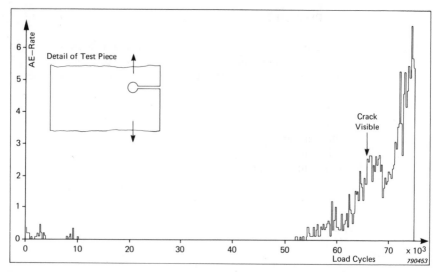

Fig.9.16. Impulse Rate as a function of load cycles for a fatigue test on a notched specimen

used, the unique detection and localization capabilities of AE monitoring are generally recognized.

Methods and instrumentation developed for AE can also be used for other applications. Faults in bearings, which often cause expensive breakdowns in industry, result in mechanical noise dependent on the type of fault and may be detected on the outside of the bearings and analysed as AE signals. Other examples of related applications are loose particle detection and leak testing. A list of industrial application areas is shown in Table 9.1.

Fabrication		Later Inspection	
Duration Fabrication	Final test	Proof testing	Continuous monitoring
Welding	Pressure testing of vessels and pipelines	Vessels and pipelines	Vessels and pipelines
Heat treatment		Bridges	Buildings — bridges
Hardening	Construction	Rotating machinery	
Phase transformation	Bonding		Mines

Table 9.1. Some industrial application areas of AE techniques

226

9.9.1. Advantages and Limitations

Some of the advantages and limitations mentioned are summarized and listed in Tables 9.2 and 9.3. On account of the low attenuation of AE signals in the 100 kHz range in metallic structures, flaws may be detected several meters from the transducer. For concrete and masonry structures low frequencies should be used or higher attenuation has to be accepted.

Acoustic emission is generated by releasing the stored energy. This energy has to be supplied, usually in the form of the normal working structural loads or by applying extra load as in proof testing.

Remote detection and location of flaws.
Integral method (The entire structure is covered).
The measuring system can be set-up quickly.
High sensitivity.
Requires only limited accessibility to test objects.
Detects active flaws.
Only relatively low loads are required.
Can sometimes be used to forecast failure load.

Table 9.2. Advantages

The structure has to be loaded.
AE activity is highly dependent on materials.
Irrelevant electrical and mechanical noise can interfere with measurements.
Limited accuracy of localization.
Gives limited information on the type of flaw.
Interpretation of results may be difficult.

Table 9.3. Limitations

9.10. EXAMPLES OF APPLICATION

Some examples are given to indicate the application of AE measurements and the interpretation of the results.

9.10.1. Tensile Test on a Brass Specimen

A tensile test was carried out on a brass specimen (Fig.9.17). The cross section was 45 mm² and the alloy was Muntz metal (60% *Cu* and 40% *Zn*). The recording (Fig.9.18) plots the output from the peak level detector of the Conditioning Amplifier Type 2638 and the weighted sum count from the AE Pulse Analyzer Type 4429. The applied force has been drawn on the same chart.

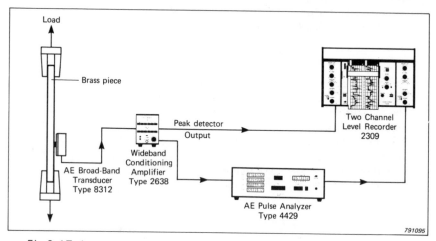

Fig.9.17. Instrumentation set-up for a tensile test on a brass specimen

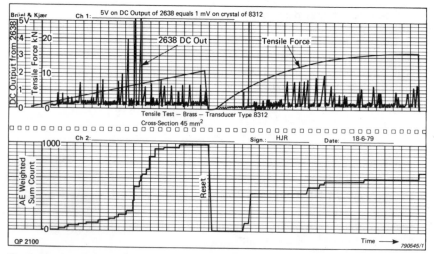

Fig.9.18. Load, peak output and "weighted sum" as a function of time for a brass specimen

In the first run the tensile force was raised from 0 to 11 kN and then released. The yeild point was expected to be reached at a force of about 6,5 kN and this is in fact very clearly confirmed in the AE activity charts. In the "weighted sum count" plot the peculiar stepwise rise characteristic of this material can be seen.

In the second run the load was raised from 0 until fracture which occurred at about 16 kN as compared to an expected value of 17 kN. The specimen was quiet below the yield point. This phenomenon, that the acoustic emission, once taken out of the material, is not repeated, is commonly known as the Kaiser effect. Above the yield point the Kaiser effect no longer applies. The level of acoustic emission is again high after the yield point but moderate during the plastic deformation.

9.10.2. Tensile Test on Carbon-Fibre Braid

A tensile test on a specimen of carbon-fibre braid of 2 × 10 mm cross section was performed with the set-up shown in Fig.9.19. Three recording channels were used, one registering the load applied to the specimen and two registering the AE activity. Fig.9.20 shows the plots obtained. It can be seen that in this particular example the weighted sum output from the Pulse Analyzer is easier to interpret than the peak detector output from the Conditioning Amplifier.

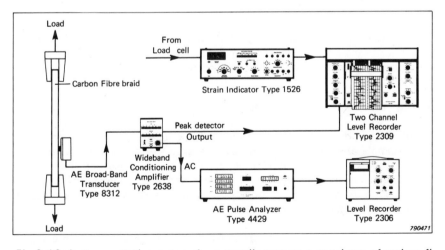

Fig.9.19. Instrumentation set-up for a tensile test on a specimen of carbon-fibre braid

229

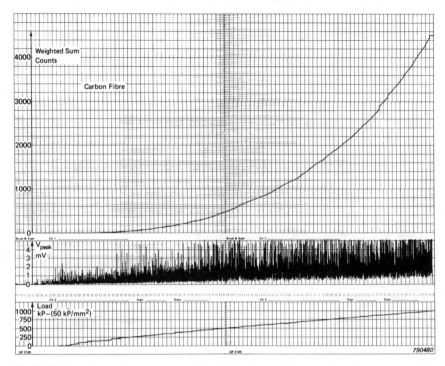

Fig.9.20. Load, peak output and "weighted sum" as a function of time for carbon-fibre braid

The curves show that while the tensile load is increased linearly, AE activity increases at an even "exponential" rate which reflects the pattern as fibres break leaving fewer intact fibres to support an ever increasing load.

9.10.3. Test on a Pressure Vessel

Part of the instrumentation set-up used for location, as described in the next example and shown in Fig.9.22, was used to monitor a proof test on a pressure vessel. A single AE channel consisting of a transducer and a conditioning amplifier fed one channel of the level recorder. A pressure transducer connected to the second level recorder channel monitored the water pressure applied to the vessel.

It was known that the previous maximum pressure applied to the vessel was 170 atm. The Kaiser effect is clearly demonstrated in the AE plot obtained (Fig.9.21). Significant activity is observed first when the applied pressure exceed 170 atm. Note that a logarithmic amplitude scale is used where

230

a linear scale was used in the previous example. It can be seen that activity decreases when the pressure is kept constant.

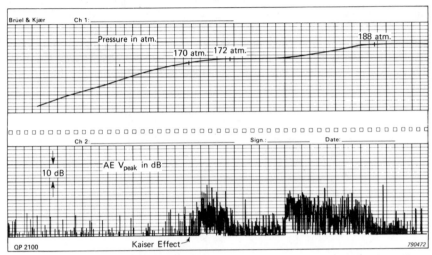

Fig.9.21. Pressure and Acoustic Emission activity as a function of time illustrating the Kaiser effect

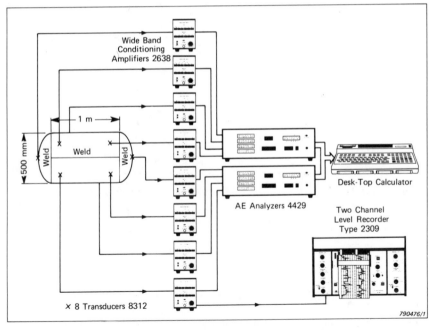

Fig.9.22. Measurement set-up for localization of sources

9.10.4. AE Source Location on a Pressure Vessel

The same vessel as used in the previous example was monitored by the eight-channel system shown in Fig.9.22 in an attempt to locate faults during a proof test. Calculations on AE pulse arrival times were carried out by a desk top calculator. The calculated AE "sources" are plotted on a folded out plan of the two vessel ends in Fig.9.23. Significant AE activity was found in the vicinity of a welded seam near transducer 5 (T_5), this enabled further efforts to be concentrated here.

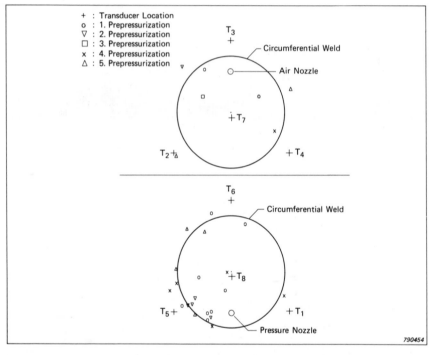

Fig.9.23. Locations of the sources of emissions on the two ends of the pressure vessel (folded out)

9.10.5. AE Source Location Using Two Measuring Channels

When a test specimen such as that shown in Fig.9.24 is loaded, acoustic emission is generated, both at the loading points due to deformation and fric-

232

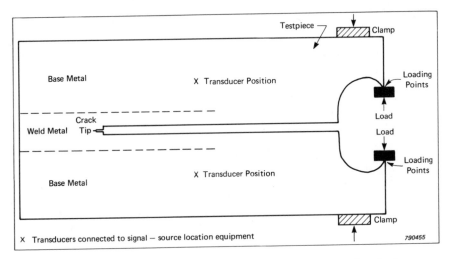

790455

Fig.9.24. Test specimen for differentiating two sources of emission

tion, and at the crack tip. To be able to distinguish between the two sources of acoustic emission, a theoretical analysis was first carried out to determine the relative time of arrival at the transducers, for signals originating at any part of the test piece.

Fig.9.25 (a) shows theoretically calculated regions with different band numbers corresponding to the various time differences. For practical measurements a pencil lead was broken at various locations on the specimen to generate an artificial source and the time differences for the signals to arrive at the two transducer positions were measured. The results are shown in Fig.9.25 (b) and are found to be in good agreement with the theoretical values. The instrumentation set-up shown in Fig.9.26 was used to store and display the time differences.

The test piece was then clamped and loaded above the expected fracture load. The acoustic emission was measured and found to be mostly in channel numbers ± 13 as shown in Fig.9.27 (a) confirming that the activity was generated at the loading points. To ensure that no deformation and friction occurred at the loading points when the clamp was removed, the specimen was loaded once again above the expected fracture load with the clamp on. Fig.9.27 (b) shows again the acoustic emission in channels ± 13 and some in channel 9. The clamp was now removed and the test performed by applying a suitable load. The acoustic emission measured is shown in Fig.9.27 (c). It can be seen that most of it lies in channel 0 indicating that the activity is generated at the crack tip.

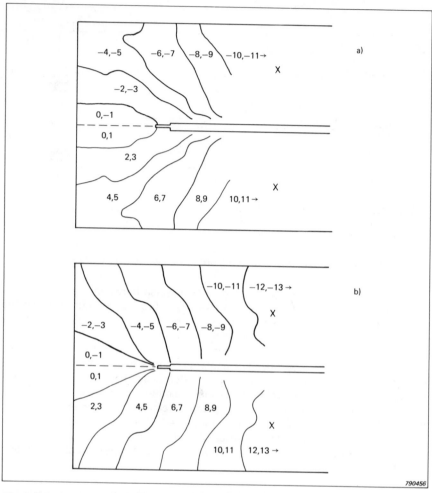

Fig.9.25. Time differences (band numbers) for the signals to arrive from the regions shown to the two transducer positions
(a) Theoretical
(b) Measured

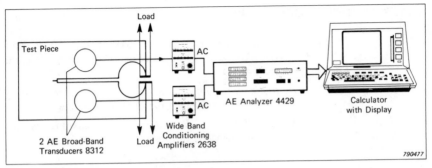

Fig.9.26. Set-up for storage and display of time differences

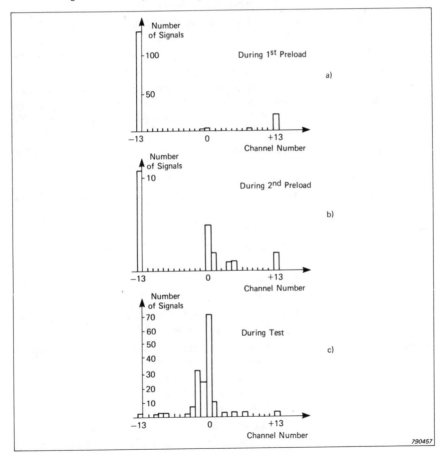

Fig.9.27. Amplitude distribution as a function of band numbers (time differences) a) During first preload b) During second preload c) During the actual test with clamp removed

9.11. SELECTED BIBLIOGRAPHY

ASTM: *Acoustic Emission,* ASTM STP 505, 1972 and ASTM STP 571, 1975, American Society for Testing and Materials

ASTY, M.:   *Acoustic emission source location on a spherical or plane surface.* NDT International, Oct. 1978

BECHT, J., EISENBLÄTTER, J. and JAX, P.:   *Werkstoffprüfung mit der Schallemissionsanalyse.* Zeitschrift für Werkstofftechnik 4 (1973) Nr.6

BOLIN, L.A.:   *A bibliography on acoustic emission.* Report LITH-IKP-R-44, Linköping University, Sweden, 1974

DROUILLARD, T.F.:   *Acoustic Emission, A Bibliography with Abstracts.* IFI-/Plenum, New York, 1979

HATANO, H. and MORI, E.:   *Acoustic emission transducer and its absolute calibration.* J.A.S.A., Vol. 59, 2 (1976), p.p. 344-349

HILL, R., and ADAMS, N.L.:   *Reinterpretation of the Reciprocity Theorem for Calibration of Acoustic Emission Transducers Operating on a Solid.* Acoustica, Vol.43, 5 (1979), p.p. 305-312

KAISER, J.:   *Untersuchungen über das Auftreten Geräuschen beim Zugversuch.* Ph.D. thesis, Technische Hochschule, München 1950

NICHOLS, R.W., (ed.):   *Acoustic Emission.* Applied Science Publishers Ltd. 1976

SCHLEGEL, D., RUNOW P. and FINK, W.:   *Schallemissionsanalyse während der Wasserdruckprüfung.* Bänder Bleche Rohre 12-1978

SPANNER, J.C., (ed.):   *Acoustic Emission: Techniques and Applications.* Intex Publishing Company 1974

SPANNER, J.C. and McELROY, J.W. (eds.):   *Monitoring Structural Integrity by Acoustic Emission.* Intex Publishing Company 1975

TOBIAS, A.:   *Acoustic-emission source location in two dimensions by an array of three sensors.* Non-Destructive Testing, Feb. 1976, p.p. 9-12

VIKTOROV, I.A.:   *Rayleigh and Lamb Waves, Physical Theory and Applications.* Plenum Press, New York 1967

Proceedings: *Journées d'études de l'émission acoustique.* Proceedings from a meeting in Lyon, March 1975. Inst. des Sciences Appliquées, Villeurbannes 1975

10. VIBRATION AND SHOCK TESTING

10.1. VIBRATION TESTING

One of the earliest workers to use a systematic form of vibration testing was Wöhler, who used special apparatus for his experiments on the fatigue of metals over 100 years ago. However, most modern vibration testing techniques have been developed since the start of World War II.

At that time it was important to develop parts and equipment capable of withstanding the service environment in aircraft. Problems were encountered not only with mechanical structural failure, but also with sophisticated electronic and electromechanical instrumentation and control systems, whose performance and reliability was sensitive to the vibration encountered in service. Furthermore, it was appreciated that theoretical prediction of the vibration response of a piece of equipment in service could be extremely difficult.

The development of such test techniques has taken place primarily in the aerospace industries, but vibration testing has a much wider application today in other areas such as the automobile, construction, electronics, machine-tool, packaging and ship-building industries. The most common uses are for:

1. Production Control
2. Frequency Response / Dynamic Performance Testing
3. Environmental Tests

The most common types of vibration testing are:

1. Sinusoidal Testing; fixed or sweeping frequency
2. Random Testing; wideband or narrow band characteristics
3. Force Testing; using mechanical impedance or mobility concepts and structural response measurements.

Electronic equipment is used widely for the generation of vibration signals, and for the provision of essential control functions. Fundamental features of reliability, stability and reproducibility are obtained, and electronic safety circuits can be built in to safeguard objects under test and the test equipment itself. Furthermore voltage analogues of frequency and vibration variables and mechanical parameters can be used readily to provide hard copies of test results using ancillary recorder or plotter equipments.

10.1.1. The Exciter

Any vibration test system requires a device which can be activated to subject the test object to the mechanical motion required. This transducer is the exciter. Useful operating regions for the two principal exciter techniques are shown in Fig.10.1.

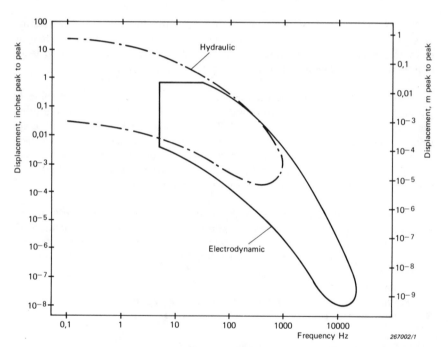

Fig.10.1. Useful operating regions of modern hydraulic and electro-dynamic vibration machines (after G.B. Booth)

For low-frequency testing, typically in the range 0 Hz to 20 Hz, where a large displacement stroke is required, the "electrohydraulic" vibrator is widely used. The use of an electronic servo-control system allows the vibration signal to be derived and regulated easily, whilst the hydraulic drive system can be designed to give long stroke and high force capabilities.

For frequencies above 10 Hz, and to match common vibration test specifica-

238

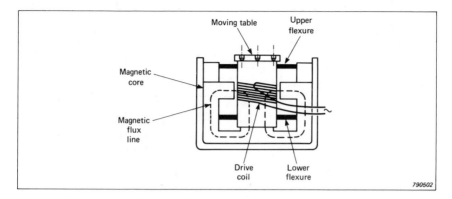

Fig.10.2. Basic construction of an electrodynamic exciter

tions, the electrodynamic vibration exciter is in general use. Its basic construction is shown in Fig.10.2. A moving coil assembly, which is connected to the work table, is positioned in a magnetic field. The electronic control system provides the exciting signal, which is amplified and fed to the moving coil to excite the test object mounted on the work table. For excitation forces up to about 200 N, a permanent magnet may be used to provide the magnetic field, whilst for higher force requirements an electro-magnetic stator assembly is desirable.

The work table of any exciter should be rigid, such that all points move in phase, and the moving element must be suspended so as to allow motion along one axis only.

10.1.2. Characteristics of the Electrodynamic Exciter

To ensure uni-axial translatory motion of the work-table, and to enable high force ratings or acceleration levels to be delivered to suit individual test specifications, severe constraints are placed on the design of an exciter. Inevitably, the effect of mass (moving assembly), springs (flexures), and damping gives every exciter its own frequency response characteristic. Different regions of the response are dominated by the stiffness of the flexures, the moving mass, and, at very high frequencies, the resonances of the moving element itself. These regions can be seen clearly from the acceleration characteristics measured on a typical exciter when the drive current to the moving coil is kept constant for a frequency sweep (Fig.10.3).

Many power amplifiers operate as constant voltage sources. The acceleration response characteristic of a voltage-fed exciter depends on the impedance of the moving coil winding, and on the mechanical damping present in the system. For a typical low-impedance, well-damped vibration exciter

239

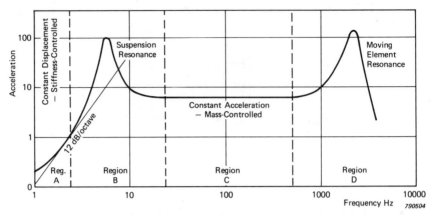

Fig.10.3. Idealized acceleration characteristics of electrodynamic vibration exciter plotted as a function of frequency for constant drive current

driven at constant voltage, the suspension resonance is eliminated owing to the damping effect introduced by the low output impedance of the power amplifier: the back-e.m.f. generated in the moving coil is short-circuited through the amplifier. Back-e.m.f. is proportional to velocity ($e \propto d\phi/dt$), and therefore the moving-element characteristic in the flexure-controlled region will be velocity-limited and the acceleration-against-frequency characteristic will show a rising slope of 6 dB / octave in this region (Fig.10.4).

Above the flexure resonance frequency, where the motion is mass con-

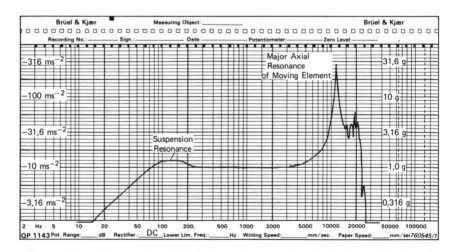

Fig.10.4. Example of the acceleration characteristic of a practical exciter recorded as a function of frequency for constant drive voltage

trolled, the acceleration level available a will be limited by the rated force of the exciter F (N), the mass of the test object M (kg), and the mass of the moving element M_e (kg), such that:

$$a = \frac{F}{M + M_e} \text{ ms}^{-2} \qquad (10.1)$$

The nominal force rating for a given exciter design will be dependent on the maximum current capability of the moving coil. This is seen from the basic relationship

$$F = [BL]I \qquad (10.2)$$

where

F = force in N
B = magnetic flux density in air gap in Wbm^{-2}
I = current in moving coil in A
L = length of conductor in air gap in m

The product BL is called the "head constant" as it is fixed for a given design. It has further significance in consideration of the "dynamo" performance of the moving coil, which produces a back e.m.f. according to:

$$E_{BACK} = [BL]v \qquad (10.3)$$

where

E_{BACK} = back e.m.f. across moving coil in V
v = velocity of conductor in air gap in ms^{-1}

For a constant-voltage source it can be seen that the flexure resonance will be largely velocity-limited, whilst an integration of the back-e.m.f. may be used to provide an analogue of displacement for control purposes. This feature may be included in more sophisticated exciter control systems.

The ultimate low-frequency performance will be limited by the physical displacement travel available for the moving element. It is usual to include mechanical bump stops in the design to allow occasional maximum travel excursions without permanent damage.

Since these constraints are functions of the moving element construction, additional versatility may be achieved by the provision of interchangeable moving elements. In this way the moving mass / work table / flexure characteristics can be optimised to suit particular requirements for high acceleration, large test objects, long stroke, etc. by interchanging exciter heads whilst retaining the same basic body (Fig.10.5 and 10.6). General-purpose vibration exciters with fixed heads offer compromise specifications for performance parameters, based on their force ratings.

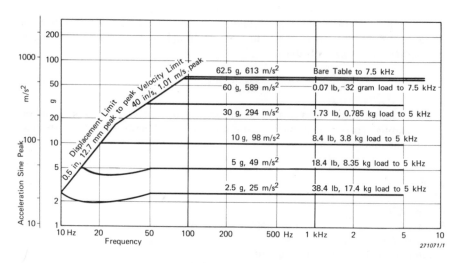

62.5 g, 613 m/s²	Bare Table to 7.5 kHz	
60 g, 589 m/s²	0.07 lb, 32 gram load to 7.5 kHz	
30 g, 294 m/s²	1.73 lb, 0.785 kg load to 5 kHz	
10 g, 98 m/s²	8.4 lb, 3.8 kg load to 5 kHz	
5 g, 49 m/s²	18.4 lb, 8.35 kg load to 5 kHz	
2.5 g, 25 m/s²	38.4 lb, 17.4 kg load to 5 kHz	

Fig.10.5. Diagram of the performance limits of an exciter showing constraints imposed by displacement, velocity and acceleration boundaries

Fig.10.6. Electrodynamic vibration exciter together with interchangeable heads

242

10.1.3. The Influences of the Resonances on the Vibration Signal

During a vibration test, the test object will be secured to the work table, or to a light-weight fixture which itself is bolted to the table. When a vibration

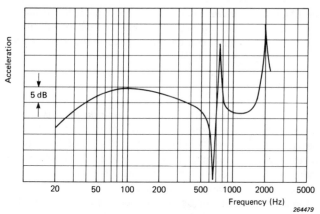

Fig.10.7. Example of a recording of the acceleration measured at the table of an electrodynamic exciter loaded by a test object having a single degree of freedom

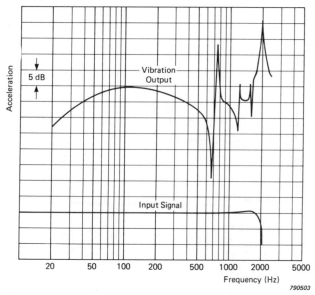

Fig.10.8. Example of a recording of the acceleration measured at the table of an electrodynamic exciter loaded by a test object and excited with a wide-band random signal

signal is fed to the exciter the electrical drive required to maintain a constant vibration amplitude will not be constant, but will be a function of the drive frequency. This effect arises because of the interactions between resonances in the test specimen, and in the exciter itself. It can be demonstrated by using a sinusoidal signal of different frequencies (Fig.10.7) or by using a wide-band random signal of uniform power spectral density (Fig.10.8). In all forms of vibration testing it is important to include some method of ensuring that the characteristics of the test signal can be reproduced at the work table.

10.1.4. Sinusoidal Excitation

When it is required to maintain a constant vibration level with a sinusoidal drive signal, the output level from a vibration sensor mounted on the work table may be used in a servo loop to control the input level to the exciter (Fig.10.9). In this way the effects of the system resonances are regulated by the control sensor, whilst behaviour of the test objects is studied using a response accelerometer connected through a preamplifier to a measuring amplifier or a graphic level recorder, or using a stroboscopic motion analyzer.

The circuit used to regulate the excitation signal is known as a compressor, and the servo-loop of which it forms a part is known as a compressor loop.

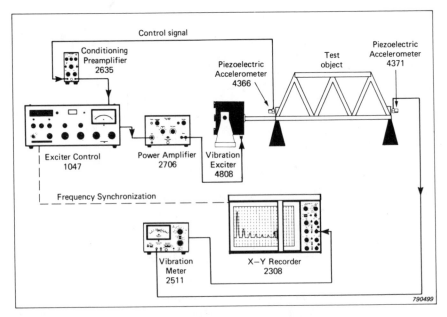

Fig.10.9. Example of a servo-controlled swept-frequency test arrangement

In such testing, it is common to include an automatic frequency sweep facility in the control oscillator. Then the regulation speed in the control loop must be greater than the speed with which resonances are built up, for any selected frequency sweep rate.

The upper limit to the regulation speed in an unfiltered loop is set by its interaction with the vibration frequency. At low vibration frequencies the compressor must not react so quickly that it attempts to regulate the instantaneous motion of the test object, since this tendency distorts the excitation sinusoid.

The regulation speed should be adjustable to permit optimization of the automatic frequency sweep. Automatic variation of regulation speed with excitation frequency is a useful facility on a vibration test installation.

Since some test objects contain a variety of non-linear elements, control and response signals may be seriously distorted, even if the signal input to the vibration exciter is a pure sinusoid. To ensure correct regulation using the fundamental frequency, a tracking band-pass filter centred at the excitation frequency may be used to ensure that the correct control signal reaches the control circuit (Fig.10.10). This filter should not be tuned too sharply, as

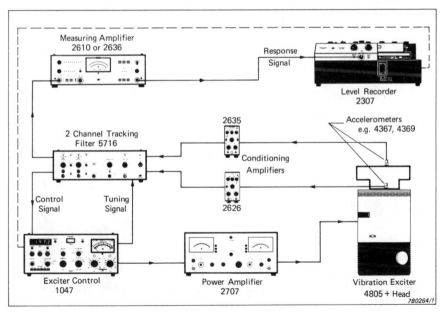

Fig.10.10. Example of a servo-controlled swept-frequency test arrangement in which the control and response signals are filtered at the excitation frequency

245

very selective filtering of the control signal reduces the effective regulation speed and the stability of the servo loop.

The most convenient vibration sensors for both control and response measurement are piezoelectric accelerometers. This type of device generates an electrical output signal proportional to instantaneous acceleration. If this signal (suitably amplified by a conditioning amplifier) is fed to the compressor, then it is the mean acceleration level of the test object which is kept constant. However, the signal may, if required, be integrated with respect to time, using an electronic integrator. One stage of integration gives a signal proportional to instantaneous velocity; a second gives a signal proportional to instantaneous displacement. Thus the incorporation of one or two integrators in the compressor loop permits regulation of velocity or displacement respectively. If the effects of mechanical or electrical noise cause the signal to be non-linear, filtering may be required.

It is sometimes required to cross-over from one required variable to another as recommended in certain standardised vibration test programmes, e.g. IEC 68-2-6 Test F. Automatic frequency-controlled cross-over switching is then necessary (Fig.10.11).

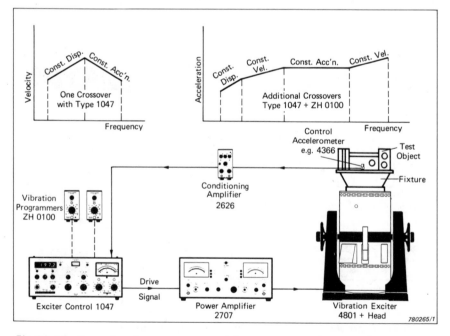

Fig.10.11. Example of an arrangement for programmed swept-sinewave testing

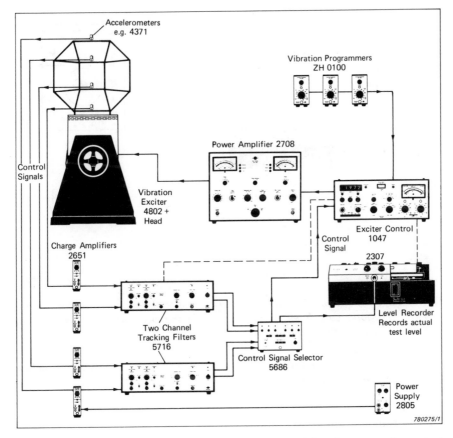

Fig.10.12. Example of a test arrangement with provision for up to six control positions (only four are illustrated)

When large, complex test specimens are bolted to the work table, control from one point may not be sufficient, owing to irregular motion in different parts of the test object. It is desirable in such cases to be able to select the control point required, or to average over a number of points, in order to avoid over-testing (Fig.10.12).

Where it is required to perform vibration tests up to high frequencies, and a very low exciting-force is acceptable, it is in some situations advantageous to use a piezoelectric accelerometer as an exciter (Fig.10.13). This is feasible because the accelerometer is a passive device obeying the reciprocity theorem. The uniformity of its frequency response as a sensor can be exploited when it is used, in reverse, as an exciter, to achieve excitation without a re-

247

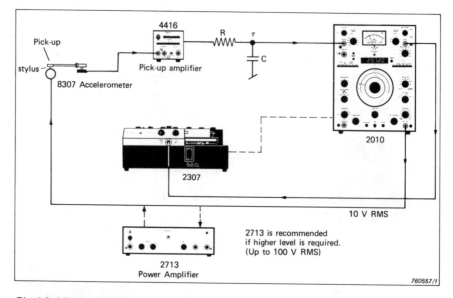

Fig.10.13. Arrangement for high-frequency response-measurement of gramophone cartridges using a piezoelectric accelerometer as a vibration exciter

gulation loop. The vibration level can be predicted from the values of applied voltage, accelerometer capacitance, and mass.

10.1.5. Random Vibration Testing

Sometimes components or sub-assemblies exhibit failure mechanisms which can be initiated by random vibration but not by sinusoidal vibration owing to nonlinear interaction between different frequency components.

Wideband random testing is therefore widely used. The drive signal has characteristics which approximate closer to the statistical characteristics of common vibration environments in service than does a pure sine signal: all specimen resonances are excited simultaneously, so that important interaction effects are accounted for.

Vibrations occurring in service, in an aircraft wing member or in a car stub-axle for example, have power spectra whose characters differ widely. The development of a realistic test specification can be extremely difficult. A common approach is to collect environmental data by recording and analysis, and to derive "envelope" limits to specify the vibration test spectrum (Fig.10.14).

248

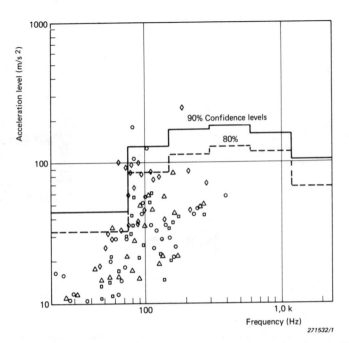

Fig.10.14. Example of the derivation of vibration test level specifications from environmental data

When a random type of input signal is applied to a vibration test system, the effect of system resonances can be avoided by using a suitable spectrum shaper, consisting of a bank of parallel band-pass filters with individually adjustable attenuation (Fig.10.15). A real-time frequency analyzer can be used to compare the resulting excitation spectrum with the desired excitation spectrum, and the attenuators of the spectrum shaper can be adjusted to achieve the spectrum desired. The same arrangement can be used to "linearize" the response of the exciter system, using a random noise source as a reference, which is replaced subsequently by a tape recorder to reproduce the measured environment at the work table.

This system has the disadvantage that it is passive and provides no control or regulation of the test whilst it is in progress. Broad-band equalizer / analyzer systems which include compressor loops for many narrow-band frequency components have been manufactured using analogue electronics, but they tend to be complex and bulky owing to the large number of electronic components used. Current generation systems make extensive use of digital techniques, where comparison of the measured signal with the desired signal allows the required signal to be synthesized.

A vibration testing technique which eases the problems associated with the

249

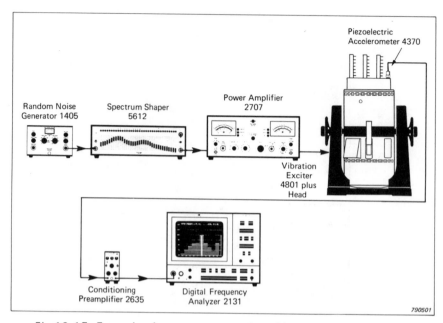

Fig.10.15. Example of an arrangement for wide-band random testing

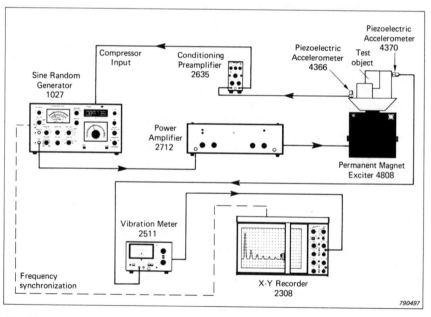

Fig.10.16. Example of an arrangement for narrow-band random testing using automatic frequency-band sweeping

250

generation and control of wide band random test signal, whilst retaining the statistical character of a random signal, is sweep random vibration testing (Fig.10.16). The narrow band nature of the signal means that the same regulation and programming facilities can be used for the sweep sine wave test. Sweep random test specifications can be written as for sweep sine tests, directly from the measured or estimated vibration environment.

10.1.6. Force Testing and Structural Response

For certain types of vibration test a force transducer may be mounted between the worktable and the test object. By comparison of the resulting vibration with the force input, the "resistance to be set in motion" or the "willingness to be set in motion" of the test object can be investigated. When used to relate vibratory motion at a point to its exciting force, these parameters are called point mechanical impedance and point mechanical mobility respectively (Fig.10.17). These concepts can give an insight into the equivalent mechanical system of a complex structure, thus being useful in mode studies, determination of dynamic properties, and evaluation of compliance. The expressions can be written:

$$Z = \frac{F}{v} \quad \text{(Mechanical Impedance)} \tag{10.4}$$

and
$$M = \frac{v}{F} \quad \text{(Mechanical Mobility)} \tag{10.5}$$

where F is the complex force vector, and v the complex velocity vector. Further definitions apply to transfer mobility, when the response is measured at a different point to the applied force.

Point Impedance $\xrightarrow[v]{F}$ Transfer Impedance $\xrightarrow{F}$ v

800374/1

Fig.10.17. The concepts of point and transfer impedance and mobility

Mechanical impedance ideas grew from lumped-parameter concepts as used for electrical circuits. It was required to try to model the behaviour of a structure in terms of discrete mechanical elements. For simple mechanical elements excited at a fixed excitation frequency such that $F = F_0 e^{j\omega t}$ and velocity $v = v_0 e^{j\omega t}$, the equation of motion for a mass is governed by:

$$F = ma = j\omega m v$$

251

since $a = j\omega v$ for vibration at fixed frequency ω.

Thus mechanical impedance:

$$Z_m = j\omega m \tag{10.6}$$

and mechanical mobility

$$M_m = \frac{1}{j\omega m} \tag{10.7}$$

Similarly for a spring element of stiffness k:

$$F = kd = \frac{k}{j\omega} v$$

since $v = j\omega d$ for vibration of fixed frequency ω.
Thus mechanical impedance

$$Z_k = \frac{k}{j\omega} \tag{10.8}$$

and mechanical mobility

$$M_m = \frac{j\omega}{k} \tag{10.9}$$

where:

$a = a_o e^{j\omega t}$ – acceleration
$v = v_o e^{j\omega t}$ – velocity
$d = d_o e^{j\omega t}$ – displacement
$m =$ mass (kg)
$k =$ spring constant (N/m)

For a damper element of damping c (N s/m),

$$F = cv$$

Thus mechanical impedance

$$Z_c = c \tag{10.10}$$

and mechanical mobility

$$M_c = \frac{1}{c} \tag{10.11}$$

Furthermore, mechanical impedances and mobilities can be represented vectorially in the complex plane (Fig.10.18). Note that other parameters such as apparent mass and dynamic stiffness may be defined when force is measured relative to acceleration or to displacement respectively. The equivalent mobility terms would be inertance, and compliance or receptance

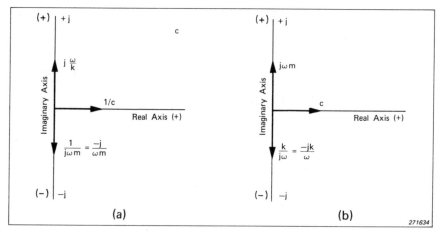

Fig.10.18. Vector representation of mechanical impedance and mobility:
(a) Mobility
(b) Impedance

(Fig.10.19). The use of velocity as the motion parameter gives resonance peaks which occur close to the undamped natural frequencies, and usually requires less dynamic range from the measuring equipment used than the use of acceleration or displacement.

For practical force and structural response testing, a vibration exciter drives

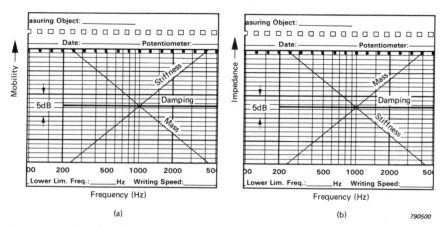

Fig.10.19. Frequency dependence of lumped impedance and mobility parameters
(a) Mobility
(b) Impedance

253

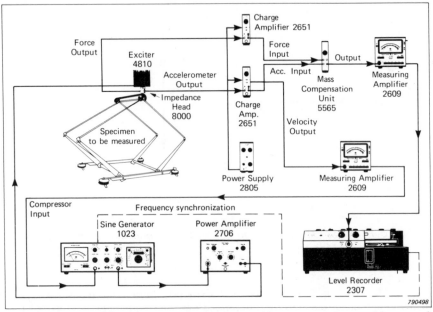

Fig.10.20. *Example of arrangement for making automatic graphic record-ings of point mechanical impedance as functions of frequency*

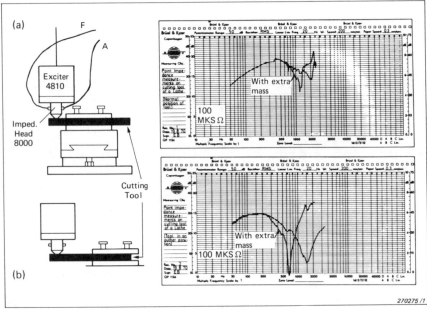

Fig.10.21. *Point impedance measurements on the cutting tool of a lathe:*
(a) Tool in normal position   (b) Tool in outer position

the object through an impedance head (Fig.6.24). This device incorporates two sensors, one delivering a signal proportion to the force being applied to the test object, and the second measuring the motion of the point at which the force is being applied. Where larger forces are required to be transmitted it is best to separate the functions by using separate force and motion sensors. Since the motion transducer is usually an accelerometer, the signal output must be integrated electrically to produce a velocity signal.

For mechanical impedance measurements the velocity level of the measuring point is kept constant, whereby a recording of the force level indicates the modulus of the impedance as $|Z| = |F| / |v|$ (Fig.10.20). This representation is particularly useful where properties of sub-systems must be combined to give the impedance matrix of a complete system. Fig.10.21 shows a typical application of mechanical impedance measurement.

Similarly, to measure the mobility, the driving force should be kept constant and the velocity level recorded as $|M| = |v| / |F|$. This representation is particularly useful when modal parameters of a system are to be found.

The phase difference between force and velocity signals can be measured by means of a phase meter. Where signal harmonics or extraneous noise interfere with measurements, tracking filters can be used (Fig.10.22).

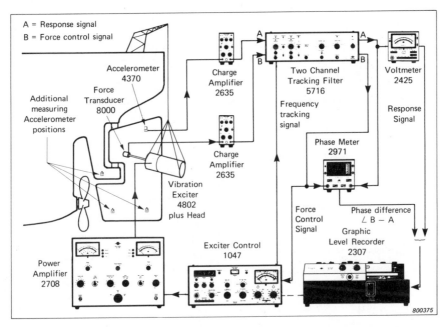

Fig.10.22. Example of arrangement for making mobility measurements on the rudder of a ship

255

10.2. SHOCK TESTING

Shock testing of equipment is a method of qualification testing to ensure that delicate equipment will operate satisfactorily in the practical shock environment. All equipment experiences some kind of shock during handling or transportation, whilst equipment mounted in vehicles may be exposed to a wide variety of shock conditions in service.

10.2.1. Laboratory Testing

In general, it is impracticable to reproduce the actual shock environment in a test. It is better to ensure that the *effects* of the test shock upon the tested equipment are similar to those of the shock(s) occurring in practice, and to ensure that these shock effects are *completely reproducible*. The latter is of prime importance when comparisons are made between test results obtained at different institutions, or when different product designs are evaluated.

One method of specifying a shock test is to define the instantaneous acceleration of the shock pulse as a function of time (IEC Recommendation 68-2-27), together with allowable tolerances on pulse shape and total velocity change produced by the pulse (Fig.10.23).

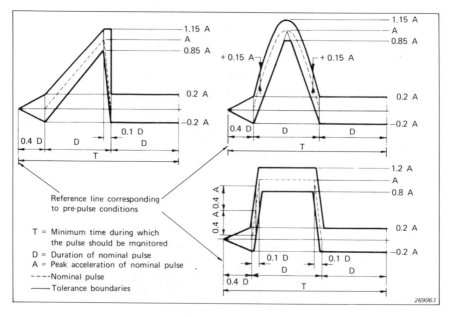

Fig.10.23. IEC preferred pulse forms for shock testing

256

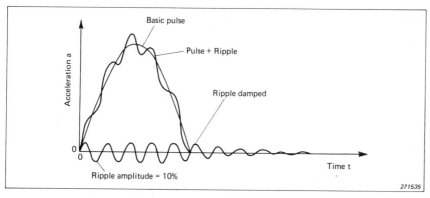

Fig.10.24. *Example of a shock pulse upon which a certain amount of ripple is superimposed*

Tolerances allow for the fact that a certain ripple (caused by resonance effects in the shock machine and test fixture) is often superimposed upon the test pulse in practice (Fig.10.24). The extra damage potential might invalidate the test results, if it were significant.

An alternative method of testing is to specify the type or manufacture of test machine to be used. The simplest design is the drop-test machine, where a test specimen is bolted on to a carriage and dropped from a certain height (Fig.10.25). The shape of the shock pulse is determined primarily by the material and shape of the impacting surfaces. Shock pulses up to 800 kms^{-2} have been obtained in this way. Further types of test machine utilize hydraulic or pneumatic principles, and do not depend upon the action of

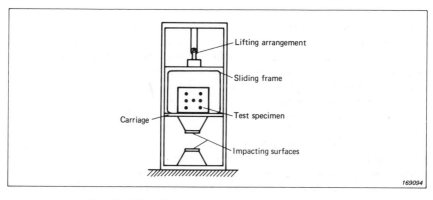

Fig.10.25. *Construction of a drop-test machine*

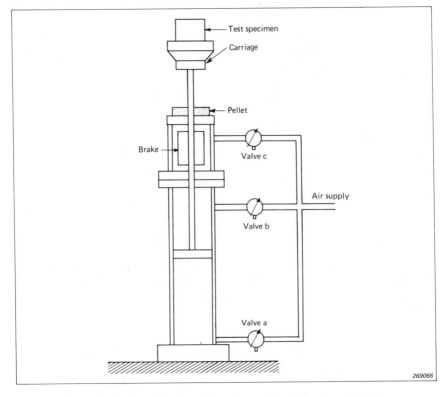

Fig.10.26. Construction of a pneumatic shock-test machine

gravity (Fig.10.26). Operation of such machines can be automated, and a brake can be actuated immediately after the impact so that rebounding of the carriage, and consequent distortion of the shock pulse, does not occur.

When a shock test is specified, the mounting method to be used, the maximum allowable transverse motion (< 30% of the nominal peak value), and the number of test shocks to be applied in each direction of three mutually perpendicular axes are normally stipulated. Furthermore, the phase characteristics of the measuring and monitoring equipment must be uniform over a relatively wide frequency range to ensure the correct frequency relationship between the various frequency components of the measured pulse (Fig.10.27).

Owing to the response of certain systems, a specified overall shock spectrum could be produced by a variety of shock pulse shapes. There is no unique time function associated with a specific shock spectrum. Damage due to accumulation of stress cycles (mechanical fatigue) may therefore differ between the tests, whilst *peak* acceleration levels and *peak* stress levels will us-

258

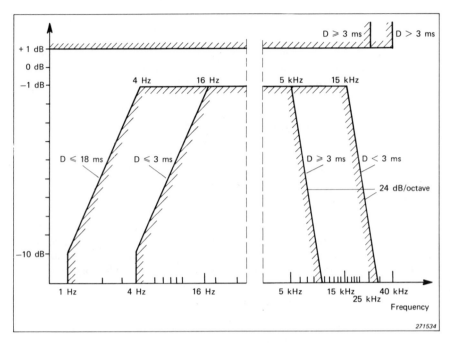

Fig.10.27.   Frequency characteristics required from shock measurement systems (I.E.C.)

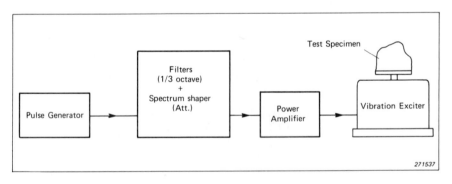

Fig.10.28.   Arrangement of equipment for a third-octave shock-spectrum synthesis system

ually be similar. As a shock test is devised to test the resistance of equipment against short-duration peak stresses, this allows for the possibility of specifying the test in terms of its shock spectrum rather than acceleration-versus-time characteristic. Furthermore, many shock-induced motions observed in service have waveforms which are predominantly oscillatory in character.

259

In practice, a shock-testing arrangement can be realised using an electrodynamic vibration exciter connected to specially-tailored electronic excitation sources (Fig.10.28). Typically, a short duration impulse, or "unit" impulse, from a pulse generator, excites a bank of parallel filters (e.g. 1/3-octave set). The time function of the summed output from the filters is termed a *synthesized shock*.

If the response of the object to this synthesized shock is analyzed, it is found that the peak response is roughly five times larger than the peak of the exciting transient (Fig.10.29). Actually, to produce a specified shock response in a specimen, a considerably lower input *force* is required than when using a conventional test machine. This occurs because the specimen is subjected to an oscillating transient, rather than to a single impulse.

Often the bandwidth of 1/3-octave filters is too wide to equalize narrowband test specimen resonances, whilst manual adjustment of multiple filters can be prohibitively time consuming. Testing has also been carried out using automatic narrow band test systems, but these are considerably more com-

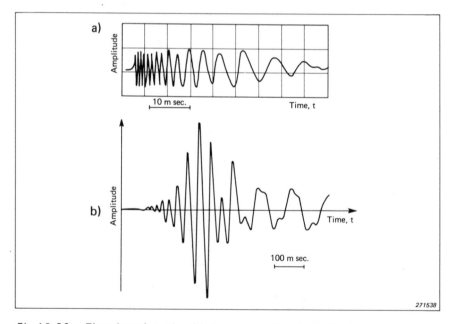

Fig.10.29. Time function of a third-octave synthesized shock
(a) Overall vibration table motion (summed output from the third-octave filter bank of Fig.10.28)
(b) Shock spectrum analyzer (narrow band) output of the signal shown in (a)

plex in operation. As in the case of broad-band vibration test systems, analogue signal generators have largely been superseded by digital systems in this field.

Oscillatory shock motions, such as those described above, are often termed *complex shocks*. While the possibility of producing a large variety of complex shocks is offered by a shock synthesis system, some "simpler" machines do exist which produce specific complex shocks. These are in general designed according to the pendulum principle (Fig.10.30).

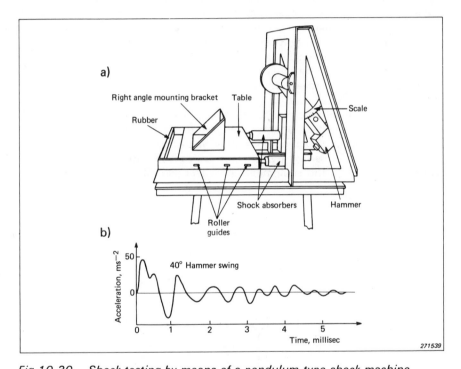

Fig.10.30. Shock testing by means of a pendulum-type shock machine
(a) Construction of the machine
(b) Typical trace of acceleration versus time produced by the machine

10.2.2. Service Testing

The transport medium or packaging method has to be specified for a piece of vulnerable equipment, so that it will not be damaged by shocks occurring during shipping or handling. This situation might arise in the delivery of consignments of delicate products such as filament devices, as well as for the

261

transport of high capital cost equipment such as large electrical transformers or turbine assemblies produced to fine tolerances. Alternatively, it may be necessary to monitor the shocks induced in the equipment at specific handling points (e.g. dock loading) or by specific transport media (e.g. belts and conveyors).

In these cases a special measuring unit can be used to measure the maximum shock values occurring in service. Typical mechanical devices are simple, and usually work on an inertia principle; they are made up of an assembly of a mass and springs or mass and magnet (Fig.10.31). However, they suffer the major disadvantages that they are single-event devices in general, and that their threshold levels of operation tend to exhibit considerable tolerance spread. Once they are tripped, subsequent shock information is lost: furthermore the maximum value of shock experienced and the time at which it occurred is unknown. The usual principle is that the mass is dislodged when the threshold level is exceeded.

The use of an electronic measuring device, activated only when a threshold shock level is exceeded, enables the information concerning the time at which shocks occur and their maximum values to be retained. In a typical bump recorder, the sensor (which may be sensitive to shocks in all three axes) is mounted on the equipment under test (Fig.10.32), or else the whole

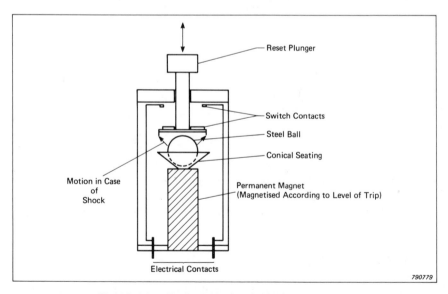

Fig.10.31. Typical mechanical shock-trip device

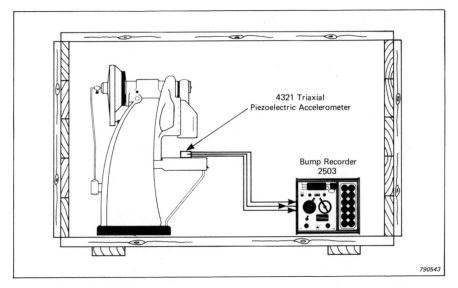

Fig.10.32. Example of application of an electronic Bump Recorder

assembly may be packaged together. The recorder may monitor the progress of the cargo over several weeks, printing out on an integral printer the time and shock value on each occasion the preset threshold level is exceeded (Fig.10.33). The inclusion of an integrator in the device enables the shock velocity values to be obtained for use in those cases where the consignment is particularly sensitive to impact velocity. A much more precise assessment of the maximum shocks occurring in service and their time of occurrence can thus be obtained using an apparatus of this kind.

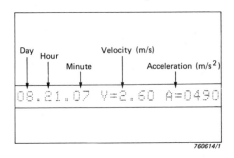

Fig.10.33. Typical print-out obtained from B & K 2503 Bump Recorder

10.3. SELECTED BIBLIOGRAPHY

ANDERSON, D.:   *"Multi-Point Excitation Techniques"*. Environmental Engineering, Dec. 1971

BOOTH, G.B. and BROCH, J.T.:   *"Analog Experiments Compare Improved Sweep Random Tests and Wide Band Random and Sweep Sine Tests*. Shock and Vibr. Bull. 34, No.5, and Brüel & Kjær Tech. Rev. No.3-1965

BOOTH, G.B.:   *"Interchangeable Head Vibration Exciters.* Brüel & Kjær Tech. Rev. No.2-1971

BROCH, J.T.:   *"Automatic Level Regulation of Vibration Exciters"*. Brüel & Kjær Tech. Rev. No. 2-1958

BROCH, J.T.:   *"Vibration Exciter Characteristics.* Brüel & Kjær Tech. Rev. No.3-1960

BROCH, J.T.:   *"An Introduction to Sweep Random Vibration"*. Brüel & Kjær Tech. Rev. No. 2-1964

BROCH, J.T.:   *"Some Aspects of Sweep Random Vibration"*. J. Sound Vibr. Vol. 3, No.2, 1966

BROCH, J.T.:   *Some Experimental Tests with Sweep Random Vibration."* Brüel & Kjær Tech. Rev. No. 2-1966

BROCH, J.T.:   *"Vibration Testing — The Reasons and the Means"*. Brüel & Kjær Tech. Rev. No.3-1967

BROCH, J.T.:   *"Some Aspects of Vibration Testing.* Proc. of Anglo Dutch Symposium on Environmental Engineering. Delft, April 1970

BROOKS, G.W. and CARDEN, H.D.:   *"A Versatile Drop Test Procedure for the Simulation of Impact Environments"*. Noise Control, Vol.7. No.5-1961

CRANDALL, S.H. et al.:   *"Random Vibration"*. John Wiley and Sons, Inc. New York 1959

CRANDALL, S.H. et al.:   *"Random Vibration II"*. MIT Press, Cambridge, Mass. 1963

CREDE, C.E. and LUNNEY, E.J.:   *"Establishment of Vibration and Shock Tests for Missile Electronics as Derived from the Measured Environment"*. WADC Tech. Report No. 56-503. ASTIA Doc. No. 1183. 1956

DAS, B.M.:   *"Non-Destructive Pavement Evaluation"*. Civil and Environmental Engineering Development Office. March 1978

DAVIS, A.G. and DUNN, C.S.: *"From Theory to Field Experience with the Non-Destructive Testing of Piles"*. Proc. Instn. Civ. Engrs. Part 2, 57, Dec. 1974, pp. 571-573

EWINS, D.J.: *"Measurement and Application of Mechanical Impedance Data"*. Journal of the Society Environmental Engineering, Dec. 1975

FRANKLAND, J.M.: *"Effects of Impact on simple Elastic Structures"*. Proceedings of the SESA, Vol.6, No.2-1949

IEC: *"Basic Environmental Testing Procedures for Electronic Components and Electronic Equipment"*. Recommendation Publication 68—2—27. Test Ea: Shock

IEC: *"Basic Environmental Testing Procedures for Electronic Components and Electronic Equipment"*. Recommendation Publication 68—2—27 Eb: Bump

IEC: *"Vibration Test for Electronic Equipments and Components"*. Recommendation Publication 68-2-6. Test F: Vibration

ISO DRAFT INTERNATIONAL STANDARD 5344: *"Electrodynamic Test Equipment for Generating Vibration — Methods of Describing Equipment Characteristics"*

JACOBSEN, L.S. and AYRE, R.S.: *"A Comparative Study of Pulse and Step-Type Loads on a Simple Vibratory System"*. Technical Report 16, Structural Dynamics, Contract N6 — ORI 154, Task 1, Stanford University, 1952

JACOBSEN, L.S. and AYRE, R.S.: *"Engineering Vibrations"*. McGraw-Hill Book Company, Inc. 1958

JORDAN, J.C.: *"Shock Response Spectrum Synthesis and Analysis"*. Proc. of the Inst. of Environmental Sciences 1967

KEEFFE, R.E. and BATHKE, E.A.: *"Shock Pulse Shaping Using Drop Test Techniques"*. Shock and Vibr. Bull. No.41. Part 5. 1970

KITTELSEN, K.E.: *"Measurement and Description of Shock"*. Brüel & Kjær Tech. Rev. No.3-1966

LEVENSON, M. and SUSSHOLZ, B.: *"The Response of a System with a Single Degree of Freedom to a Blast Load"*. Taylor Model Basin Report No. 572. 1947

MASSOUD, M. and PASTOREL, H.: *"Impedance Methods for Machine Analysis"*, Shock and Vibration Digest, Sept. 1978

McGRATH, M.B.: *"A Discussion of Pyrotechnic Shock Criteria"*. Shock and Vibr. Bull. No.41. Part 5. 1970

265

METZGAR, K.J.: "Test Oriented Appraisal of Shock Spectrum Analysis and Synthesis". Proc. of the Inst. of Environmental Sciences 1967

MONROE, J.: "A Problem of Sinusoidal vs. Random Vibration". Proc. Inst. Env. Sci. April 1961

MORROW, C.T. and MUCHMORE, R.B.: "Shortcomings of Present Methods of Measuring and Simulating Vibration Environments". J. Appl. Mech. 1955

MORROW, C.T. and SARGEANT, H.I.: "Sawtooth Shock as a Component Test". J.A.S.A. Vol.28, No.5. September 1956

MORROW, C.T.: "The Shock Spectrum as a Criterion of Severity of Shock Impulses". J.A.S.A. Vol.29, No.5. May 1957

MORROW, C.T.: "Shock and Vibration Engineering". John Wiley and Sons, Inc. New York 1963

MORROW, C.T.: "Measures of Blast Wave Damage Potential". Shock and Vibr. Bull. No.41. Part 5. 1970

MORROW, C.T.: "Application of the Mechanical Impedance Concept to Shock and Vibration Testing". Noise Control. Vol.6, No.4, 1960

MORROW, C.T.: "Significance of Power and Probability Distributions in Connection with Vibration". Noise Control. Vol.6. No.5, 1960

MØLLER PETERSEN, P.E.: "Problems in Feedback Control of Narrow Band Random Noise". Brüel & Kjær Tech. Rev. No.4-1962

OLESON, M.W.: "A Narrow Band Vibration Test". Shock and Vibr. Bull. 25. No.1. 1957

OTTS, J.V.: "Methods Used to Realistically Simulate Vibration Environments". Shock and Vibr. Bull. 41. Part 2. 1970

PIERSOL, A.G.: "Generation of Vibration Test Specifications". Measurement Analysis Corp. 1965

PIERSOL, A.G.: "Investigation of Statistical Techniques to Select Optimal Test Levels for Spacecraft Vibration Tests". Report 10909801 — F, Digitek Corporation, Marina del Rey, California. October 1970

REGIER, A.A. and HUBBARD, H.H.: "Response of Structures to High Intensity Noise". Noise Control, Vol.5, No.5. 1959

SMITH, P.W. Jr.: "Sound-Induced Vibration". Noise Control. Vol.4. No.6. 1958

SPANG, K.:   *"The Advantages of Using Initial Sawtooth Pulse Shapes in Shock Testing".* Environmental Engineering No.23 1966

STAHLE, C.V.:   *"Phase Separation Technique for Ground Vibration Testing".* Aerospace Engineering. July 1962

SØRENSEN, O.B.:   *"High Frequency Testing of Gramophone Cartridges using an Accelerometer".* B & K Technical Review No. 2-1976

TROTTER, W.D.:   *"An Experimental Evaluation of Sinusoidal Substitutes for Random Vibration".* Shock and Vibr. Bull. 29. No.4. 1961

TRULL, R.V.:   *"Sweep Speed Effects in Resonant Systems".* Shock and Vibr. Bull.41. Part 2. 1970

VIGNESS, I.:   *"Some Characteristics of Navy "High Impact" Type Shock Machines".* Proceedings of the SESA, Vol.5, No.1, 1947

VIGNESS, I.:   *"Navy High-Impact Shock Machines for Lightweight and Mediumweight Equipment".* NRL Report 5618. U.S. Naval Research Laboratory. June 1961

WITTE, A.F.:   *"Specification of Sine Vibration Test Levels Using a Force-acceleration Product Technique".* Shock and Vibr. Bull. 41. Part 2. 1970

WITTE, A.F.:   *"Dual Specifications in Random Vibration Testing, an Application of Mechanical Impedance".* Shock and Vibr. Bull. 41. Part 2. 1970

11. BALANCING OF ROTATING MACHINES

11.1. INTRODUCTION

Unbalance in rotating machinery has become an increasingly important factor in the development of modern equipment especially where the needs for speed and/or reliability are high. Techniques for balancing such equipment have advanced significantly in recent years, enabling both production and field balancing to be executed systematically and with a minimum of fuss and experimentation. Balancing of machines is important to prevent fatigue failure in associated structures, to prevent excessive loading of support bearings, to prevent transmission of excessive external noise and vibration, and to improve the durability and usefulness of the machines in service.

11.2. UNBALANCE OF RIGID ROTORS

The simplest case of unbalance can be considered for a uniform thin disc

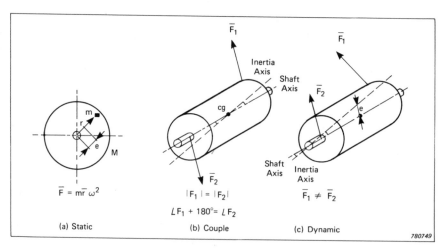

(a) Static
$$\bar{F} = m\bar{r}\,\omega^2$$

(b) Couple
$$|F_1| = |F_2|$$
$$\angle F_1 + 180° = \angle F_2$$

(c) Dynamic
$$\bar{F}_1 \neq \bar{F}_2$$

780749

Fig.11.1. Illustration of the three different kinds of unbalance

of mass M (kg), rotationally symmetrical about its axis of rotation. When a small mass m (g) is fixed to the disc at a distance r (mm) from that axis, the disc is said to be in a state of "unbalance". This type of unbalance can be detected by supporting the axle on a pair of knife edges to find the "heavy spot": for this reason it is often called *static* (or single-plane) unbalance Fig.11.1(a)). The centrifugal force F generated by the uncompensated mass, when the disc rotates a speed ω (rad/s), is given by

$$F = mr\omega^2* \tag{11.1}$$

This force is equivalent to the force generated by a small eccentricity e of the centre of mass of the disc from the axis of rotation:

$$F = Me\omega^2 \tag{11.2}$$

The unbalance of the disc, or rotor, is defined as u g-mm, where:

$$u = mr \tag{11.3}$$

It is also possible to eliminate F between (11.1) and (11.2) to see that the eccentricity term e in m also represents the specific unbalance of the rotor in g-mm/kg:

$$e = \frac{mr}{M} \tag{11.4}$$

The term for specific unbalance is particularly useful for reference and comparison purposes, as the effects of unbalance in practice are found to be dependent upon the mass of the rotor itself.

From expression (11.1) certain important conclusions can be drawn. Unbalance effects are:

(i)   synchronous with rotation speed
(ii) radial in their line of action
(iii) vector quantities possessing both size and direction
(iv) the result of a discrepancy between the geometric- and mass-symmetries of a rotor.

As such, unbalance is the most common source of vibration in rotating equipment; common rotors include electric armatures, turbomachinery, drive shafts, grinding wheels, machine tool elements, and crankshafts. In principle

---

* F, r have a definite line of action with respect to the geometry of the rotor, and are thus denoted as vector quantities. $\omega = 2\pi n / 60 \approx n/10$, where n is rotation speed in r/min.

The units quoted are consistent with ISO 1940.

the procedure of balancing involves an adjustment of the mass distribution of the rotor, so that the resulting geometrical and inertial axes more nearly coincide with one another. The task is to minimise

$$F = \sum_{i=1}^{n} m_i r_i \omega^2$$

Many practical machines, such as grinding wheels, industrial blowers and flywheels, can be considered as though their mass were concentrated in a single disc, but the majority of rotors have mass distributed along their length. This gives the possibility of a second form of unbalance. For the case of a right cylinder, it is possible to have two equal uncompensated masses symmetrically placed about the centre of mass, but positioned at 180° to one another. The rotor is in static balance, yet centrifugal forces will produce a moment about the centre of mass when the rotor turns. This type of unbalance is called couple unbalance (Fig.11.1(b)), and it results in a tilting or pendulum action of the principal inertia axis about the shaft axis at the centre of mass. To counteract the couple it is necessary to make corrections on two planes.

The general condition when both static and couple unbalance are present is called *dynamic* unbalance (Fig.11.1(c)). The principal inertia axis is now inclined to the geometric shaft axis, but there is also an eccentricity at the centre of mass. This unbalance condition can be resolved by suitable instrumentation for correction in two planes. Correction is made by mass addition (welding, rivets, etc.) or mass removal (boring, planing etc.), using ancillary equipment.

11.3. ROTOR SUPPORT SYSTEM

In an assembled machine, the rotor is supported by a bearing and base assembly. This must restrain the unbalance-excited motion of the rotor journal. For the case of a single bearing, the rotor/support assembly may be modelled as a single degree of freedom system. The differential equation of motion can be expressed:

$$M\ddot{x} + c\dot{x} + kx = mr\omega^2 \sin \omega t \qquad (11.5)$$

For sinusoidal motion the displacement x can be written:

$$x = x_o \sin (\omega t - \phi)$$

giving the solution:

$$x_0 = \frac{mr\left(\frac{\omega}{\omega_0}\right)^2}{M\sqrt{\left[1 - \left(\frac{\omega}{\omega_0}\right)^2\right]^2 + 4D\left(\frac{\omega}{\omega_0}\right)^2}}, \qquad (11.6)$$

where

$$\omega_0 = \sqrt{\frac{k}{M}}$$

$$D = \frac{c}{\sqrt{kM}}$$

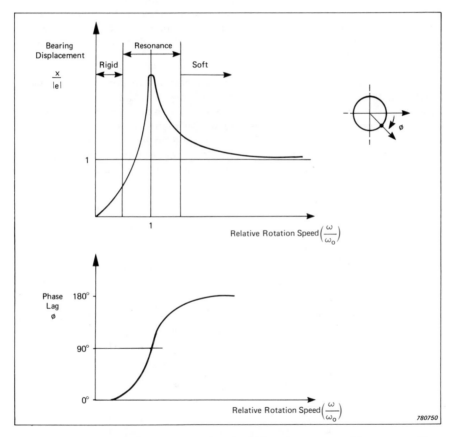

Fig.11.2. Characteristic response of a single bearing suspension system, illustrating the distinction between a hard-bearing (rigid) balancing machine and a soft-bearing one

271

and ω_0 = natural (angular) frequency of suspension, in rad/s,

k = stiffness of suspension in N/m,

c = damping of suspension in N/ms^{-1}

$$\omega = \frac{2\pi n}{60} \approx \frac{n}{10} \; rad/s$$

n = rotation speed in r/min.

The solution indicates different regimes of interest, depending on the relative values of rotor angular velocity, ω, and the natural frequency of the suspension system ω_0 (Fig.11.2). Where the support resonance is much higher than the rotation speed ($\omega \ll \omega_0$) unbalance forces are reacted by elastic forces in the supports (*hard* supports) as given by expression (11.1). Where the support resonance is much lower than the rotation speed ($\omega \gg \omega_0$, *soft* supports), unbalance forces are reacted by inertia forces in the rotor itself as given by expression (11.2). In the general case unbalance forces are reacted by some combination of the two effects depending on the characteristics of the supports and foundation.

For a rotor moving in one plane, but possessing two degrees of freedom (Fig.11.3), the geometry and the moment of inertia of the rotor become important. That is, the existence of unbalance in one plane will excite vibrations in both suspension systems depending on geometric location of the unbalance on the moment of inertia of the rotor, and on the support characteristics. This interaction is called the *cross effect* between the two support systems. For rotation at a fixed frequency this relation can be written as a matrix of complex terms:

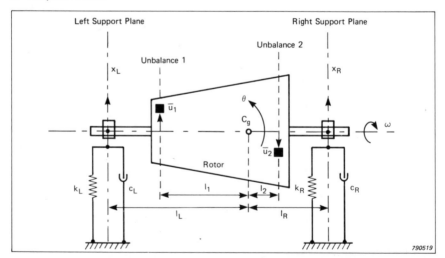

Fig.11.3. Unbalance of a rotating body vibrating with two degrees of freedom x, θ

272

$$\begin{bmatrix} x_L \\ x_R \end{bmatrix} = \begin{bmatrix} \alpha \end{bmatrix} \begin{bmatrix} u_1 \\ u_2 \end{bmatrix} \qquad (11.7)$$

where [α] is called the influence coefficient matrix and

$$\begin{bmatrix} \alpha \end{bmatrix} = \begin{bmatrix} \alpha_{L1} & \alpha_{L2} \\ \alpha_{R1} & \alpha_{R2} \end{bmatrix}$$

1, 2 refer to unbalance planes 1, 2.

L, R refer to support planes L, R.

In this way, it is possible to build up increasingly more sophisticated models of the dynamic system. However, the simple single- and two-degree of freedom models can be very useful for describing the behaviour of real machines.

11.4. SETTING THE STANDARDS

Ideally, a completely balanced machine would show no unbalance at all. In practice, though, owing to machining tolerances, mechanical play, run-out, misalignment distortion etc. perfect balance can never be achieved. In any production or maintenance situation an appropriate residual unbalance, "balance quality" or vibration tolerance must be selected which depends on the performance required from the machine and the economics of the balancing process.

In the fifties much work was done in West Germany to collect the experiences of engineers working in this field. VDI 2060, "Beurteilungsmaßstäbe für den Auswuchtzustand rotierender, starrer Körper", has now been adopted internationally as recommendation ISO Standard 1940, "Balance Quality of Rotating Rigid Bodies". The recommendations relate acceptable residual unbalance to the maximum service speed of the rotor, and associate various types of representative rotors with ranges of recommended quality grades (Figs.11.4 and 11.5). The quality grade, G, (equivalent to the product $e\omega$ for an unrestrained rotor) is introduced, as it enables the physically observed behaviour of machines running at different speeds to be compared. The values of G in the Standard are numerically equivalent to the eccentricity e in μm for a rotor running at 9500 RPM. The quality grade, or unbalance, of a rotor can be assessed using a calibrated balancing machine.

For machines in service, unbalance vibrations are influenced considerably

Balancing Grades for Various Groups of Representative Rigid Rotors

Quality grade G	e_ω [1] [2] mm/sec	Rotor types — General examples
G 4000	4000	Chrankshaft-drives [3] of rigidly mounted slow marine diesel engines with uneven number of cylinders [4].
G 1600	1600	Crankshaft-drives of rigidly mounted large two-cycle engines.
G 630	630	Crankshaft-drives of rigidly mounted large four-cycle engines. Crankshaft-drives of elastically mounted marine diesel engines.
G 250	250	Crankshaft-drives of rigidly mounted fast four-cylinder diesel engines [4].
G 100	100	Crankshaft-drives of fast diesel engines with six and more cylinders [4]. Complete engines (gasoline or diesel) for cars, trucks and locomotives [5].
G 40	40	Car wheels, wheel rims, wheel sets, drive shafts. Crankshaft-drives of elastically mounted fast four-cycle engines (gasoline or diesel) with six and more cylinders[4]. Crankshaft-drives for engines of cars, trucks and locomotives.
G 16	16	Drive shafts (propeller shafts, cardan shafts) with special requirements. Parts of crushing machinery. Parts of agricultural machinery. Individual components of engines (gasoline or diesel, for cars, trucks and locomotives. Crankshaft-drives of engines with six and more cylinders under special requirements.
G 6.3	6.3	Parts of process plant machines. Marine main turbine gears (merchant service). Centrifuge drums. Fans. Assembled aircraft gas turbine rotors. Fly wheels. Pump impellers. Machine-tool and general machinery parts. Normal electrical armatures. Individual components of engines under special requirements.
G 2.5	2.5	Gas and steam turbines, including marine main turbines (merchant service). Rigid turbo-generator rotors. Rotors. Turbo-compressors. Machine-tool drives. Medium and large electrical armatures with special requirements. Small electrical armatures. Turbine-driven pumps.
G 1	1	Tape recorder and phonograph (gramophone) drives. Grinding-machine drives. Small electrical armatures with special requirements.
G 0.4	0.4	Spindles, discs, and armatures of precision grinders. Gyroscopes.

Notes:

1. $\omega = 2 \pi n/60 \approx n/10$, if n is measured in revolutions per minute and ω in radians per second.

2. In general, for rigid rotors with two correction planes, one half of the recommended residual unbalance is to be taken for each plane; these values apply usually for any two arbitrarily chosen planes, but the state of unbalance may be improved upon at the bearings. For disc-shaped rotors the full recommended value holds for one plane.

3. A crankshaft-drive is an assembly which includes the crankshaft, a flywheel, clutch, pulley, vibration damper, rotating portion of connecting rod, etc.

4. For the present purposes, slow diesel engines are those with a piston velocity of less than 9 m/s; fast diesel engines are those with a piston velocity of greater than 9 m/s.

5. In complete engines the rotor mass comprises the sum of all masses belonging to the crankshaft-drive described in footnote 3 above.

800624

Fig.11.4. Maximum residual unbalance corresponding to recommended Balance Quality Grades, G, as laid down in ISO 1940 (1973)

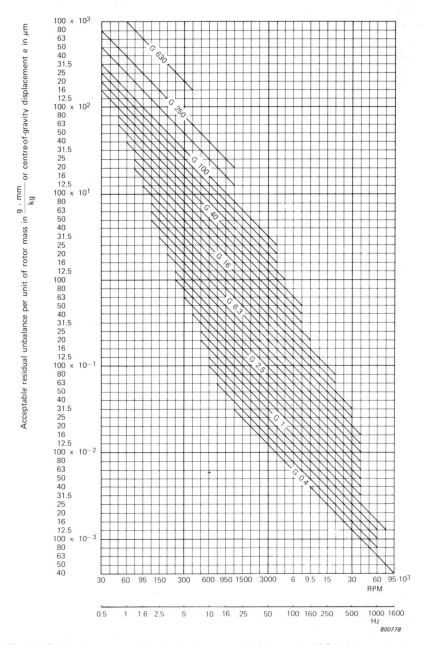

Fig.11.5. Maximum residual unbalance as laid down in ISO 1940 (1973)

275

by the physical characteristics of the bearings and base. Consequently it is most convenient to assess the run quality of the machine using vibration levels as recommended in standards such as VDI 2056, "Beurteilungsmaßstäbe für mechanische Schwingungen von Maschinen", adopted internationally as ISO 2372, "Mechanical Vibration of Machines with Operating Speeds from 10 to 200 rev/s". These standards give guidance as to when maintenance might be required on a machine in service (Fig.11.6). Where the major source of vibration is unbalance the Standard can be used as a basis for specifying the acceptable residual vibration level.

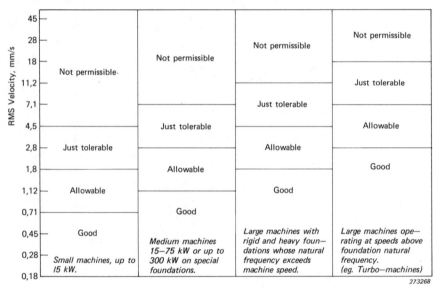

Fig.11.6. Vibration criterion chart (from VDI 2056)

Other useful Standards related to balancing equipment itself include ISO 2953 "Balancing Machines — Description and Evaluation" and ISO 2371 "Field Balancing Equipment — Description and Evaluation".

In all cases, these Standards represent committee decisions made by groups of engineers for the guidance of others: experience is often required to indicate how they can be interpreted best for any given balancing problem.

11.5. BALANCING MACHINES

A dynamic balancing machine consists of a bed assembly (Fig.11.7) and an associated measurement unit (Fig.11.8). Instrumented support pedestals carry the rotor to be balanced, which is driven at constant speed by a motor

276

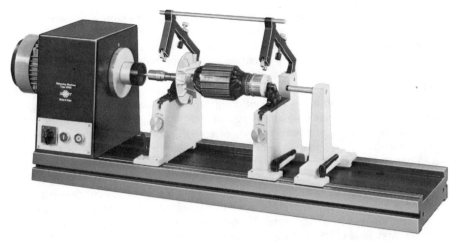

Fig.11.7. An example of a soft-bearing universal balancing machine, the B & K Type 3905

Fig.11.8. An example of the console for a dynamic balancing machine, B & K Type 2504

and drive system. Most two-plane machines operate with the rotor axis horizontal, and are described as "universal". Typically, drive to the rotor is provided via an axial cardan shaft or a circumferential belt arrangement, depending on the size and specification of the balancing requirement. The support pedestals can be set at any convenient position along the bed to suit different rotor geometries within the mass range of the machine, whilst the measurement head, or console, is designed to accommodate any likely combination of measuring and correction planes presented to it. The electrical signals sensed at the supports are analysed in the console to display directly the *amount* and *angle* of unbalance to be corrected on the two correction planes selected for the rotor. The balancing bench and the console complement one another; if they are used correctly, an *unbalance reduction ratio* of 80 — 90% might be typical for a single run.

277

Balancing machines may be designed with *soft* bearings or with *hard* bearings. These descriptions refer to the characteristics of the support systems as discussed in Section 11.3. In a soft-bearing machine, sensors are used to measure the vibratory motion at the journals. The moving element, operating above resonance, is decoupled from external vibration effects, enabling the bed and support posts to be of relatively light-weight construction, to give a transportable machine offering high sensitivity over its mass range. Hard-bearing machines measure force at the bearings. To restrain the rotor adequately, a stronger, heavier form of construction is necessary to give the high mechanical impedance required at the bearings. This form of construction has the disadvantage of greater sensitivity to extraneous vibrations.

Whichever type of transducer is used in the supports, the console must process the raw unbalance signals to yield calibrated correction values. In practice, the signals from the sensors must be filtered to eliminate higher-order effects and noise. The resulting cleaned-up sinusoidal signals are processed through a network of sensitivity and mixing potentiometers so that appropriate calibrated correction values, for the correction planes to be used, appear and are held on the display. The display is usually selectable to indicate mass addition or mass removal on the chosen correction planes. Single-variable analogue displays are less common than the vector-meter display, which gives a pictorial representation of the state of unbalance: alternatively, the use of digital electronics permits very consistent and stable operation and lends itself to application to a digital display for clear, unambiguous interpretation in the industrial workplace.

The front panel controls of the console are adjustable by the operator to achieve *plane separation* and calibration of the unbalance, measured in terms of mass corrections (practical correction units). In this way the operator can obtain independent readings for each correction plane, and the confusing *correction plane interference*, or cross effect, is eliminated. A dynamic calibration procedure is used to set up soft-bearing machines, whereas geometric dimensions are dialled-in statically to set up the hard-bearing machine. Once the balancing machine is calibrated, unbalance corrections can be found for any subsequent rotor in the series with a single *balancing run*.

11.6. FIELD BALANCING

Sometimes access to a balancing machine is not available; the rotor to be balanced is too large to suit a balancing machine, or the rotor must be balanced in its normal service conditions. In these cases "field" or "in-situ" balancing can be carried out using suitable portable instruments. Generally, such instruments require more know-how on the part of the user than a balancing machine, but are more versatile in application owing to their portability and the range of different transducer sensitivities which can be used with

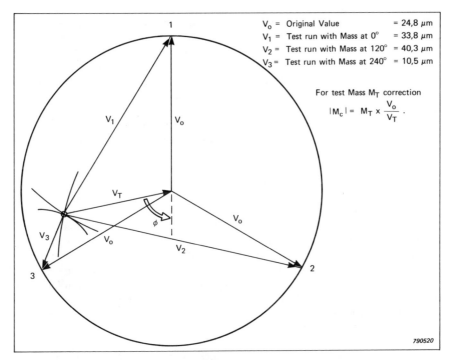

Fig.11.9. Three-point method for single-phase balancing - Siebert's Construction

the same instruments. Such instruments are also useful for machinery condition monitoring, vibration spectrum analysis, and fault diagnosis.

For a machine in operation, it is normally only possible to mount sensors externally, for example on the bearing housings. Thus it is the motion of the bearing housings which is measured. In practice, the dynamic system has many degrees of freedom, as the spring/damper characteristics of each of the two bearings will be different not only from each other but also in the two orthogonal radial directions at each bearing. By analogy with equation 11.6 for the single degree of freedom system, the only way of calibrating the dynamic system is to introduce a value of known unbalance to the system, and measure the transfer characteristics between the unbalance plane and the measuring position. If linearity and phase fidelity between unbalance changes and corresponding vibration changes (at least over a limited range) can be assumed, corresponding correction values can be calculated. It is important, though, that the machine should be run up to the same speed, and that the sensors should not be moved, during the balancing runs.

One method of determining the size and position of the unbalance for a single plane is to use a simple vibration meter connected to an accelerometer mounted on the bearing. First the initial unbalance is measured. Then a trial mass is used to introduce a known unbalance by attaching it to the rotor at the same radius to be used for the final correction mass. Three test runs are carried out with the trial mass placed at 0°, 120°, 240° on the rotor. Geometrically, *Siebert's construction* (Fig.11.9) can be used to evaluate the correction values. Three vectors of equal length, corresponding to initial unbalance V_o, at 0°, 120°, 240° respectively, are drawn out from the origin. Vectors corresponding to V_T (0°), V_T (120°), V_T (240°) are constructed by centring a compass point on each of the V_o vectors in turn: the point of intersection of these arcs enables the vectors corresponding to the trial mass alone to be constructed. The correction mass can be calculated directly.

Usually it is impracticable to carry out three trial runs; furthermore it is necessary to use a filter synchronised to rotation speed, to ensure that the unbalance component of the vibration signal can be isolated from other mechanical influences. The inclusion of some form of phase-measuring device in the system enables a more practical procedure to be implemented. One way of determining the phase is to tape or mark a scale graduated in angular units on the rotor, and illuminate the scale during the trial balancing runs with the light from a stroboscope triggered by the filtered vibration signal. An example of such a system is shown in Fig.11.10.

Purpose-built field-balancing sets, however, employ a non-contact tachometer probe to trigger an all-electronic phase indicator from a single arbitrary mark on the rotor. The example shown in Fig.11.11 is designed to be equally suitable for monitoring and analysis tasks as mentioned above.

For single-plane balancing, such as for a grinding wheel, an initial reading of vibration amplitude, $|V_o|$, and phase angle, α_0 (with reference to a fixed

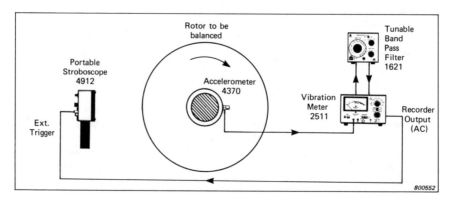

Fig.11.10. Field balancing with a stroboscopic motion analyzer

280

Fig.11.11. *Example of a portable field balancing set, giving direct digital in-dication of phase by the use of a non-contacting probe*

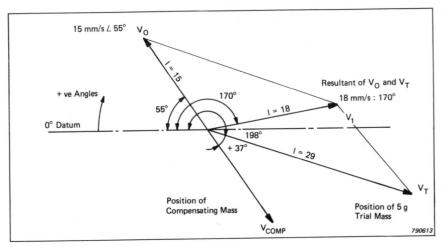

Fig.11.12. *Single-point phase-angle method for single-plane balancing*

V_O = *initial unbalance*

V_1 = *resultant of V_O + V_T*

point on the rotor) are obtained (Fig.11.12). The machine is then stopped and a trial mass M_T is fixed to the rotor at some arbitrary position. Running the machine at the same speed as before yields a new vibration amplitude, $|V_1|$, and phase angle, α_1, enabling a vector diagram to be constructed directly.

281

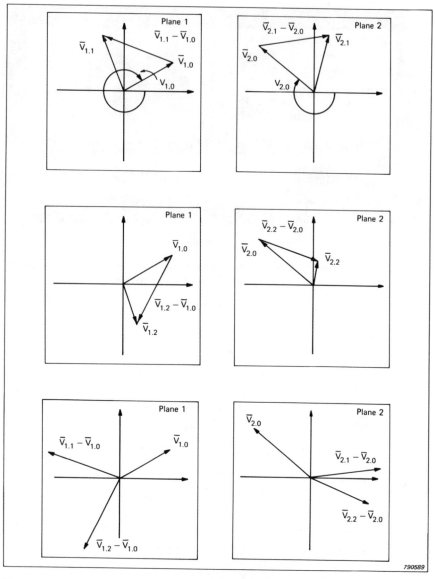

*Fig.11.13. Vectorial representation of vibration levels for two-plane balan-
cing*

The difference ($V_1 - V_o$) represents the effect of trial mass, M_T, on the measured vibration. Thus the size of the correction mass is given by:

282

$$M_c = \frac{|V_0|}{|V_1 - V_0|} M_T \qquad (11.8)$$

placed at an angle α_c to counteract V_0. Where non-linearities, or incorrect choice of trial mass, do not allow acceptable residual unbalance to be achieved in the first run, it may be necessary to repeat the procedure.

Where field balancing in two planes is to be carried out, two trial runs must be made, introducing known unbalance in two correction planes and making measurements on two bearing housings. These runs are necessary to enable all the terms of the influence coefficient matrix, defined in equation (11.7), to be generated (Fig.11.13).

In run 0, the initial condition of unbalance is assessed measuring $|V_{10}|$ $\angle\alpha_0$ and $|V_{20}|$ $\angle\beta_0$. (β signifies phase in the second measuring plane).

In run 1, a trial mass M_{T1} is placed on correction plane 1, measuring $|V_{11}|$ $\angle\alpha_1$ and $|V_{21}|$ $\angle\beta_1$.

In run 2, a trial mass M_{T2} is placed on correction plane 2, measuring $|V_{12}|$ $\angle\alpha_2$ and $|V_{22}|$ $\angle\beta_2$.

It can be seen that:

$(V_{11} - V_{10})$ = effect of M_{T1} at measuring position 1.
$(V_{12} - V_{10})$ = effect of M_{T2} at measuring position 1.
$(V_{21} - V_{20})$ = effect of M_{T1} at measuring position 2.
$(V_{22} - V_{20})$ = effect of M_{T2} at measuring position 2.

To balance the rotor, correction masses should be placed in planes 1 and 2 to generate vibrations equal in magnitude but opposite in direction to V_{10} and V_{20}. A graphical solution is possible, but manipulation of the six vector values in the two measuring planes is tedious. It is much easier to execute the required calculations on an electronic computer (Fig.11.14) or calculator. The widespread availability of programmable pocket calculators now makes it possible for balancing-set users to obtain commercial magnetic card-programs pre-programmed specifically for balancing. These can be fed directly into the user's own calculator to solve balancing equations automatically without any involvement on the part of the operator in programming or mathematics. Mathematically, it is required to calculate correction values M_{c1}, M_{c2} which satisfy the equations:

```
DYNBAL WW 1326
LIST
10   DIM C(2,2),D(2,2),E(2,2),F(2,2),G(2,2),H(2,2),I(2,2),J(2,2)
12   DIM K(2,2),L(2,2),M(2,2),N(2,2),J(2,2),P(2,2),Q(2,2),R(2,2)
14   DIM S(2,2),T(2,2),U(2,2),V(2,2),X(2,2)
20   FOR Y= 1 TO  6
30   READ A(Y),B(Y)
35   LET B(Y)=B(Y)*ATN( 1)/ 45
40   NEXT Y
50   LET C( 1, 1)=A( 1)*COS(B( 1))
60   LET C( 1, 2)=A( 1)*SIN(B( 1))
62   LET C( 2, 1)=-C( 1, 2)
65   LET C( 2, 2)=C( 1, 1)
70   LET D( 1, 1)=A( 2)*COS(B( 2))
75   LET D( 1, 2)=A( 2)*SIN(B( 2))
80   LET D( 2, 1)=-D( 1, 2)
85   LET D( 2, 2)=D( 1, 1)
90   LET E( 1, 1)=A( 3)*COS(B( 3))
95   LET E( 1, 2)=A( 3)*SIN(B( 3))
100  LET E( 2, 1)=-E( 1, 2)
105  LET E( 2, 2)=E( 1, 1)
110  LET F( 1, 1)=A( 4)*COS(B( 4))
115  LET F( 1, 2)=A( 4)*SIN(B( 4))
120  LET F( 2, 1)=-F( 1, 2)
125  LET F( 2, 2)=F( 1, 1)
130  LET G( 1, 1)=A( 5)*COS(B( 5))
135  LET G( 1, 2)=A( 5)*SIN(B( 5))
140  LET G( 2, 1)=-G( 1, 2)
145  LET G( 2, 2)=G( 1, 1)
150  LET H( 1, 1)=A( 6)*COS(B( 6))
155  LET H( 1, 2)=A( 6)*SIN(B( 6))
160  LET H( 2, 1)=-H( 1, 2)
165  LET H( 2, 2)=H( 1, 1)
200  MAT I=E-C
205  MAT J=F-D
210  MAT K=G-C
215  MAT L=F-D
220  MAT M=H-D
225  MAT N=E-C
230  MAT O=D*I
235  MAT P=C*J
240  MAT Q=K*L
245  MAT R=M*N
250  MAT S=O-P
255  MAT T=Q-R
260  MAT U=INV(T)
265  MAT V=S*U
270  MAT I=C*N
275  MAT J=D*K
280  MAT K=I-J
285  MAT X=K*U
290  LET Y1=SQR(V( 1, 1)↑ 2+V( 1, 2)↑ 2)
300  LET Y2=SQR(X( 1, 1)↑ 2+X( 1, 2)↑ 2)
310  IF V( 1, 1)< 0 THEN 340
320  LET Y3= 0
330  GOTO 350
340  LET Y3= 180
350  IF X( 2, 2)< 0 THEN 380
360  LET Y4= 0
370  GOTO 390
380  LET Y4= 180
390  LET Y5=Y3+(ATN(V( 1, 2)/V( 1, 1)))/ATN( 1)* 45
400  LET Y6=Y4+(ATN(X( 1, 2)/X( 1, 1)))/ATN( 1)* 45
410  PRINT "MODULUS AND ARGUMENT OF C1:",Y2,Y6
420  PRINT "MODULUS AND ARGUMENT OF C2:",Y1,Y5
499  DATA 170, 112, 53, 73, 235, 94, 53, 68, 185, 115, 77, 104
510  END
RUN
MODULUS AND ARGUMENT OF C1:     1.70127          236.17
MODULUS AND ARGUMENT OF C2:     .930379          121.844
READY
```

Fig.11.14. Computer programme in Basic for dynamic balancing

$$\begin{pmatrix} M_{C1} \\ M_{C2} \end{pmatrix} = \begin{bmatrix} \dfrac{V_{11} - V_{10}}{M_{T1}} & \dfrac{V_{12} - V_{10}}{M_{T2}} \\ \dfrac{V_{21} - V_{20}}{M_{T1}} & \dfrac{V_{22} - V_{20}}{M_{T2}} \end{bmatrix} \begin{pmatrix} -V_{10} \\ -V_{20} \end{pmatrix} \qquad (11.9)$$

When a phase meter and an accurate numerical calculation technique are used, the residual unbalance is often reduced to acceptable levels after the first run. Where difficulties are experienced, it may be necessary to verify the linearity and phase reproduceability between trial unbalance placed on the correction planes and vibration measurements in the measuring planes. In this case, some experiments with positioning of the sensors, or selection of correction planes, may enable a technique to be evolved to give more satisfactory results.

11.7. DIFFICULT BALANCING TASKS

11.7.1. Fine Balancing

To achieve unbalance quality grades as low as $G1$ and $G0,4$ for equipment such as record players and gyroscopes, special techniques are required. For example at $G0,4$ a rotor running at 6 000 r/min will require an eccentricity of the centre of mass of less than 0,63 μm. Considering that instrument ball bearings may themselves be manufactured to a radial run-out tolerance of 1 μm, whilst the typical tolerance on fine machining (boring, turning, grinding) is 25 μm, it is clear that the unbalance introduced at all stages of production and assembly must be controlled to achieve precision. This will necessitate balancing at the final stage.

Simple support rollers, or prismatic blocks which are used to support the rotor journals for general-purpose tasks on industrial balancing machines, are inadequate in these cases. For grades better than $G1$ the rotor should be mounted in its own support bearings on the balancing machine; for grade $G0,4$ the rotor should be driven as it would in service, so that the actual service environment in terms of electrical and aerodynamic effects may be reproduced. Examples are gyroscopes excited by a half-stator assembly, and turbochargers driven by compressed air.

11.7.2. Flexible Rotors

At high rotational speeds, the rotor can no longer be regarded as rigid. For rotational speeds greater than 50% of the first critical speed it may be said to be flexible (Fig.11.15). The axial distribution of unbalance along the rotor will tend to excite the various mode shapes of the rotor, depending on its speed

285

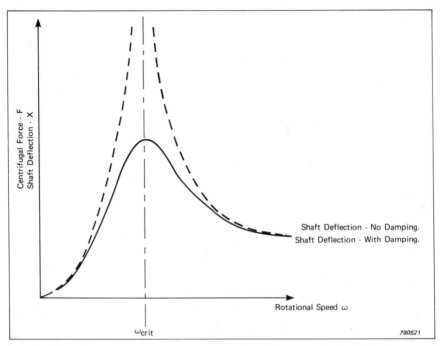

Fig.11.15. Relationship between centrifugal force, shaft deflection and shaft speed for one critical speed

of rotation and form of support. Theoretically, such a shaft possesses an infinite number of principal modes, each with its corresponding natural frequency. In the absence of damping and/or non-linear effects the deflections at these critical frequencies would become infinitely large, and destroy the machine. Balancing is now a process to "dynamically straighten" the rotor to re-align its principal inertia axis with the axis of rotation in order that the machine can be run up safely to its operating speed (Fig.11.16). One technique is to perform a sequence of balancing operatings in the vicinity of each of the critical speeds in turn, to reduce the internal bending moments for each mode to zero. The procedure is to start at the first critical frequency, and proceed to each of the others in turn until service speed is achieved. This is satisfactory where service speed is less than 50% of the subsequent critical speed. At each speed, correction mass sets are fitted on selected planes, such that unbalance is not introduced which would excite the lower, previously balanced, principal modes.

For example, to correct the first (V-) principal mode, a correction mass M will be located at the centre, with two masses each of $M/2$ at 180° positioned adjacent to the support bearings in order not to effect the rigid balance condition. Corresponding mass sets allow compensation of higher modes.

286

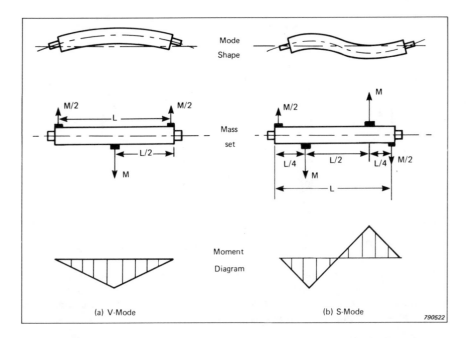

Fig.11.16. Dynamic straightening of first and second principal modes

This technique is called modal balancing. Where computing facilities are available the "influence coefficient" matrix may be used, but this will require relative displacement transducers to establish the deflections at intermediate points between support bearings. A typical example of this type of rotor is the automotive cardan shaft, balanced by welding sheet-metal compensating-weights. As the shaft does not run at uniform speed it is possible to achieve only a compromise solution to the balancing problem.

11.7.3. Crankshaft Balancing

Crankshafts are used to convert the reciprocating motion of a piston into rotary motion of a shaft. For design purposes the moving elements can be divided into purely rotary components (big-end pin, connecting rod big-end) and purely reciprocating components (piston assembly, connecting rod small-end). Therefore suitable counterbalance weights can be devised and incorporated in the crankshaft webs, which balance the rotary components plus a proportion (or factor) of the reciprocating components (Fig.11.17). In the production process, such crankshafts can be balanced on balancing machines: sophisticated automated handling and correction equipment is widely used in the car industry for this purpose. In certain configurations such as in V-4 and V-6 designs, the component of unbalance at twice the rotation frequency of the

287

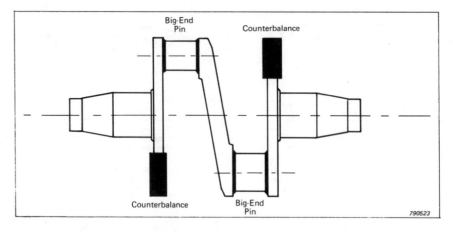

Fig.11.17. Twin-cylinder crankshaft with counterbalance weights

shaft, owing to the complex motion of the connecting rods, can be unacceptable. In these cases, balance can be achieved by provision of a contra-rotating balance shaft driven at twice engine speed. These shafts are fabricated with specially calculated counterbalance webs.

11.7.4. Multiple-Span Shafts

The majority of current techniques have evolved for use with single-span rotors, supported in bearings at each end. The problems of rotor assemblies supported in three or more bearings is the subject of current research (Fig.11.18).

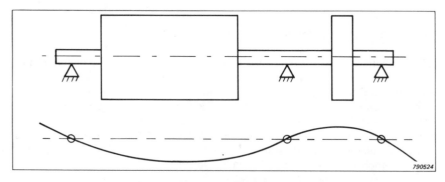

Fig.11.18. Mode shape for a three-bearing turbo-alternator assembly

For a rigid rotor, measured values will depend not only on rotor unbalance, but also on the accuracy of the alignment of the bearings and on the run-out at the journals. In contrast to unbalance forces, the latter effects are predominantly speed-independent, causing a constant centre-of-mass eccentricity. Rebuilding of the machine (e.g. for line-boring of the bearing housings and rotor balancing) would be necessary to correct such a fault. For flexible rotors, it is extremely difficult if not impossible to predict how the bearing systems will affect the mode shapes and vibration response at the critical speeds. It is common to consider the rotor spans in turn, as separate simply-supported systems. The shaft-stiffness is often such that intermediate bearing assemblies are assumed to decouple separate rotor spans. Alternatively, where linearity and phase fidelity is observed between unbalance added on any correction plane and the vibration measurements on every support bearing, then the influence coefficient method may be used. In general, one extra correction plane is required for every extra bearing measurement. Portable measuring equipment may be used for this work, with switches to allow connection of extra vibration sensors; but, as the number of bearings increases, the solution of the resulting matrix equations becomes increasingly complex and calls for substantial computing facilities.

11.8. SELECTED BIBLIOGRAPHY

ADKINS, F.E. and GRAY, A.: *"Dynamic Balancing at Heaton Works".* Parsons, Newcastle upon Tyne, 1960

BISHOP, R.E.D. and GLADWELL, G.M.L.: *"The Vibration and Balancing of an Unbalanced Flexible Rotor".* J. Mech. Eng. Sci., Vol. 1, No.1. June 1959

BRUNNENGRÄBER, H. and DRUST, P.: *"Messverfahren in der Auswuchttechnik".* Messen und Prüfen / Automatik May 1978

BISHOP, R.E.D., PARKINSON, A.G.: *"On the use of Balancing Machines for Flexible Rotors".* ASME Paper No. 71-Vibr.-73

BISHOP, R.E.D. and GLADWELL, G.M.L.: *"The Vibration and Balancing of an Unbalanced Flexible Rotor".* Journal Mechanical Engineering Science Vol.1, No.1. 1959

EL-HADI, I.: *"Zusammenstellung, Kritische Untersuchung und Weiterentwicklung der Verfahren zum Auswuchten betriebsmäßig aufgestellter Maschinen mit starren und mit elastischen Läufern".* Diss. Darmstadt 1962

FEDERN, K.:   *"Grundlagen einer systematischen Schwingungsent-störung wellenelastischer Rotoren"*. VDI Berichte, Band 24, 1957

FEDERN, K.:   *"Auswuchttechnik Band 1"*. Springer-Verlag 1977

GRGIČ, A.:   *"Zwei Verfahren zum Bestimmen der Eigenfrequen-zen des Systems Welle-Fundament"*. VDI-Z120 Nr.5, March 1968, pp. 213—219

GUINS, S.B. and BURMIST, J.:   *"Precision Balancing of Rotating Machine Parts"*. Machine Design. Vol.24, No.12, December 1952

HIMMLER, G.:   *"Technologien und Mittel zum Massenausgleich"*. Werkstatt und Betrieb 110 (1977) 11

JUDGE, A.W.:   *"The Testing of High Speed Internal Combustion En-gines with Special Reference to Automobile and Air-craft Types, Including Gas Turbines"*. Chapman & Hall, 4th ed., London, 1955

KELLENBERGER, W.: *"Should a Flexible Rotor be Balanced in N or (N + 2)* *"Planes "*. ASME Paper No. 71-Vibr.-55

KOLBE, W.:   *"Wuchten großer Induktoren"*. Elektrizitätswirtschaft, 57. Jahrg. Heft 1, Feb. 1958

LAWRIE, G.C.:   *"Precision Production Balancing"*. Tool Engineer, Vol. 3, No.4, April 1953

LUND, J.W. and TØNNESEN, J.: *"Experimental and Analytic Investigation of High Speed Rotor Balancing"*. Research Report No. FR8. Dept. of Mach. Design. Tech. Univ. of Denmark. December 1970

LUND, J.W. and TØNNESEN, J.: *"Analysis and Experiments on Multi-Plane Balancing of a Flexible Rotor"*. ASME Paper No. 71-Vibr.-74

MACDUFF, J.N.:   *"A Procedure for Field Balancing Rotating Machin-ery"*. Sound and Vibration. July 1967

MOORE, L.S. and DODD, E.G.:   *"Mass Balancing of Large Flexible Rotors"*. Proc. I. Mech.E. Vol.177 1963 pp.811-841

PETERMANN, J.E.:   *"Balancing Heavy Shafts and Rotors"*. Allis Chalmers Electrical Review. Vol. XXIII, No. 1 1958

290

RIEGER, N.F.:   "Rotor Bearing Dynamics — State of the Art". Mechanism and Machine Theory, Pergamon 1977. Vol.12 pp.261—270

SCHNEIDER, H.:   "VDI Taschenbücher T29 Auswuchttechnik". VDI Verlag Düsseldorf 1977

THEARLE, E.L.:   "Dynamic Balancing in the Field". Trans. ASME, 56 (10). 1935

TESSERZIK, J.M., BADGLEY, R.H. and ANDERSON, W.J.:   "Flexible Rotor Balancing by the Exact Point-Speed Influence Coefficient Method". ASME Paper No. 71-Vibr.-91

THEARLE, E.L.:   "Dynamic Balancing of Rotating Machinery in the Field". Applied Mechanics APM-56-19

TØNNESEN, J.:   "Further Experiments on Balancing of a High-Speed Flexible Rotor". ASME Paper No. 73-DET-99

WILCOX, J.B.:   "Dynamic Balancing of Rotating Machinery". Pitman, London 1967

12. FUNDAMENTALS OF SHOCK AND VIBRATION CONTROL

12.1. ISOLATION OF VIBRATION AND SHOCK

Undesired vibration and shock may originate from a wide variety of sources, such as unbalance and reciprocating motion in mechanical machinery, aerodynamic turbulence, rough sea movements, earthquakes, road and rail transportation, rough handling of equipment, etc.

Even though ideally all undesirable vibrations should be eliminated at the source it is obvious from the above "list" of sources that this may be possible only in very few cases. In other cases, however, it may be possible to *"isolate" the source* by means of shock and vibration isolators, or to reduce the shock and vibration effects by means of effectively designed vibration absorbers, or the use of damping treatments.

On the other hand, "natural" vibration sources like aerodynamic turbulence, rough sea movements and earthquakes cannot be "isolated" in the usual sense of the word. The only way to diminish undesirable vibration effects originating from these types of sources is to *"isolate" the equipment* to which the vibrations may cause serious damage.

Now, whether it is the source or the equipment that is going to be isolated, the physical principles involved are similar.

12.1.1. Vibration Isolation

Fig.12.1 shows the "universal" solution to isolation problems, i.e. the proper mounting of the source (machine), Fig.12.1 a), or the equipment, Fig.12.1 b), on springs and dampers. (If the springs consist of cork or rubber-like materials damping is automatically built-into the spring in the form of internal material damping).

Consider first the vibration *isolation of the source,* Fig.12.1 a).

The equation of motion for the mass, *m*, in the system, Fig.12.1 a), was for-

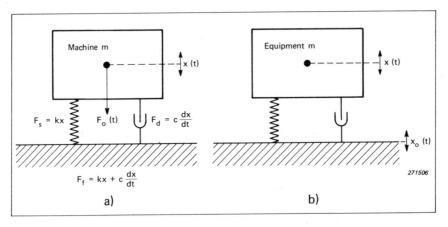

Fig.12.1. Illustration of the basic principles involved in vibration isolation, i.e. The mounting of the machine producing the vibration, or the equipment to be isolated from the vibration, m, on springs and dampers

mulated and solved in Chapter 3, section 3.1, for an arbitrary sinusoidal force, $F_0 e^{j2\pi ft}$:

$$x(f) = H(f)F_0 e^{j2\pi ft}$$

$$\text{where } H(f) = \frac{\dfrac{1}{4\pi^2 f_0^2 m}}{1 - \left(\dfrac{f}{f_0}\right)^2 + \dfrac{jf}{Qf_0}}$$

In the case of vibration isolation, one is not normally interested in $x(f)$ but in the force transmitted to the foundation. This force is the vector sum of the force transmitted through the spring element and that transmitted through the damper, i.e.:

$$F(f) = kx + c\frac{dx}{dt} = kx(f) + c\frac{d[x(f)]}{dt} = F_f e^{j(2\pi ft + \alpha)}$$

$$F_f e^{j(2\pi ft + \alpha)} = [kH(f) + j2\pi fcH(f)]F_0 e^{j2\pi ft}$$

whereby:

$$\frac{F_f}{F_0} e^{j\alpha} = T = \frac{\dfrac{1}{4\pi^2 f_0^2}\left(\dfrac{k}{m} + \dfrac{j2\pi fc}{m}\right)}{1 - \left(\dfrac{f}{f_0}\right)^2 + \dfrac{jf}{Qf_0}}$$

293

where T is the force *transmissibility*. Manipulation of this equation results in

$$|T| = \frac{\sqrt{1 + \frac{1}{Q^2}\left(\frac{f}{f_o}\right)^2}}{\sqrt{\left[1 - \left(\frac{f}{f_o}\right)^2\right]^2 + \frac{1}{Q^2}\left(\frac{f}{f_o}\right)^2}} \tag{12.1}$$

Here f_o is the natural undamped resonant frequency of the spring-mass system and $\frac{1}{Q}$ is a measure of the system damping:

$$\frac{1}{Q} = 2\xi = 2\frac{c}{c_c} = \frac{c}{\sqrt{km}} \tag{12.2}$$

ξ = damping ratio
c_c = critical damping coefficient ($c_c = 2\sqrt{km}$)

Fig.12.2 shows a graphical representation of the formula given for $|T|$ for various damping ratios.

The basic principle of vibration isolation now consists in selecting a spring mounting so that the natural frequency, f_o, of the spring-mass system is considerably lower than the lowest frequency component in the forcing spectrum produced by the machine.

With regard to the choice of *damping ratio* this should be selected with a view *both* to give a relatively low transmissibility amplification at the spring-mass resonant frequency, *and* to give satisfactory isolation (low transmissibility) at frequencies well above resonance.

There are, however, other factors which enter the picture in practice. Some of these are briefly discussed in the following.

A rigid machine which is mounted on four springs as shown in Fig.12.3 may exhibit more than one degree-of-freedom in its motion. Generally speaking it is a *six degree-of-freedom system*, in that it may have translatory motions in three directions, as well as rotary motions about three mutually perpendicular axes. (See also section 3.3). In selecting a proper isolation mounting the lowest frequency component in the forcing spectrum of the machinery must then be considerably higher than the highest resonant frequency of the (multi-degree-of-freedom) mounting system.

Another factor to be considered is the *lateral stability* of the mounting system. This, in many cases, sets a limit to how soft the mounting springs can be chosen. In practice a resonant frequency of the simple spring-mass system, Fig.12.1, of the order of 5 — 10 Hz is often used.

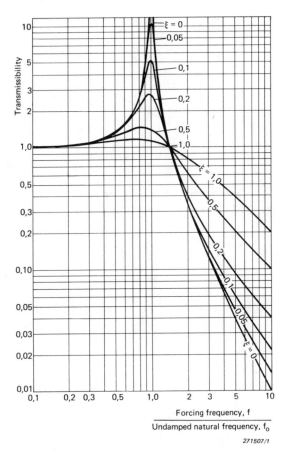

Fig.12.2. Curves showing the absolute transmissibility as a function of the frequency ratio f/f_o for various damping ratios

At high frequencies so-called *"wave"* effects may sometimes occur in the mounting springs. These are due to longitudinal standing waves (chapter 3, section 3.6) in the springs. They seem, however, not to pose too serious problems in practice when the springs are produced from materials with relatively high internal damping. A curve illustrating theoretically the concept of wave-effects is shown in Fig.12.4.

Another effect which may be of some concern in the design of practical vibration isolation mountings is *the effect of foundation reaction.* In the above discussion the foundation has been assumed to be infinitely rigid, i.e. the motion of the mass, *m*, in Fig.12.1 a), is completely taken up by the spring and the damper. This is not always the case, although in many practical situations it may represent a proper approximation.

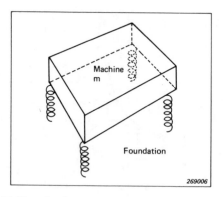

Fig.12.3. Sketch of a machine mounted on four springs

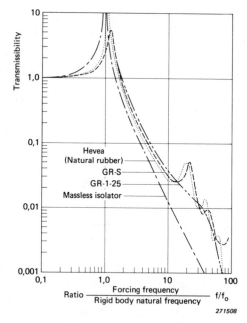

Fig.12.4. Curves showing wave-effects in isolators

A somewhat better approximation is to represent the foundation in the form of a mass which is able to move in the X-direction, Fig.12.5. By solving the differential equations of motion for this sytem one finds that the resonant frequency is now:

$$f'_o = f_o \sqrt{1 + \frac{m}{B}} \qquad (12.3)$$

296

where f_o is the "original" resonant frequency of the system with mass, m, and stiffness k ($B = \infty$). If the foundation is best represented by a plate, a theoretical treatment of the situation involves the theory of structures (chapter 3, section 3.6) and may become extremely complicated.

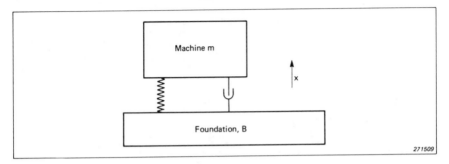

Fig.12.5. Illustration of the approximation of the machine foundation by a mass, B

A practical approach to vibration problems of the type sketched in Fig.12.1 a), is to frequency analyze the vibrations produced by the machine. From the measured (or estimated) spectrum the lowest frequency component to be "isolated" can be determined.

By then utilizing the curves, Fig.12.2, the resonant frequency of the mounted system, as well as the damping, necessary to provide sufficient isolation, can be estimated.

To find the stiffness required from the isolation mount (spring) when the desired resonant frequency has been determined the formula:

$$k \approx 39{,}2 \cdot P \cdot f_o^2 \quad \text{N/m} \qquad (12.4)$$

can be used. Here P is the weight of the machine to be isolated in kilograms and f_o is the resonant frequency of the machine and isolation mount system. Figs.12.6, 12.7 and 12.8 illustrate a practical case. In Fig.12.6 the frequency spectrum measured on a rotating electrical machine is shown, while Fig.12.7 shows the measuring arrangement used. From the spectrum, Fig.12.6 it is seen that the major vibrations (acceleration) are found in the frequency range from around 200 Hz to just above some 1000 Hz. Although there are some disturbing vibrations also at frequencies lower than 100 Hz, an effective vibration isolation is relatively easy to obtain in this case.

If the resonant frequency of the isolated system is chosen around 10 Hz the isolation of frequency components higher than 100 Hz will be nearly perfect, and this is taken as a basis for the isolation design. Since, in general it

297

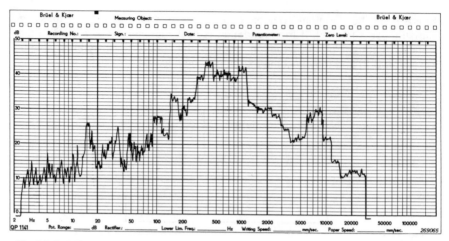

Fig.12.6. Vibration frequency spectrum produced by a rotating electrical machine

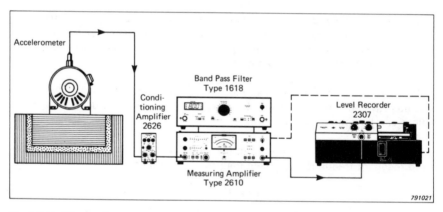

Fig.12.7. Measuring arrangement used to determine the frequency spectrum shown in Fig.12.6.

is necessary to use at least four vibration isolators in practice, Fig.12.3, each of the isolators carries only one quarter of the total weight of the machine. For the machine in question which has a total weight of 8 kg this means that each isolator will carry a weight of 2 kg. The required isolator stiffness then becomes (see Equation (12.4)):

$$k = 39,2 \cdot 2 \cdot 10^2 = 7840 \text{ N/m}$$

From the manufacturer's catalogue it was found, however, that he did not supply a vibration isolator with exactly this stiffness, and use therefore had to be made of isolators with a stiffness of 11800 N/m.

298

Actually, it should be mentioned here that most vibration isolator manufacturers do not publish their data in terms of stiffness but rather in terms of the static deflection corresponding to a certain (maximum) static load. If it is assumed that the isolator in question behaves linearly the stiffness can, on the other hand, be readily estimated from the manufacturer's data by means of the simple relationship.

$$k = \frac{P\,(max)}{d\,(max)}$$

Where P is the weight of the machine per isolator and d is the static deflection produced by this load. In the above example the maximum weight per isolator was given by the manufacturer to be 3,6 kgf, and the corresponding deflection 3 mm thus

$$k = \frac{3,6\,\text{kgf}}{3\,\text{mm}} = \frac{3,6 \cdot 9,81}{0,003}\ \text{N/m} = 11800\ \text{N/m}$$

It is now necessary to check how this influences the resonant frequency of the isolation system. Rearranging Eqn. (12.4) gives:

$$f_o = \sqrt{\frac{k}{39,2\,P}} = \sqrt{\frac{11800}{39,2 \cdot 2}} = 12,3\ \text{Hz}$$

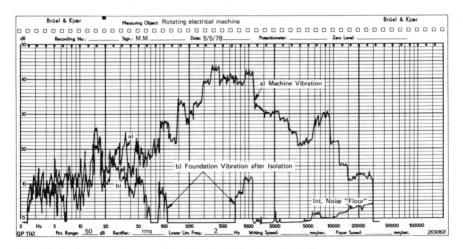

Fig.12.8. Curves showing the effect of vibration isolation
a) Vibration frequency spectrum produced by the machine
b) Vibration frequency spectrum measured on the foundation after isolation of the machine

Considering that the major frequency components to be isolated are considerably higher than 12,3 Hz this change in resonant frequency is quite acceptable. The resulting isolation can be seen from the curves, Fig.12.8. Here the curve a) corresponds to that shown in Fig.12.6, while the curve b) was measured on the foundation after isolation of the machine.

Note that it has been assumed here that acceleration was the important vibration parameter to isolate. In many cases it would be considered that velocity is more relevant, and that would change the picture somewhat. The dominant frequency component would then be at 15 Hz which would require a considerably lower mounting resonance frequency to isolate it, but the same principles can be used.

Before leaving the subject of vibration isolation of mechanical (or electrical) machinery a few further considerations should be briefly touched upon.

Firstly, it is important that the vibration isolators are placed correctly with respect to the motion of the center of gravity of the machine, see Figs.12.11 and 12.9.

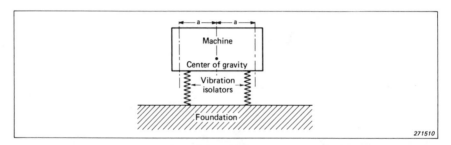

Fig.12.9. Illustration of proper mounting of the machine. The vibration isolators should be placed symmetrically with respect to the center of gravity of the motion

Secondly, the center of gravity of the machine should be located as low as possible. If serious "rocking" effects (section 3.3), or other instabilities, become a problem in the mounting, the effective center of gravity may be lowered by first mounting the machine on a heavy mass and then isolating the mass + machine, Figs.12.10 and 12.11. Fig.12.11 actually also illustrates the principle of the "floating" floor.

Thirdly, it is possible by means of a compound vibration isolation system, Fig.12.12, to obtain a force transmissibility characteristic which gives greater attenuation for frequency components above the (compound) system reson-

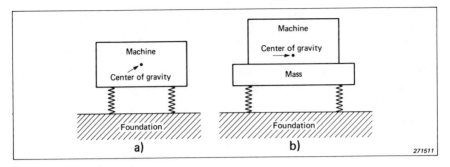

Fig.12.10. Sketch showing the center of gravity of a machine can be "artificially" lowered by adding mass (weight) directly onto the machine
a) Machine
b) Machine with properly added mass (weight)

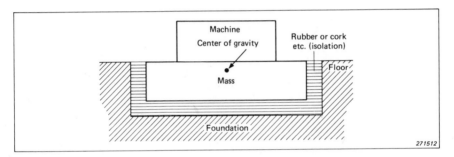

Fig.12.11. Sketch showing how the addition of mass is utilized in the so-called "floating" floor

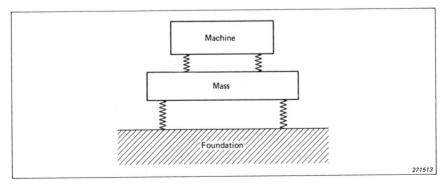

Fig.12.12. Illustration of a compound system

ances than does the "simple" system discussed above, see Fig.12.13. The design of such compound systems is, on the other hand, more complicated and critical than the design of a "simple" vibration isolator.

For readers who are familiar with electrical filter theory and electro-mechanical analogies the design problems involved may, however, not seem too formidable.

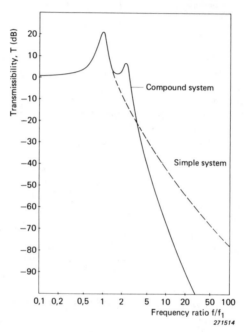

Fig.12.13. Transmissibility curves illustrating the difference in transmissibility between the simple and the compound system

Returning now to the second "case" of vibration isolation, i.e. the case where *equipment* is to be isolated from a vibrating foundation, Fig.12.1 b), the equation of motion for the mass, *m*, is:

$$m \frac{d^2x}{dt^2} + c \frac{d\,(x-x_o)}{dt} + k\,(x-x_o) = 0 \qquad (12.5)$$

Again solving the equation for an arbitrary sinusoidal foundation vibration $x_o = X_o e^{j2\pi ft}$ results in:

$$x = \frac{1 - \left(\frac{f}{f_o}\right)^2 + \frac{jf}{Qf_o}}{\frac{1}{4\pi^2 f_o^2}\left(\frac{k}{m} + j\frac{2\pi fc}{m}\right)} X_o$$

$$\left|\frac{x}{x_o}\right| = \frac{\sqrt{1 + \frac{1}{Q^2}\left(\frac{f}{f_o}\right)^2}}{\sqrt{\left[1 - \left(\frac{f}{f_o}\right)^2\right]^2 + \frac{1}{Q^2}\left(\frac{f}{f_o}\right)^2}} = |T| \qquad (12.6)$$

Thus the *displacement transmissibility* is now given by exactly the same relationship, $|T|$, as was the force transmissibility in the case where the vibration source was to be isolated from the foundation. Simple manipulations with the above formula show that the same relationship is also obtained for the velocity and acceleration transmissibility of the system of Fig.12.1 b).

The transmissibility formula (and the curves shown in Fig.12.2) are therefore generally valid in vibration isolation problems. This again means that the same procedures as outlined in the foregoing are involved in designing a vibration isolation system whether it is the source or equipment that has to be isolated.

There is, however, one significant difference which should be borne in mind. In determining the vibration frequency spectrum of the source, Fig.12.1 a) and Fig.12.6, the effects of internal resonances in the machine are automatically taken into account. As the foundation on which the machine (and isolator) is placed is assumed to exhibit no disturbing resonance the isolation problem consists here simply in selecting an isolator/machine configuration with a resonant frequency, f_o, which is low enough to ensure sufficient isolation of the forcing frequency components.

When the vibrations originate in the foundation and are transmitted to equipment Fig.12.1 b), it is not *only* important to know the forcing vibration frequency spectrum, but also the internal resonances in the equipment. These may be excited and could cause serious damage, even if the exciting frequency components are heavily attenuated by the vibration isolation system. This is due to resonance amplification effects within the equipment itself. It is therefore necessary when an effective vibration isolation system is to be designed *also to take such internal equipment resonances into account.*

If these resonances cannot be predicted theoretically the equipment may be subjected to a vibration test (see Chapter 10) prior to the design of a proper vibration isolation system. By means of suitable vibration testing, dangerous resonances and their effects can be detected experimentally, and corresponding isolation criteria established.

12.1.2. Shock Isolation

Even though the principles involved in shock isolation are very similar to those involved in vibration isolation some differences exist due to the transient nature of a shock. *The reduction in shock severity, which may be obtained by the use of isolators, results from the storage of the shock energy within the isolators and its subsequent release in a "smoother" form i.e. over a much longer period of time.* However, the energy storage can only take place by deflection of the isolators.

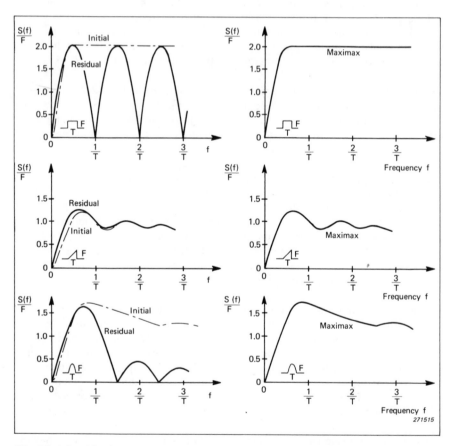

Fig.12.14.   Maximax (overall) undamped shock response spectra for rectangular, final peak sawtooth, and half-sine shock pulses

As a shock pulse may contain frequency components ranging from 0 to ∞ it is, generally speaking, not possible to avoid excitation of the isolator/mass resonance. On the other hand, *if the duration of the shock pulse is short in comparison with one half period of the isolation system resonant frequency* (f_o), *the response of the system may not have serious consequences*. This may be best illustrated by means of Fig.3.13, section 3.5, and the shock response spectrum type of description, also outlined in section 3.5.

In this case the shock response spectrum of greatest interest is the so-called *maximax*, or *overall*, spectrum (section 3.5). Fig.12.14 shows the maximax shock spectra for the three types of shock pulses discussed in section 3.5. From the figure it can be seen that as long as the resonant frequency, f_o, of the isolation system is considerably lower than $\frac{1}{2T}$ where T is the duration of the shock pulse, the shapes of the maximax spectra are quite similar. This is in conformity with the statement made in Chapter 2, section 2.3, that "when the duration of the shock pulse is short compared with the natural period of the mechanical system on which it acts, the *severity of the shock is determined by the area of the shock pulse alone*". In Fig.12.15 the statement may be illustrated even clearer in that here the three maximax shock spectra shown in Fig.12.14 are redrawn to scales where the ordinate is no longer $S(f)/F$ but

$$S(f) \Big/ \frac{1}{T} \int_0^T F(t)\, dt.$$

$\int_o^T F(t)\, dt$ is the area of the shock pulse and $\frac{1}{T}\int_o^T F(t)\, dt$ is the "effective pulse height", see Fig.12.16. Fig.12.15 may actually be used as basis for the design and evaluation of an undamped shock isolation system, as described below. Consider first the system shown in Fig.12.17 a), which is actually the same system as shown in Fig.12.1 a), but without damping. Let the time dependency of the force $F(t)$, in this case be as indicated in Fig.12.18 a).

The maximum force acting on the foundation F_r, can now be found from Fig.12.18 b) and Fig.12.15, provided that the resonant frequency, f_o, of the system Fig.12.17 is known. Assuming that this is $f_o = 1/10\ T$ the maximum force acting on the foundation is found from Fig.12.15 to be approximately 0,6 times the "effective" force, Fig.12.18 b), i.e.:

Maximum force "response" $= 0,6\ F_o = F_r$

The maximum displacement of the mass, m, is equal to the force divided by the stiffness, k, of the isolator:

$$x_r = \frac{F_r}{k} = \frac{0,6\ F_o}{k}$$

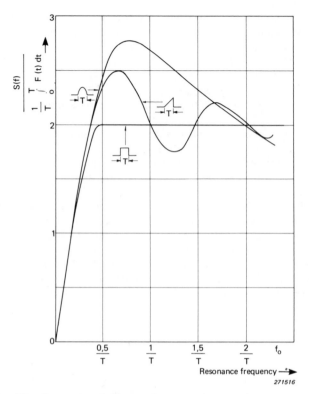

Fig.12.15. The first part of the maximax to different scales. The spectra are here normalized to pulses of the same "effective" height

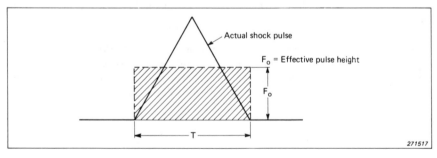

Fig.12.16. Illustration of the concept of "effective" pulse height

As the motion of the mass will consist of an oscillation with a frequency equal to the natural frequency (resonant frequency) of the isolation system,

306

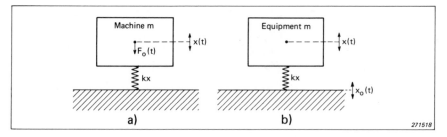

Fig.12.17. Sketch of basic spring-mass systems (without damping

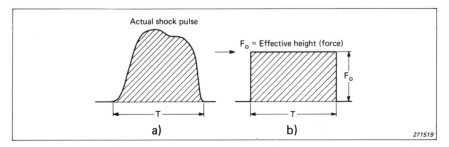

Fig.12.18. Shock force pulse acting upon the system shown in Fig.12.17
a) Actual shock pulse
b) "Effective" shock pulse

the maximum velocity and acceleration of the mass, m, can then be found directly from the relationships:

$$v_r = \left| \frac{dx}{dt} \right|_{max} = 2\pi f_0 \, x_r = 2\pi f_0 \frac{F_r}{k} = 1,2\pi f_0 \frac{F_0}{k}$$

and

$$a_r = \left| \frac{d^2x}{dt^2} \right|_{max} = (2\pi f_0)^2 x_r = 4\pi^2 f_0^2 \frac{F_r}{k} = 2,4\pi^2 f_0^2 \frac{F_0}{k}$$

When the forcing function, $F(t)$, is unknown, or difficult to measure, it is often convenient to measure istead the acceleration, a, of the mass, by means of an accelerometer. Calculations may then be performed "backwards" to determine the "effective" force, F_0, as well as other quantities of interest.

If viscous damping is included in the isolation system, and it normally is, the above calculations must be modified.

Starting again with the maximax shock spectrum for a damped system, such a "spectrum" is shown in Fig.12.19 for half sine shock pulses. In this case, F_r, is found from Fig.12.19, utilizing the curve which corresponds to

307

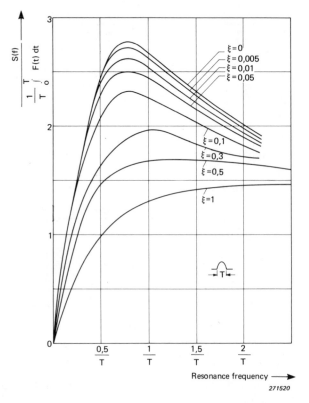

Fig.12.19. Damped shock response spectrum for half sine shock pulses

the damping included in the system. The relationship between F_r and x_r is however, in this case no longer quite so simple, because F_r is the vector sum of the forces transmitted through both the spring element and the damper (Fig.12.1 a)).

Also, because of the damping, f_0 is no longer simply equal to $\frac{1}{2\pi}\sqrt{\frac{k}{m}}$ but rather*):

$$f_0 = \frac{1}{2\pi} \sqrt{\frac{k}{m}} \sqrt{1-\xi^2}$$

where

$$\xi = \frac{c}{c_c} = \frac{c}{2\sqrt{km}} = \frac{1}{2Q}$$

---

*) In effect this difference in resonant frequency between damped and undamped resonances also applies to *vibration* isolation systems. However, the damping included in these systems in practice is often so small ($\xi \ll 1$) that the resonance shift is normally neglected.

Taking these factors into account the maximum displacement, x_r, of the mass, m, becomes:

$$x_r = \frac{F_r}{k\sqrt{1+(2\xi)^2}} \qquad (12.7)$$

Utilizing the relationships between x_r, v_r and a_r one has:

$$v_r = \sqrt{\frac{k}{m}}\, \frac{\sqrt{1-\xi^2}}{\sqrt{1+(2\xi)^2}}\, \frac{F_r}{k} \qquad (12.8)$$

and
$$a_r = \frac{1-\xi^2}{\sqrt{1+(2\xi)^2}}\, \frac{F_r}{m} \qquad (12.9)$$

When the shock pulse duration is no longer short compared with one half period of the isolation system motion, utilization of the shock spectrum technique becomes somewhat more complicated.

It seems, however, that utilization of the "spectrum" shown in Fig.12.19 and the method of estimation described above for damped systems may result in reasonably good approximations to actual practical problems.

In conjunction with the practical application of shock isolators certain facts should be noted:

Firstly, as mentioned above, reduction in shock force transmissibility can only take place by allowing the isolator to deflect, i.e. by motion which allows the shock energy to be dissipated over a much longer period of time than that occupied by the shock itself. Thus certain space clearances must be allowed for the isolated equipment.

Secondly, if the resonant frequency of the isolation system is chosen incorrectly the isolator may "amplify" the destructive effects of the shock rather than provide the desired isolation. This requires that the resonant frequency of the isolation system is away from all resonances within the machine or equipment to be isolated.

Thirdly, if the isolator turns out to have unexpected non-linear characteristics (and many practical isolator materials *do* perform non-linearly) a great number of "extra" response effects may take place at harmonic or sub-harmonic frequencies.

In some cases isolators are, on purpose, designed to be non-linear. If, for instance, space limitations do not allow for the required (linear) motion of equipment one may be temped to employ non-linear isolators of the "hardening" spring type (see also Chapter 3, section 3.2). This kind of isolator will, when deflecting into the non-linear region, firstly change the resonant frequency of the isolation system (f_o increases with increasing isolator deflection), and secondly produce a number of harmonic force components which may excite internal resonances in the isolated equipment. Also the *peak* acceleration of the equipment may be considerably increased by the use of "hardening" spring type isolators.

On the other hand, *if the isolation system contains a fair amount of damping*, the deteriorating effects mentioned above are drastically reduced. Thus, *a heavily damped, "hardening" spring type isolation system may in some cases provide the appropriate solution to a difficult isolation problem.*

BASIC TYPES OF ISOLATORS

Material	Frequency Range	Optimum Frequencies	Damping	Limitations	Remarks
Metal Springs: Helical Compression Springs	All (theoretically)	Low frequencies (with high static deflections)	Very low 0.1% of critical	Readily transmit high frequencies	Widely used and easy to produce with required characteristics
Helical Tension Springs	All (theoretically)	Low frequencies	Very low	–	Little used
Leaf Springs	Low	Low	Fairly good (due to friction)	–	Limited to specific applications
Belleville Washers	–	–	High with parallel stacking	Subject to fatigue: more complicated assembly	Compact. Stiffness depends on method of stacking. Controlled non-linear stiffness
Rubber: (i) In Shear (ii) In Compression (iii) Shear-Compression	depends on composition and hardness	High	Increases with rubber hardness	limited load-carrying capacity	(i) Small energy storage (ii) No change in volume (iii) Has secondary snubbing action
Cork	Depends on density	High	Low (6% of critical)	Practical limit to minimum natural frequency attainable	Highly compressible without lateral expansion
Felt	Depends on density & thickness. Extends into audio-frequency range	High (usually above 40 Hz)	High	Practical limit to minimum natural frequency dependent on load & thickness	1/2" to 1" thickness normally used
Sponge Rubber	–	Low	Fair	Low stiffness with high compressibility	Used in the form of moulded pads or cut slabs
Steel Mesh	–	Low	Fair to high	Limited load-carrying capacity	Used in form of pads; also as inserts
Pneumatic (Cushions, Air Bellows)	Frequency controlled by air volume	–	Low		Relatively undeveloped
Rubber Composites	Depends on design & rubber hardness	High	Depends on design	–	Moulded rubber mounting pads with metallic casings and/or inserts
Spring and Rubber Composites	Wide range depends on design	Depends on design	Low		Basically metal springs encased in rubber. May incorporate damping
Rubberised Fabric	–	10–12 Hz typical	6–8% typical	–	Properties intermediate between rubber and steel springs
Cork-Rubber	–	High	Low	–	Alternative to rubber or cork
Studded or Ribbed Rubber Mats	–	Moderately low	depends on rubber hardness	–	Properties similar to solid rubber but with increased static deflections
Steel-Bound Cork	Depends on density	High	Up to 6% of critical	–	Cork composition with bonded metal faces. Particularly applicable for isolation of concrete mounting blocks

Table 12.1

310

Another type of nonlinear shock isolator is that with "softening" spring characteristics. These are found less frequently in practice, but their main advantage is that they very effectively reduce the transmitted force via large deflections. In cases where equipment is to be protected against *one* severe shock only, use may profitably be made of "softening" or collapsing spring isolators. The landing system of the american Lunar Excursion Module (1969) is a good example of the use of this type of isolator.

It should also be mentioned that, in analogy with vibration isolation systems, shock isolation may also be provided in the form of compound systems (Fig.12.12). This seems, however, to be less frequently utilized in practice than is the case for compound vibration isolation systems.

Finally, to give the reader an idea of some important characteristics and features of commonly used isolators the table 12.1 above has been reproduced from R.H. Warring (ed.): "Handbook of Noise and Vibration Control" (1970 edn.).

12.2. DYNAMIC VIBRATION CONTROL AND VIBRATION DAMPING

In the previous section the basic aspects involved in the *isolation* of vibrations and shocks were outlined. There are, however, practical cases where vibration isolation is not suitable, or difficult to arrange, and other methods of vibration reduction must be sought. One way of reducing the vibration may then be to utilize the principle of the *dynamic vibration absorber*. This principle can, in general, only be used effectively when the "original" vibrations contain one major frequency component only (or they consist of a very narrow band of frequencies such as a lightly damped, randomly excited single resonance).

If vibration reduction is to be achieved in cases of randomly excited multi-degree-of-freedom systems (plates and beams) the application of dynamic vibration absorbers is normally complicated and use is then preferably made of some sort of general *damping treatment*.

12.2.1. The Dynamic Vibration Absorber

The basic physical principle of the dynamic vibration absorber is that of attaching to a vibrating structure a resonance system which counteracts the original vibrations. *Ideally such a system would completely eliminate the vibration of the structure, by its own vibrations.*

Fig.12.20 illustrates these ideas. The mass, M, is here assumed to be the mass of a (rigid) machine structure producing the vibrating force, $P_0 \sin(2\pi ft)$.

311

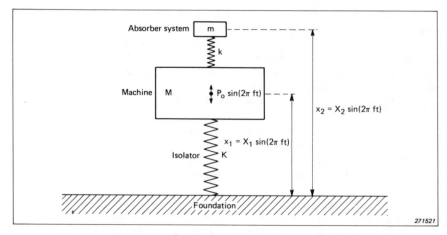

Fig.12.20. Illustration of the principle of the dynamic vibration absorber

The machine is mounted on a vibration isolator with a stiffness, K. Attached to the machine is a resonance (dynamic absorber) system consisting of the mass, m, and the spring element, k. It is now a simple matter to write down the equations of motion for the complete system:

$$M \frac{d^2x_1}{dt^2} + Kx_1 - k(x_2 - x_1) = P_o \sin(2\pi ft)$$

$$m \frac{d^2x_2}{dt^2} + k(x_2 - x_1) = 0$$

(12.10)

Assuming that the stationary solutions to these equations can be written (where X_1 and X_2 can be either positive or negative)

$$x_1 = X_1 \sin(2\pi ft)$$

and

$$x_2 = X_2 \sin(2\pi ft)$$

then

$$\left(1 + \frac{k}{K} - M \frac{(2\pi f)^2}{K}\right) X_1 - \frac{k}{K} X_2 = \frac{P_o}{K}$$

and

$$X_1 = \left[1 - \left(\frac{f}{f_a}\right)^2\right] X_2$$

(12.11)

where $f_a = \frac{1}{2\pi}\sqrt{\frac{k}{m}}$ = resonant frequency of the attached (absorber) system

By setting

$$1 - \left(\frac{f}{f_a}\right)^2 = 0 \text{ i.e. } f_a = f$$

312

the motion, X_1, of the machine will be zero, i.e. *the machine will not vibrate at all*. The maximum amplitude of the mass, m, is in this case:

$$- \frac{k}{K} X_2 = \frac{P_0}{K} \ i.e. \ X_2 = - \frac{P_0}{k}$$

This again means that by tuning the absorber system resonant frequency to equal the "disturbing" frequency, the vibration of the machine can be eliminated.

Actually, in practical cases the "disturbing" frequency region often covers the resonant frequency of the machine-isolator system, and both the absorber and the isolation system contain some mechanical damping. The equations of motion for the complete system then become considerably more complex, and so do their solutions.

Figs.12.21, 12.22 and 12.23 illustrate the effects upon the vibration transmissibility of a machine/isolator system when the machine is supplied with a dynamic vibration absorber.

From Fig.12.21 it is seen that when the complete system contains no damping at all and the absorber system is tuned to the resonant frequency of the machine/isolator system the transmissibility at this frequency is zero, in conformity with the above statements and mathematical derivations. However, on both "sides" of the resonant frequency two, theoretically infinitely

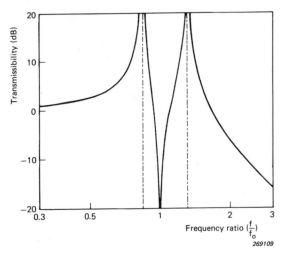

269109

Fig.12.21. Theoretical transmissibility curves for a vibration isolated system supplied with an undamped dynamic vibration absorber, see also Fig.12.20

313

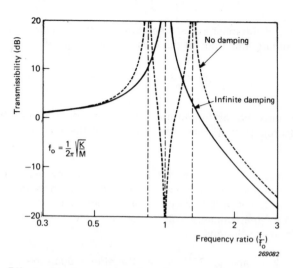

Fig.12.22. *Effect of extreme absorber damping upon the transmissibility ratio of an undamped machine/isolator system*

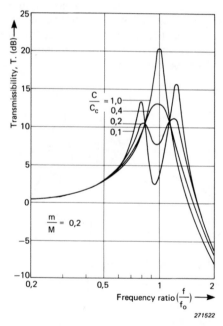

Fig.12.23. *Transmissibility of a machine/isolator system when the machine is supplied with a damped vibration absorber. The degree of damping is indicated on the curves. (Snowdon)*

high, transmissibility "peaks" are found. The shape of the curve is caused by the dynamic coupling between the machine/isolator system and the absorber system. Coupling effects of this sort are quite common in many branches of physics.

If the absorber damping is infinite, the absorber mass is virtually clamped to the machine and the absorber system does not function at all, Fig.12.22. In practice, when a damped vibration absorber is applied to a machine/isolator system the transmissibility curve must lie between the two extremes sketched in Fig.12.22. This is illustrated in Fig.12.23 for various values of absorber damping ratio.

Theory has shown that when damping is added to the absorber the "optimum" performance conditions*) are, in general, no longer obtained by tuning the resonant frequency of the absorber system to equal the resonant frequency of the machine/isolator system. Actually the most favourable tuning depends upon the ratio between the absorber mass and the mass of the machine i.e. m/M. It has been found that when the damping is of the viscous type then the ratio between the absorber resonant frequency, f_a, and the machine/isolator resonant frequency f_o, should be:

$$\frac{f_a}{f_o} = \sqrt{\frac{M}{m+M}} = \sqrt{\frac{1}{1+\dfrac{m}{M}}} \qquad (12.12)$$

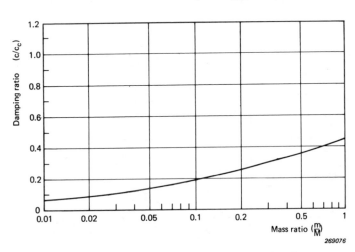

Fig.12.24. Curve showing "optimum" viscous damping factor as a function of the mass ratio $\frac{m}{M}$ (Snowdon)

*) "Optimum" conditions are assumed to be those which ensure a maximally "flat" peak-notch region of the transmissibility curve, Fig.12.23, to be obtained.

From this equation it is noted that when m/M is small the difference between the two resonant frequencies is negligible, while for an increasing

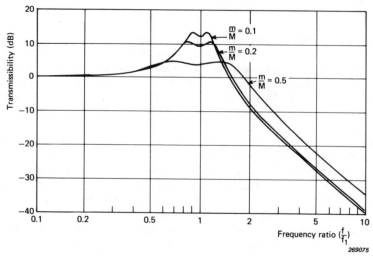

Fig.12.25. Theoretical transmissibility curves for a system of the type shown in Fig.12.20 supplied with a viscously damped dynamic vibration absorber. Optimum absorber tuning and damping for mass ratios of $\frac{m}{M} = 0,1$, $\frac{m}{M} = 0,2$, $\frac{m}{M} = 0,5$. (Snowdon)

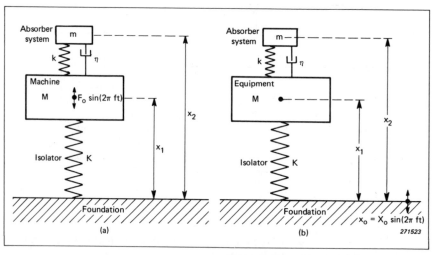

Fig.12.26. Dynamic vibration absorber applied to:
a) Machine (source)
b) Equipment

mass-ratio the "de-tuning" of the absorber may become very significant. Also the "optimum" viscous damping factor depends upon the mass-ratio, see Fig.12.24. Finally, Fig.12.25 shows some theoretical transmissibility curves calculated for various mass-ratios and "optimum" damping. Note the decrease in resonant amplification with increasing mass-ratios.

As pointed out in section 12.1 the theoretical treatment of the vibration transmissibility from a vibrating source (machine) to its foundation, and that

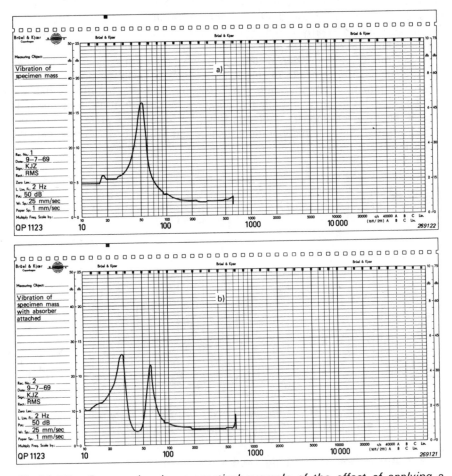

Fig.12.27. Curves showing a practical example of the effect of applying a dynamic vibration absorber to a simple vibrating system
a) Transmissibility curve for the system before the dynamic vibration absorber was applied
b) Transmissibility curve for the system with absorber

317

of the vibration transmissibility from a vibrating foundation to a mounted equipment is more or less identical. This, of course, also applies with respect to the use of dynamic vibration absorbers see, Fig.12.26.

To illustrate this statement consider a rigid equipment (mass: M) elastically mounted on an electro-dynamic vibration machine (see also section 10.1). The transmissibility curve for this system was measured and automatically recorded on a Brüel & Kjær Level Recorder, Fig.12.27 a). By attaching a damped dynamic absorber system (mass: $m = 0,5\,M$) to the mass M the transmissibility curve was changed into the one shown in Fig.12.27 b). The effect of the absorber is clearly noted. For the sake of completion the vibration of the absorber mass, m, was also measured and recorded, Fig.12.28. Before finishing this brief discussion of the dynamic vibration absorber it should be mentioned that the principle of the absorber may be used not only to reduce resonance effects in vibration and shock isolation systems, but also to reduce the vibration of beams and plates vibrating in one of their fundamental modes. Thereby the acoustic radiation from, for instance, a plate, may be reduced, making the dynamic vibration absorber an efficient tool in the "battle" against acoustic noise.

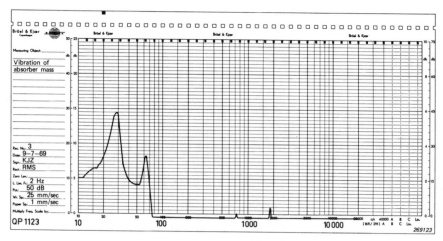

Fig.12.28. *Vibration of the absorber mass, m, in the system used to obtain the transmissibility curve shown in Fig.12.27 b)*

12.2.2. Application of Damping Treatments

As pointed out in section 3.6, structural elements like beams and plates exhibit a, theoretically infinite, number of resonances (normal modes). If these elements are subjected to vibrations of variable frequency (motor with variable speed), or to wide band random vibrations, a number of resonances

318

might be excited and the application of separate dynamic vibration absorbers becomes impractical. Because most engineering materials like steel, aluminium, copper etc. contain little inherent damping, resonant vibrations must be reduced by some "external" means. In the case of plates, use is sometimes made of some sort of "stiffening" arrangements. These arrangements do, however, not *damp* the resonances, they merely shift them towards higher frequencies. If the resonances can be shifted to frequencies which will not be excited during normal operation of the equipment this solution to the problem of reducing plate vibrations may be acceptable.*)

On the other hand, in complicated machinery, the shifting of resonant frequencies in one element *may* cause serious vibration troubles to occur in some other element. The most general solution to the problem will therefore be, in some way or other, to apply some sort of external damping to the elements considered.

External damping can be applied in several ways: (1) By means of interface damping (friction), (2) by spraying a layer of material with high internal losses over the surface of the vibrating element or (3) by designing the critical elements as "sandwich" structures.

Interface damping is obtained by letting two surfaces "slide" on each other under pressure, see Fig.12.29 a). If there is no lubricating material between the surfaces the damping effect is produced by dry friction (Coulomb damping). The force versus displacement relationship for this type of damping is shown in Fig.12.29 b), and the total dissipated vibrational energy (damping energy) is given by the area enclosed by the curve B — C — D — E — B. Even if dry friction can be a very effective means of damping excessive vibrations it has the disadvantage that it may lead to fretting corrosion of the two surfaces. To avoid the fretting corrosion use is sometimes made of an adhesive separator. The arrangement then, however, turns into what is commonly termed a sandwich structure, a type of damping arrangement which is further discussed later in this section.

One of the "simplest" methods of applying damping to a structural element vibrating in bending is to spray a layer of viscoelastic material with high internal losses over the surface of the element. This kind of damping technique has been widely used in the automotive industry for many years. The most well-known materials, solely made for the purpose, are the so-called mastic deadeners made from an asphalt base.

---

*) Actually because internal material damping often increases with frequency a certain "damping" effect may also be achieved by shifting the resonant frequencies.

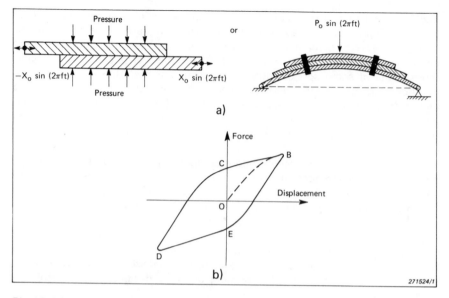

Fig.12.29. Example of interface damping
  a) Sketch showing a physical system producing dry friction type of interface damping
  b) Force versus displacement relationship for this type of damping

Other types of "deadening" materials are at present commercially available. Common to all of them are that they are made from high polymer materials possessing optimum damping properties over certain frequency and temperature regions. These regions may, however, for some mastic materials, be fairly wide.

To obtain optimum damping of the combination structural element + damping material, not only must the internal loss factor of the damping material be high, but so also must its modulus of elasticity (Young's modulus).

An approximate formula governing the damping properties of a treated panel in practice is given by the expression:

$$\eta \simeq 14 \left(\frac{\eta_2\, E_2}{E_1}\right) \left(\frac{d_2}{d_1}\right)^2 \qquad (12.13)$$

where (see also Fig.12.30):

$$\eta = \frac{1}{Q} = 2\,\xi = 2\frac{c}{c_c}$$

= Loss factor of the combination structure element (panel) + damping material

η_2 = Loss factor of the damping material

E_1 = Modulus of elasticity (Young's modulus) of the structural element

E_2 = Modulus of elasticity of the damping material

d_1 = Thickness of the structural element (panel)

d_2 = Thickness of the layer of damping material

One fact, which is immediately obvious from the above formula, is that the relative thickness of the layer of damping material, (d_2/d_1), plays a very important role in the resultant damping. In practice the ratio is normally chosen to be of the order of three to one. Also, it can be seen that it is generally advantageous to apply *one* (thick) layer of damping material rather than dividing the layer in two by using doublesided coating.

A third method of applying damping to structural elements is the use of sandwich structures, Fig.12.31. Several types of such constructions exist: The original structure may be supplied with a constrained viscoelastic layer, i.e. the damping material is covered with a thin metal sheet, Fig.12.31 a); a thin visco-elastic layer is placed between two equally thick plates (adhesive separator), Fig.12.31 b); or finally use may be made of a thick visco-elastic layer between the two plates, Fig.12.31 c).

A considerable number of theoretical and experimental investigations have been carried out to allow the prediction and comparison of damping properties of sandwich structures. The general results of these investigations indicate that, contrary to the above discussed application of mastic deadeners, the thickness of the visco-elastic layer is not a factor of *prime* importance. It seems, however, that the overall geometry of the construction (symmetrical, unsymmetrical) is important, the symmetrical construction showing the most favourable overall damping properties. On the other hand, when the thickness of the visco-elastic layer is increased, the temperature and frequency ranges within which optimum damping can be obtained also increases.

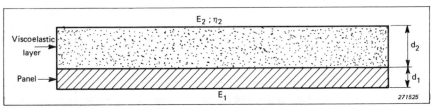

Fig.12.30. Sketch illustrating the use of a single visco-elastic layer to obtain the required vibration damping effect

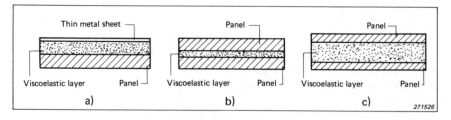

271526

Fig.12.31. Examples of sandwich structures
a) Use of a constrained visco-elastic layer
b) Sandwich structure with a thin visco-elastic layer
c) Sandwich structure with a thick visco-elastic layer

To illustrate the general difference in damping obtained between a system using single-layer mastic deadening and a sandwich construction, some measured results (Cremer and Heckl) are reproduced in Fig.12.32.

The measurement of material damping properties is normally carried out by one of two basic measurement methods:

1. The frequency response method, and

2. The decay-rate (reverberation) method.

The practical application of the frequency response method normally consits of cutting a bar-shaped sample from the material to be tested, clamping

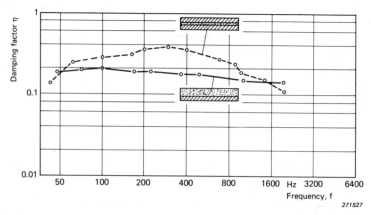

271527

Fig.12.32. Results of loss factor measurements on a sandwich structure with a thin visco-elastic layer, and on a plate supplied with single-layer mastic deadening ($d_2/d_1 \approx 2,5$). (After Cremer and Heckl)

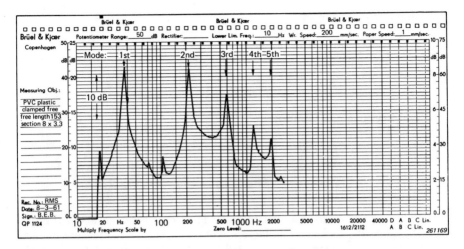

Fig.12.33. Complete frequency response curve obtained from measurements on a sample bar clamped at one end

the sample bar at one end, or both ends, and exciting it into bending vibrations with a variable frequency, sinusoidal force.

The amplitude of the response vibrations is then plotted as a function of frequency, see Fig.12.33. From such a curve, at a resonance peak, the loss factor can be calculated as

$$\eta = \Delta f_n / f_n \qquad (12.14)$$

where Δf_n is the bandwidth at the half power points (3 dB points) and f_n is the resonant frequency. The index n is the order of the resonance, or mode number. The modulus of elasticity*) (Young's modulus) can be found from the resonant frequency and the mechanical dimensions of the bar:

$$E = 48\pi^2 \varrho \left(\frac{l^2}{h} \frac{f_n}{K_n^2}\right)^2 \text{N/m}^2 \qquad (12.15)$$

l is the active length (m) of the bar,
h is the thickness in the plane of vibration (m)
ρ is the material density (kg/m^3)
K_n depends on the boundary conditions of the bar:

---

*) The modulus of elasticity found according to the described technique actually is the real part of a complex modulus of elasticity (dynamic modulus). In most practical cases, however, the difference between the modulus of elasticity found from the formula given here and Young's modulus is negligible.

both ends free or clamped:

$$K_1 = 4,73; \ K_2 = 7,853; \ K_3 = 10,996$$

$$K_n = \left(n + \frac{1}{2}\right)\pi; \qquad\qquad n > 3$$

one end free, one end clamped:

$$K_1 = 1,875; \ K_2 = 4,694; \ K_3 = 7,855$$

$$K_n = \left(n - \frac{1}{2}\right)\pi; \qquad\qquad n > 3$$

This measuring method is suitable for values of η between about 0,6 and 0,001. When the loss factor is large it will be impossible to measure the amplitude because no standing waves will be present, and if it is too small the resonance peaks will be too narrow to allow the bandwidth to be measured with reasonable accuracy.

For the second method mentioned above, i.e. the decay rate method, the external exciting force is tuned to a resonant frequency of the sample which will start a forced oscillation with steady amplitude when equilibrium is reached. If the exciting force is stopped instantly, the vibration amplitude decays exponentially with time. (Thus linearly with time if plotted out logarithmically.) The loss factor η is found from

$$\eta = \frac{D}{27,3 \, f_n} \qquad\qquad (12.16)$$

where D is the decay rate in dB/s and f_n is the resonant (modal) frequency. The modulus of elasticity, E, is found as described above for the frequency response method (Eqn. (12.15)).

In the decay rate method, the upper limit for measuring the loss factor depends on the measuring instruments. There is no theoretical lower limit.

A type of decay-rate measurement which has been extensively used in the past, especially in the U.S.A., is the so-called Geiger thick-plate test. The basic principle of this test is the same as already outlined for cut-out sample bars, only that the sample in this case consists of a suspended plate, see Fig.12.34.

Normally decay measurements according to the Geiger test are made at one frequency only. As this test has been used mainly in conjunction with automotive panels the frequency has commonly been chosen around 160 Hz.

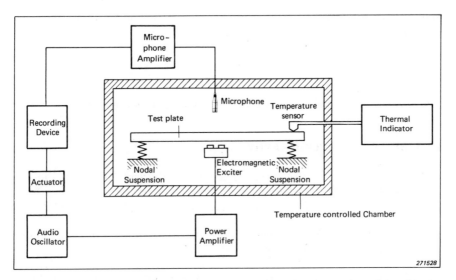

Fig.12.34. *Measuring arrangement suitable for use in conjunction with the Geiger thick-plate test*

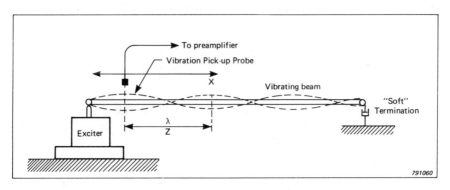

Fig.12.35. *Sketch showing how the attenuation of progressive mechanical waves may be measured*

So far the decay-rate type of tests discussed have been based on the interruption of a steady state normal mode (resonant) vibration, i.e. time decay measurements. Other types of decay-rate measurements are sometimes used: the determination of the decay-rate of progressive waves. This is based on decay-rate determinations in space rather than in time, as described below. When a long strip of material is excited in transverse vibration at one end, and terminated at the other end in such a way that practically no reflection takes place, Fig.12.35, one-dimensional mechanical waves progress

325

along the strip. The attenuation of these waves may then be used a measure of the damping properties of the material strip:

$$\eta = \frac{D_\lambda}{27,3} \qquad (12.17)$$

where D_λ is the attenuation along the strip in dB per wavelength.

12.3. SELECTED BIBLIOGRAPHY

BLAY, D., BOURGAIN, L., and SAMSON, G.: *Application of Electro-Acoustical Techniques to the Determination of the Modulus of Elasticity by a Non-Destructive Process.* B & K Tech. Rev. No.4, 1971

CRANDALL, S.H.: *The Role of Damping in Vibration Theory.* J. Sound Vib. Vol. 11. No. 1. 1970

CREDE, C.E.: *Vibration and Shock Isolation.* John Wiley and Sons, Inc. New York 1951 (1962)

CREMER, L. and HECKL, M.: *Körperschall.* Springer Verlag. Berlin, Heidelberg / New York, 1967

DERBY, T.E. and RUZICKA, J.E.: *Loss Factor, Resonant Frequency of Viscoelastic Shear Damped Structural Components.* NASA Report CR 1269, 1969

GROOTENHUIS, P.: *Measurement of the Dynamic Properties of Damping Material.* Proc. Int. Symp. Assoc. Belge Acoustieus, Leuwen 1967

GROOTENHUIS, P.: *Sandwich Damping Treatment Applied to Concrete Structures.* Trans. R. Soc. A 263, 455. 1968

GROOTENHUIS, P.: *The Control of Vibrations with Viscoelastic Materials,* J. Sound Vib. Vol. 11, No. 4. 1970

GROOTENHUIS, P.: *The Anti-Shock Mounting of Testing Machines.* Proc. Inst. Mech. Engrs. 1965-1966

KUNICA, S.: *Servo-controlled Pneumatic Isolators — Their Properties and Applications.* ASME Paper No.65-WA/MD-12. Nov. 1965

KURTZE, G.: *Physik und Technik der Lärmebekämpfung.* Verlag G. Braun. Karlsruhe, 1964

MEAD, D.J.: The Practical Problems of Assessing Damping Treatments. Journal of Sound and Vibration. Vol. 1, No. 3, July 1964

MUSTIN, G.S.: Theory of Cushion Design. Monograph No. SVM-2, Shock and Vibration Information Center Washington, D.C. 1968

OBERST, H.: Schwingungsdämpfenden Kunststoffe aus optimal eingestellten Polymeren. Kolloid-Zeitschrift. Zeitschrift für Polymere. Band 216-217, S. 64-80, 1967

OLESEN, H.P. and DELPY, D.T.: Shock and Vibration Isolation of a Punch Press. Brüel & Kjær Tech. Rev. No. 1-1971

ROSS, D.,UNGAR, E.E., and KERWIN, E.M.: Damping of Plate Flexural Vibrations by Means of Viscoelastic Laminae. ASME Publ. Structural Damping. Section 3. 1969

RUZICKA, J.E.: Resonance Characteristics of Unidirectional Viscous and Coulomb-Damped Vibration Isolation Systems. Trans. ASME, Journ. of Eng. for Industry, 89, Series B, No.4, Nov. 1967

SNOWDON, J.C.: Rubberlike Materials, Their Internal Damping and Role in Vibration Isolation. Journal of Sound and Vibration. Vol. 2, No. 2, April 1965

SNOWDON, J.C.: Vibration and Shock in Damped Mechanical Systems. John Wiley and Sons, Inc. New York, 1968

SNOWDON, J.C.: Isolation and Absorption of Machinery Vibration. US Navy Report TM 76-188, 1976

SOLIMAN, J.I. and HALLMAN, M.G.: Vibration Isolation Between Non-rigid Machines and Non-rigid Foundations. Journal of Sound and Vibration. Vol. 8, No. 2, September 1968

ZAVERI, K., and OLESEN, H.P.: Measurement of Elastic Modulus and Loss Factor of Asphalt. B & K Tech. Rev. No.4, 1972

UNGAR, E.E. and DIETRICH, C.W.: High Frequency Vibration Isolation. Journal of Sound and Vibration. Vol.4, No.2, September 1966

WARRING, R.H. ed.: Handbook of Noise and Vibration Control. Trade and Technical Press, Ltd. Morden, Surrey, England 1978 (Previous edition, 1970)

APPENDICES

APPENDIX A

On the Statistical Interpretation of the RMS-Value

In conjunction with the brief discussion in Chapter 2, section 2.2, on the probabilistic description of random vibration signals it might be of considerable interest to relate the concept of the signal RMS-value to this kind of data.

The definition of *probability density* given in section 2.2

$$p(x) = \lim_{\Delta x \to 0} \frac{P(x) - P(x + \Delta x)}{\Delta x} \tag{A.1}$$

immediately leads to the following expression for the *probability* of finding instantaneous amplitude values within the (small) amplitude interval, Δx:

$$P(x) - P(x + \Delta x) = P(x; \; x + \Delta x) = \int_x^{x+\Delta x} p(x)\, dx$$

When x is a function of time as indicated in Fig.A.1, then

$$P(x; \; x + \Delta x) = \int_x^{x+\Delta x} p(x)\, dx = \frac{\Sigma \Delta t_n}{T} = \frac{\Delta t}{T}$$

Defining now the statistical quantity

$$\sigma^2 = \int_{-\infty}^{\infty} x^2\, p(x)\, dx \tag{A.2}$$

this may be expressed as follows:

$$\sigma^2 = \int_{-\infty}^{\infty} x^2\, p(x)\, dx = \lim_{\Delta x \to 0} \sum_{-\infty}^{\infty} x^2\, P(x; \; x + \Delta x)$$

$$= \lim_{\Delta t \to 0} \sum_o^T x^2 \frac{\Delta t}{T} = \int_o^T \frac{x^2}{T}\, dt = \frac{1}{T} \int_o^T x^2 dt \tag{A.3}$$

328

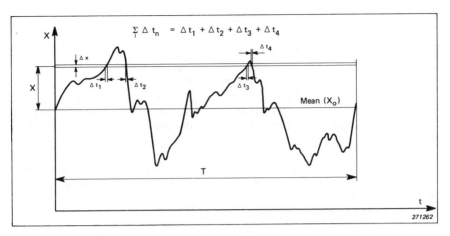

Fig.A.1. Example of a stationary random time function (vibration)

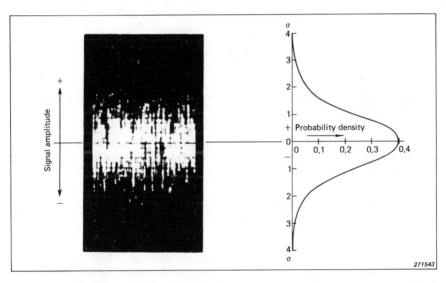

Fig.A.2. Illustration of the relationship between the instantaneous magnitude values in a Gaussian random vibration signal and the Gaussian probability density curve

σ^2 is, in the literature on statistics, commonly termed *variance* and the square-root of the variance is called the *standard deviation, σ.* However, when the statistical phenomenon being studied is a stationary time-function as shown in Fig.A.1, then

$$\sigma = \sqrt{\frac{1}{T} \int_0^T x^2(t)\, dt} \qquad (A.4)$$

which is nothing but the expression used in engineering dynamics for the signal *RMS-value*. Thus, besides being related to the power involved in the process, the RMS-value is also directly related to the process statistics. This may be best appreciated by considering the fact that most probability density curves are expressed in terms of standard deviations (RMS-deviations), see also Fig.2.9.

Finally, Fig.A.2 illustrates the relationship between the instantaneous amplitude values in a Gaussian random vibration signal and the Gaussian probability density curve.

APPENDIX B

Response Versus Excitation Characteristics for Linear Single Degree-of-Freedom Systems

In Chapter 3, section 3.1, the differential equation of motion for a *force-excited*, linear, single degree-of-freedom system was formulated (see also Fig.3.1 b) and Fig.B.1 a) below):

$$m\frac{d^2x}{dt^2} + c\frac{dx}{dt} + kx = f(t)$$

By Fourier transformation it was shown, furthermore, that the displacement response, x, of the mass, m, to a sinusoidal exciting force can be written:

$$x = H(f)F_0 e^{j2\pi ft} \qquad (B.1)$$

where $H(f)$ was termed the *complex frequency response function*.

$$H(f) = \frac{1}{k\left[1 - \left(\frac{f}{f_0}\right)^2\right] + \frac{j}{Q}\left(\frac{f}{f_0}\right)} \qquad (B.2)$$

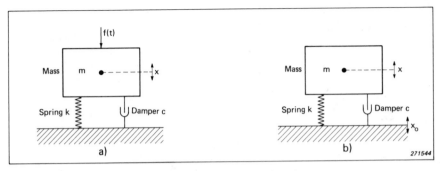

Fig.B.1. Models of a single degree-of-freedom system
a) System excited by a force acting upon the mass
b) System excited by motion of the foundation

from which

$$|H(f)| = \frac{1}{k\sqrt{\left[1 - \left(\frac{f}{f_0}\right)^2\right]^2 + \frac{1}{Q^2}\left(\frac{f}{f_0}\right)^2}}$$ (B.3)

$$\phi(f) = tan^{-1}\left[\frac{1}{Q\left(\frac{f_0}{f} - \frac{f}{f_0}\right)}\right]$$ (B.4)

where $|H(f)|$ is the absolute value of the displacement frequency response function and $\phi(f)$ is the *phase lag* between the displacement of the mass, m, and the exciting force.

By utilizing the relationships

$$v(t) = \frac{dx}{dt} \qquad a(t) = \frac{d^2x}{dt^2}$$

the velocity and acceleration frequency response functions can be readily found. The results are given in the first table and the corresponding functions are graphically illustrated in Fig.B.2.

If the excitation of the system is not a force, but a *motion of the foundation* Fig.B.1 b) a large number of response versus excitation functions can be formulated. The response of interest may, for instance, be the absolute motion of the mass, m, or it may be the relative motion between the mass and the foundation (the loading on the spring element).

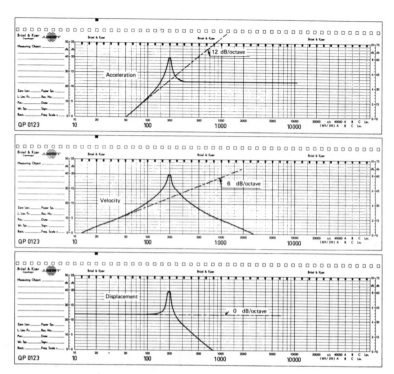

Fig.B.2. Curves showing the displacement, velocity and acceleration response of a force-excited single degree-of-freedom system. Note that the curves for velocity and acceleration response can be found simply by adding respectively 6 and 12 dB/octave to the displacement response

Force-excited, linear, single degree-of-freedom system	
Response quantity	Frequency response function
Displacement of mass, m, Fig. B. 1a)	$$H_x(f) = \frac{1}{k\left[1-\left(\frac{f}{f_0}\right)^2\right] + \frac{j}{Q}\left(\frac{f}{f_0}\right)}$$
Velocity of mass, m, Fig. B. 1a)	$$H_v(f) = \frac{j2\pi f}{k\left[1-\left(\frac{f}{f_0}\right)^2\right] + \frac{j}{Q}\left(\frac{f}{f_0}\right)}$$
Acceleration of mass, m, Fig. B. 1a)	$$H_a(f) = \frac{-4\pi^2 f^2}{k\left[1-\left(\frac{f}{f_0}\right)^2\right] + \frac{j}{Q}\left(\frac{f}{f_0}\right)}$$

800129

332

Response versus excitation functions for the absolute *motion of the mass* are tabulated in the second table.

Response Quantity, Fig.B. 1b)	Excitation Quantity Fig.B. 1b)		
	Displacement	Velocity	Acceleration
Displacement $x(t)$	$\|H(f)\| = \dfrac{D_1}{D_2}$	$\|H(f)\| = \dfrac{D_1}{2\pi f D_2}$	$\|H(f)\| = \dfrac{D_1}{4\pi^2 f^2 D_2}$
Velocity $v_x(t)$	$\|H(f)\| = \dfrac{2\pi f D_1}{D_2}$	$\|H(f)\| = \dfrac{D_1}{D_2}$	$\|H(f)\| = \dfrac{D_1}{2\pi f D_2}$
Acceleration $a_x(t)$	$\|H(f)\| = \dfrac{4\pi^2 f^2 D_1}{D_2}$	$\|H(f)\| = \dfrac{2\pi f D_1}{D_2}$	$\|H(f)\| = \dfrac{D_1}{D_2}$

800130

where

$$D_1 = \sqrt{1 + \frac{1}{Q^2}\left(\frac{f}{f_0}\right)^2}$$

and

$$D_2 = \sqrt{\left[1 - \left(\frac{f}{f_0}\right)^2\right]^2 + \frac{1}{Q^2}\left(\frac{f}{f_0}\right)^2}$$

Similarly response versus excitation functions for the *relative motion between* the mass and the foundation are tabulated in the third table:

Response Quantity, Fig.B. 1b)	Excitation Quantity Fig.B. 1b)		
	Displacement, $x_o(t)$	Velocity, $v_{xo}(t)$	Acceleration, $a_{xo}(t)$
Relative Displacement $x(t) - x_o(t)$	$\|H(f)\| = \dfrac{f^2}{f_0^2 D_2}$	$\|H(f)\| = \dfrac{f}{2\pi f_0^2 D_2}$	$\|H(f)\| = \dfrac{1}{4\pi^2 f_0^2 D_2}$
Relative Velocity $v_x(t) - v_{xo}(t)$	$\|H(f)\| = \dfrac{2\pi f^3}{f_0^2 D_2}$	$\|H(f)\| = \dfrac{f^2}{f_0^2 D_2}$	$\|H(f)\| = \dfrac{f}{2\pi f_0^2 D_2}$
Relative Acceleration $a_x(t) - a_{xo}(t)$	$\|H(f)\| = \dfrac{4\pi^2 f^4}{f_0^2 D_2}$	$\|H(f)\| = \dfrac{2\pi f^3}{f_0^2 D_2}$	$\|H(f)\| = \dfrac{f^2}{f_0^2 D_2}$

800131

where D_2 has the same meaning as before.

By studying the three tables it is readily noticed that *when one of the desired response versus excitation functions, $|H(f)|$, has been formulated the other follows immediately by manipulating with the quantity $2\pi f$, see also the curves,* Fig.B.2. That this must be so follows immediately from the mathematical relationships between the displacement, velocity and acceleration.*)

APPENDIX C

On the Wave-Shape Distortion in Non-Linear Mechanical Systems

While a linear resonance system may act as a signal "wave filter" suppressing possible harmonic distortion a *non-linear resonance system actually produces waveform distortion.* The degree of distortion depends on the type of non-linearity and upon the excitation of the system.

As a first example consider a non-linear, single degree-of-freedom system of the *hardening spring* type, Fig.C.1 (see also Chapter 3, section 3.2). Assume further that the foundation of the system moves sinusoidally at a frequency close to the system resonance. The waveform of the displacement of the mass may then look as shown in Fig.C.2 a).

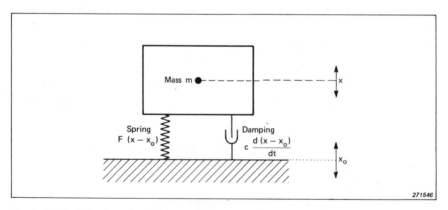

Fig.C.1. Model of a single degree-of-freedom system containing a non-linear spring element

---

*) For the special case $|H(f)| = \dfrac{D_1}{D_2}$, see also Fig.12.2 of the text.

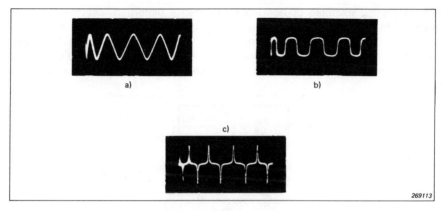

Fig.C.2. *Typical resonance wave-shapes for the motion of the mass in a single degree-of-freedom system containing a hardening spring type stiffness element*
a) Displacement
b) Velocity
c) Acceleration

By differentiation of the displacement signal with respect to time one finds that the corresponding velocity of the mass will have a wave-shape as indicated in Fig.C.2 b). Finally, a second differentiation yields the acceleration wave-shape shown in Fig.C.2 c).

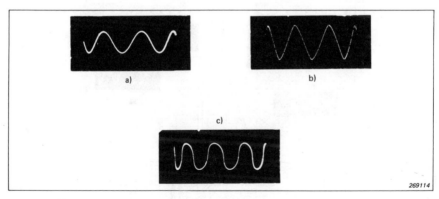

Fig.C.3. *Similar to Fig.C.2, the stiffness element in this case being of the softening spring type*
a) Displacement
b) Velocity
c) Acceleration

As a second example of non-linear resonance distortion, assume that the system, Fig.C.1, is of the *softening spring* type. Under the same excitation conditions as stated above the motion of the mass then produces wave-shapes as shown in Fig.C.3. Although the wave-shape distortion is here not nearly as heavy as in the hardening spring case it can be clearly noticed.

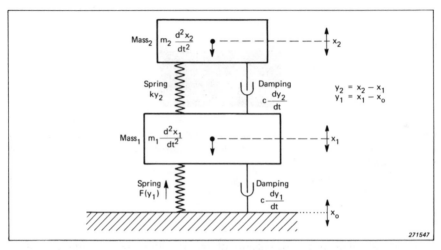

Fig.C.4. Model of a two degree-of-freedom system containing one non-linear stiffness element of the hardening spring type

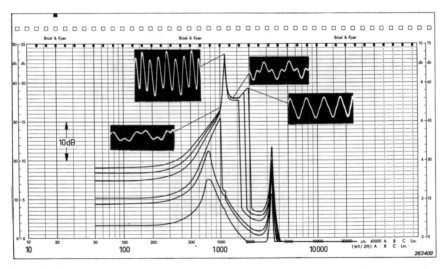

Fig.C.5. Frequency response curves for the motion of the second mass in the system sketched in Fig.C.4. Curves are shown for different levels of excitation of the foundation

Wave-shape distortion will also be produced when the non-linearity is situated in the damping element of the system. It seems, however, that *the most pronounced distortion effects are produced by the hardening spring type resonant non-linearities.* This is important to remember as the use of hardening springs in practice is not at all uncommon (Chapter 12, section 12.1).

Before closing this brief discussion on waveform distortions in mechanical systems it should be mentioned that non-linearities in one or more elements in a multi degree-of-freedom system may cause many "unexpected" effects in the response. As an example of such effects the response of the second mass in a two degree-of-freedom system, Fig.C.4, to a sweeping sinusoidal excitation of the foundation is illustrated in Fig.C.5. The sweep was here carried out with increasing frequency and both the change in wave-shape and the "jump" phenomenon, described in section 3.2, are demonstrated.

APPENDIX D

Connection Between the Fourier Spectrum of a Shock Pulse and the Residual Shock Spectrum

To demonstrate the relationship between the Fourier spectrum of a shock pulse and the undamped residual shock spectrum consider the following.

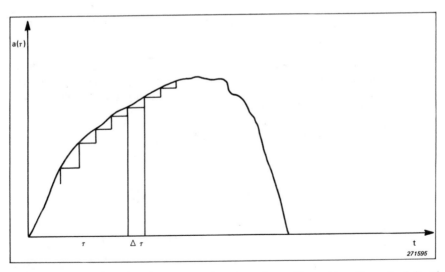

Fig.D.1. Example of a shock excitation waveform illustrating the principle of superposition in the time domain

337

Fig.D.1 shows an arbitrary acceleration shock amplitude as a function of time.

Assuming a linear resonance system, its response to such a shock can be calculated as the superposition of the responses to a number of *step* functions approximating the shock pulse.

The change in *excitation velocity* per step is

$$\Delta v = a(\tau)\Delta\tau$$

where $a(\tau)$ is the value of the acceleration excitation at time τ and $\Delta\tau$ is the width of the step.

The partial velocity response at some time t after the step has occurred is

$$\Delta v_R = h(t-\tau)a(\tau)\Delta\tau$$

where $h(t-\tau)$ is the *velocity response to a unit velocity step*. The total response at a time t after the shock has occurred is then

$$v_R = \Sigma h(t-\tau)a(\tau)\Delta\tau$$

Letting the width of the steps, $\Delta\tau$, approach zero, the sum turns into an integral

$$v_R = \int_{-\infty}^{t} h(t-\tau)a(\tau)d\tau \qquad (D.1)$$

Now, the velocity response to a unit velocity step can be found by solving the linear differential equation for the system under consideration (single degree-of-freedom, undamped system), utilizing the boundary conditions given by the unit velocity step. The solution is simply:

$$h(t-\tau) = 1 - \cos[2\pi f(t-\tau)]$$

thus:

$$v_R = \int_{-\infty}^{t} [1-\cos\{2\pi f(t-\tau)\}]a(\tau)d\tau$$

$$= \int_{-\infty}^{t} a(\tau)d\tau - \int_{-\infty}^{t} \cos\{2\pi f(t-\tau)\}a(\tau)d\tau$$

$$v_R = v(t) - \int_{-\infty}^{t} a(\tau)\cos\{2\pi f(t-\tau)\}d\tau$$

Letting $t \to \infty$ (residual spectrum) then $v(t) = Const.$ (see Fig.D.1) and

$$v_R = - \int_{-\infty}^{\infty} a(\tau) \cos\{2\pi f(t-\tau)\} d\tau + const. \qquad (D.2)$$

This is also the expression for the Fourier spectrum of the *acceleration* shock pulse except for the phase (see Chapter 2, section 2.3). Thus

$$Max. \ v_R = |F_a(f)| \qquad (D.3)$$

For each frequency component in the response "spectrum" the relationship $a_R = 2\pi f v_R$ is valid, whereby

$$S_a(f) = 2\pi f |F_a(f)| \qquad (D.4)$$

APPENDIX E

Electronic Integration of Accelerometer Output Signals

It was stated in Chapter 6, section 6.1, that it does not normally matter which of the three quantities acceleration, velocity or displacement is actually measured in an experimental vibration study, because they are all interrelated by simple differentiating and integrating operations. It was furthermore mentioned that these operations can be readily performed electronically on the output signal from the transducer.

There are, however, certain practical restrictions imposed upon these statements.

Firstly, as will be obvious from the succeeding description of electronic integration, this cannot include zero frequency (D.C), and a certain *low* frequency does therefore always exist in practice below which no integration takes place. Similarly, electronic differentiators must exhibit a certain *upper* frequency limit.

Secondly, electronic differentiators are very sensitive to high frequency noise, and to the high frequency performance of the transducer used for the actual measurement.

Due to the preference given today to acceleration sensitive transducers only the problem of electronic *integration* is considered in detail in the following.

If an arbitrary Fourier component, $a = A_0 e^{j2\pi ft}$, of an acceleration signal spectrum is integrated the result will be the corresponding Fourier component of the corresponding velocity signal spectrum:

$$v = \int a\, dt = \int A_0 e^{j2\pi ft}\, dt = \frac{A_0}{j2\pi f} e^{j2\pi ft} = V_0 e^{j2\pi ft}$$

Thus:

$$V_0 = \frac{A_0}{j2\pi f} \qquad\qquad\qquad (E.1)$$

Similarly, a second integration of the acceleration signal component yields the displacement signal component:

$$x = \iint a\, dt\, dt = \int v\, dt = \int V_0 e^{j2\pi ft}\, dt = \frac{V_0}{j2\pi f} e^{j2\pi ft} = -\frac{A_0}{(2\pi f)^2} e^{j2\pi ft} = X_0 e^{j2\pi ft}$$

Thus:

$$X_0 = \frac{V_0}{j2\pi f} = -\frac{A_0}{(2\pi f)^2} \qquad\qquad\qquad (E.2)$$

Note that for the continuous sinusoidal components assumed above, the constants of integration have been assumed to be zero. This assumption is not valid for transient signals which are discussed later.

Now, if the output signal from an accelerometer (or rather accelerometer + preamplifier), e_a, is fed to an electronic circuit of the type shown in Fig.E.1, the voltage across the capacitor C, i.e. the circuit output voltage, e_c, is:

$$e_c = \frac{1}{1 + j2\pi fRC}\, e_a$$

Thus when $2\pi fRC \gg 1$ then

$$e_c \approx \frac{1}{RC} \cdot \frac{e_a}{j2\pi f} \qquad\qquad\qquad (E.3)$$

By comparing the expressions (E.1) and (E.3) it is readily seen that when e_a represents a particular acceleration signal component then e_c must represent the corresponding velocity signal component, i.e. *an electronic integration has taken place in the network,* Fig.E.1. (The multiplying factor *1/RC* is taken care of in the internal calibration of the integrator).

340

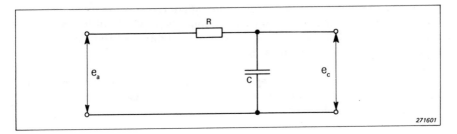

Fig.E.1. *Typical electrical integration network of the simple RC-type*

The absolute value of the expression

$$\left|\frac{e_c}{e_a}\right| = \left|\frac{1}{1 + j2\pi fRC}\right| \qquad \text{(E.4)}$$

is plotted in Fig.E.2 and demonstrates clearly the meaning of the condition $2\pi fRC \gg 1$ stated above. It also illustrates the fact that a certain low frequency limit, f_L, exists below which no integration takes place. Between f_L and f_T, i.e. in the frequency region around $f_n = 1/(2\pi RC)$, the signal is only "partly" integrated.

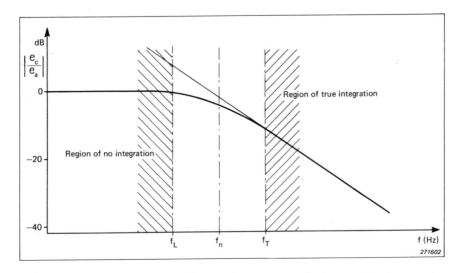

Fig.E.2. *Graphical illustration of the function* $\left|\frac{e_c}{e_a}\right| = \left|\frac{1}{1 + j2\pi fRC}\right|$

indicating the frequency region where true integration of the input signal, e_a, takes place

341

The low frequency limit for "true" integration, f_T, is in the integrators produced by Brüel & Kjær taken to be the frequency at which an integration error of 1,5 dB ($\approx 15\%$) exists. To ensure true integration of the signal it must therefore not contain frequencies below f_T.

If frequency components lower than f_T exist in the signal to be integrated the problem can sometimes be solved by the use of magnetic tape recording and tape speed transformations.

As mentioned previously, the above discussion does not apply fully to the integration of transients.

As an illustration of general principles, the example will be taken of a single "period" sine pulse as the acceleration signal which is to be integrated to both velocity and displacement.

Fig.E.3 a) illustrates the transient which may be described by the formula:

$$a(t) = A_0 \sin(2\pi ft), \qquad 0 \le t \le T, \qquad f = \frac{1}{T}$$
$$= 0, \qquad \text{otherwise} \tag{E.5}$$

The corresponding velocity signal is obtained as follows by integration:

$$v(t) = \int a(t)\,dt = \int_0^t A_0 \sin(2\pi f\tau)\,d\tau$$

$$= \left[-\frac{A_0}{2\pi f}\cos(2\pi f\tau) \right]_0^t = \frac{A_0}{2\pi f}\left[1 - \cos(2\pi ft) \right] \tag{E.6}$$

$$\text{for } 0 \le t \le T$$

i.e. a raised cosine because of the constant of integration. This is illustrated in Fig.E.3.b).

Thus, the peak value is $2A_0/2\pi f$ which is twice that obtained for a continuous signal in Equation (E.1).

Continuing in the same way the displacement may be obtained by a further integration:

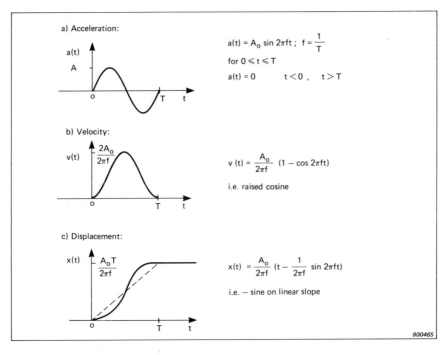

a) Acceleration:

$$a(t) = A_0 \sin 2\pi ft \; ; \; f = \frac{1}{T}$$

for $0 \leqslant t \leqslant T$

$$a(t) = 0 \qquad t < 0 , \quad t > T$$

b) Velocity:

$$v(t) = \frac{A_0}{2\pi f} (1 - \cos 2\pi ft)$$

i.e. raised cosine

c) Displacement:

$$x(t) = \frac{A_0}{2\pi f} (t - \frac{1}{2\pi f} \sin 2\pi ft)$$

i.e. – sine on linear slope

800465

Fig.E.3. Integration of an acceleration pulse to velocity and displacement

$$x(t) = \int v(t)\,dt = \int_o^t \frac{A_0}{2\pi f} \left[1 - \cos\left(2\pi f\tau\right)\right] d\tau$$

$$= \frac{A_0}{2\pi f}\left[\tau - \frac{1}{2\pi f}\sin\left(2\pi f\tau\right)\right]_o^t = \frac{A_0}{2\pi f}\left[t - \frac{1}{2\pi f}\sin\left(2\pi ft\right)\right] \qquad (E.7)$$

for $0 \leqslant t \leqslant T$

which is a negative sine superimposed on a linear slope as depicted in Fig.E.3.c).

Fig.E.4 shows the results of some actual measurements made with the integrator Type ZR 0020 with single period sine pulses of 10 ms (100 Hz) and 1 ms (1 kHz) duration respectively, where the main frequency in the pulse is respectively a factor of 10 and 100 above the nominal cut-off frequency of the integrator. The results are normalised so as to compare directly with the theoretical result in each case. It is seen that both results for peak velocity are acceptable (max. error 8% for the 10 ms pulse), but that the 16% error on double integration of the 10 ms pulse may not be acceptable. It is empha-

343

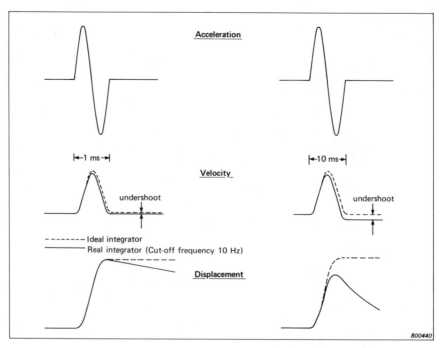

Fig.E.4. Practical integration of 2 different length acceleration pulses to velocity and displacement using the same integration cutoff frequency

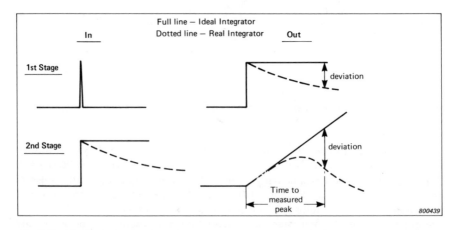

Fig.E.5. Ideal and practical impulse responses for an integrator with single and double integration

344

sized that it is only meaningful to talk of peak displacement when the "DC" component of the acceleration transient is zero, so that the final velocity is zero.

It can be seen that the problem is very similar to that discussed in Section 7.3.3 in relation to the exponential averaging (RC integration) of impulses, and this gives a guide to the way in which the error can be estimated. The actual impulse response of the integrator can be compared with those for ideal single and double integrators (Fig.E.5), and the deviation estimated for the time delay of the measured peak value. Assuming a uniform (or at least symmetrical) energy distribution along the transient, the error would be approximately half this deviation. This procedure would only be valid where the maximum velocity (or displacement) comes after the first lobe of the acceleration (or velocity) impulse, and where the deviation is small.

APPENDIX F

On the Use of Decibels

Modern day engineering requires that accurate measurements are made over wide dynamic ranges.

When the dynamic range considered covers more than one or two decades the graphical presentation of the measured results on linear scales often becomes impractical. The major reason for this is that the accuracy of the graph near the zero axis becomes extremely difficult to interpret. A commonly used solution to the problem is then to present the data in terms of *logarithmic scales*. One such logarithmic scale which is becoming increasingly popular in various fields of engineering is the *decibel (dB) scale*. Although the decibel scale originates from transmission line theory and telephone engineering it is at present widely used not only in the general field of electronic engineering but also in the fields of sound and vibration engineering.

The original definition of the decibel is based on *power ratios:*

$$dB = 10 \, log_{10}\left(\frac{W}{W_0}\right) \qquad (F.1)$$

where W_0 is a reference power. However, as the power measured across a certain impedance is related to the square of the force acting upon this impedance, Z, a more commonly used definition is

$$dB = 10 \log_{10}\left(\frac{F^2/Z}{F_0^2/Z}\right) = 20 \log_{10}\left(\frac{F}{F_0}\right) \qquad \text{(F.2)}$$

where F and F_0 are the RMS (root mean square) values of the forces.

Actually, *as long as the measurements are related to one and the same impedance the decibel-notation in the form* $20 \log_{10}(X/X_0)$ *may be used as a convenient relative magnitude scale for a variety of quantities,* not only forces. X may, for instance, be an RMS displacement, a velocity or an acceleration. X_0, however, must always be a reference quantity of the same type as X. That is when X represents a displacement then X_0 represents a reference displacement, and when X represents an acceleration then X_0 represents a reference acceleration.

A useful application of the decibel scale is evident in the frequency analysis of mechanical vibrations where large changes in amplitudes occur at resonance. The use of decibels (dB) compresses a range of displacement or acceleration magnitudes of 1 : 1000 to 0 - 60 dB, at the same time attaining constant relative accuracy in the graphical presentation. A further consequence that arises from the decibel scale is that multiplicative factors become additive terms in their logarithmic equivalents.

Also, when the ratio X/X_0 is smaller than 1,0 the logarithm to the base ten of the ratio, and thus the decibel value, becomes negative. In the table given below only ratios X/X_0 larger than unity have been considered. The same table can, however, also be used in cases where X/X_0 is smaller than unity remembering that

$$20 \log_{10}\left(\frac{X}{X_0}\right) = 20 \log_{10}\left(\frac{1}{X_0/X}\right) = -20 \log_{10}\left(\frac{X_0}{X}\right)$$

i.e. by finding the decibel value for the *inverse ratio* (X_0/X) and assigning to it a negative value.

Example

Find the number of dB corresponding to:

$$\frac{X}{X_0} = 0,5$$

As X/X_0 is smaller than one it is necessary to calculate the inverse ratio:

$$\frac{X_0}{X} = \frac{1}{0,5} = 2$$

From the table the corresponding decibel value is found to be 6,021 dB, and because of the inverting operation the actual decibel value is —6,021.

To find X/X_0 when the decibel value is given, the nearest dB-value is sought in the table and the corresponding ratio read off the left hand and top columns.

Examples

a) *Find the ratio corresponding to 3,5 dB.*
From the table it is seen that the nearest dB-value tabulated is 3,522, corresponding to a ratio of 1,5.

b) *Find the ratio corresponding to —3 dB.*
The nearest dB-value given in the table is 2,984 corresponding to a ratio of 1,41. However, as the dB-value stated above has a negative sign it is necessary to invert the ratio 1,41, i.e. —3 dB corresponds to a ratio of

$$\frac{1}{1,41} = 0,706.$$

When the ratio is >10 it may be possible to use Table F.2 directly, or in fact Table F.1 may be used if the ratio is divided by 10 a sufficient number of times to bring it into the range 1 — 10. To the result for this factor is added 20 dB for each factor 10 by which the original ratio was divided.

Examples

a) *Find the number of dB corresponding to:*

$$\frac{X}{X_0} = 32,5$$

Either: from Table F.2 the dB value is approx.

$$\frac{30,103 + 30,370}{2} = 30,237 \, dB$$

or: 32,5 = 3,25 × 10 and from Table F.1 the dB value for 3,25 = 10,238 ∴ for 32,5 it equals 10,238 + 20 dB = 30,238 dB.

b) *Find the ratio corresponding to 68 dB.*

68 = 8 + (3 × 20)

Ratio $\frac{X}{X_0} = 2,51 \times 10^3$

Since ratio 2,51 in Table F.1 gives 7,993 dB ($\approx$ 8).

Table F.1. Table of (Amplitude) Ratio-to-Decibel Conversion

$\left(\dfrac{x}{x_0}\right)$	.00	.01	.02	.03	.04	.05	.06	.07	.08	.09
1.0	.000	.086	.172	.257	.341	.424	.506	.588	.668	.749
1.1	.828	.906	.984	1.062	1.138	1.214	1.289	1.364	1.438	1.511
1.2	1.584	1.656	1.727	1.798	1.868	1.938	2.007	2.076	2.144	2.212
1.3	2.279	2.345	2.411	2.477	2.542	2.607	2.671	2.734	2.798	2.860
1.4	2.923	2.984	3.046	3.107	3.167	3.227	3.287	3.346	3.405	3.464
1.5	3.522	3.580	3.637	3.694	3.750	3.807	3.862	3.918	3.973	4.028
1.6	4.082	4.137	4.190	4.244	4.297	4.350	4.402	4.454	4.506	4.558
1.7	4.609	4.660	4.711	4.761	4.811	4.861	4.910	4.959	5.008	5.057
1.8	5.105	5.154	5.201	5.249	5.296	5.343	5.390	5.437	5.483	5.529
1.9	5.575	5.621	5.666	5.711	5.756	5.801	5.845	5.889	5.933	5.977
2.0	6.021	6.064	6.107	6.150	6.193	6.235	6.277	6.319	6.361	6.403
2.1	6.444	6.486	6.527	6.568	6.608	6.649	6.689	6.729	6.769	6.809
2.2	6.848	6.888	6.927	6.966	7.008	7.044	7.082	7.121	7.159	7.197
2.3	7.235	7.272	7.310	7.347	7.384	7.421	7.458	7.495	7.532	7.568
2.4	7.604	7.640	7.676	7.712	7.748	7.783	7.819	7.854	7.889	7.924
2.5	7.959	7.993	8.028	8.062	8.097	8.131	8.165	8.199	8.232	8.266
2.6	8.299	8.333	8.366	8.399	8.432	8.465	8.498	8.530	8.563	8.595
2.7	8.627	8.659	8.691	8.723	8.755	8.787	8.818	8.850	8.881	8.912
2.8	8.943	8.974	9.005	9.036	9.066	9.097	9.127	9.158	9.188	9.218
2.9	9.248	9.278	9.308	9.337	9.367	9.396	9.426	9.455	9.484	9.513
3.0	9.542	9.571	9.600	9.629	9.657	9.686	9.714	9.743	9.771	9.799
3.1	9.827	9.855	9.883	9.911	9.939	9.966	9.994	10.021	10.049	10.076
3.2	10.103	10.130	10.157	10.184	10.211	10.238	10.264	10.291	10.317	10.344
3.3	10.370	10.397	10.423	10.449	10.475	10.501	10.527	10.553	10.578	10.604
3.4	10.630	10.655	10.681	10.706	10.731	10.756	10.782	10.807	10.832	10.857
3.5	10.881	10.906	10.931	10.955	10.980	11.005	11.029	11.053	11.078	11.102
3.6	11.126	11.150	11.174	11.198	11.222	11.246	11.270	11.293	11.317	11.341
3.7	11.364	11.387	11.411	11.434	11.457	11.481	11.504	11.527	11.550	11.573
3.8	11.596	11.618	11.641	11.664	11.687	11.709	11.732	11.754	11.777	11.799
3.9	11.821	11.844	11.866	11.888	11.910	11.932	11.954	11.976	11.998	12.019
4.0	12.041	12.063	12.085	12.106	12.128	12.149	12.171	12.192	12.213	12.234
4.1	12.256	12.277	12.298	12.319	12.340	12.361	12.382	12.403	12.424	12.444
4.2	12.465	12.486	12.506	12.527	12.547	12.568	12.588	12.609	12.629	12.649
4.3	12.669	12.690	12.710	12.730	12.750	12.770	12.790	12.810	12.829	12.849
4.4	12.869	12.889	12.908	12.928	12.948	12.967	12.987	13.006	13.026	13.045
4.5	13.064	13.084	13.103	13.122	13.141	13.160	13.179	13.198	13.217	13.236
4.6	13.255	13.274	13.293	13.312	13.330	13.349	13.368	13.386	13.405	13.423
4.7	13.442	13.460	13.479	13.497	13.516	13.534	13.552	13.570	13.589	13.607
4.8	13.625	13.643	13.661	13.679	13.697	13.715	13.733	13.751	13.768	13.786
4.9	13.804	13.822	13.839	13.857	13.875	13.892	13.910	13.927	13.945	13.962
5.0	13.979	13.997	14.014	14.031	14.049	14.066	14.083	14.100	14.117	14.134
5.1	14.151	14.168	14.185	14.202	14.219	14.236	14.253	14.270	14.287	14.303
5.2	14.320	14.337	14.553	14.370	14.387	14.403	14.420	14.436	14.453	14.469
5.3	14.486	14.502	14.518	14.535	14.551	14.567	14.583	14.599	14.616	14.632
5.4	14.648	14.664	14.680	14.696	14.712	14.728	14.744	14.760	14.776	14.791
5.5	14.807	14.823	14.839	14.855	14.870	14.886	14.902	14.917	14.933	14.948
5.6	14.964	14.979	14.995	15.010	15.026	15.041	15.056	15.072	15.087	15.102
5.7	15.117	15.133	15.148	15.163	15.178	15.193	15.208	15.224	15.239	15.254
5.8	15.269	15.284	15.298	15.313	15.328	15.343	15.358	15.373	15.388	15.402
5.9	15.417	15.432	15.446	15.461	15.476	15.490	15.505	15.519	15.534	15.549
6.0	15.563	15.577	15.592	15.606	15.621	15.635	15.649	15.664	15.678	15.692
6.1	15.707	15.721	15.735	15.749	15.763	15.778	15.792	15.806	15.820	15.834
6.2	15.848	15.862	15.876	15.890	15.904	15.918	15.931	15.945	15.959	15.973
6.3	15.987	16.001	16.014	16.028	16.042	16.055	16.069	16.083	16.096	16.110
6.4	16.124	16.137	16.151	16.164	16.178	16.191	16.205	16.218	16.232	16.245

Ratio $\left(\dfrac{x}{x_0}\right)$	.00	.01	.02	.03	.04	.05	.06	.07	.08	.09
6.5	16.258	16.272	16.285	16.298	16.312	16.325	16.338	16.351	16.365	16.378
6.6	16.391	16.404	16.417	16.430	16.443	16.456	16.469	16.483	16.496	16.509
6.7	16.521	16.534	16.547	16.560	16.573	16.586	16.599	16.612	16.625	16.637
6.8	16.650	16.663	16.676	16.688	16.701	16.714	16.726	16.739	16.752	16.764
6.9	16.777	16.790	16.802	16.815	16.827	16.840	16.852	16.865	16.877	16.890
7.0	**16.902**	**16.914**	**16.927**	**16.939**	**16.951**	**16.964**	**16.976**	**16.988**	**17.001**	**17.013**
7.1	17.025	17.037	17.050	17.062	17.074	17.086	17.098	17.110	17.122	17.135
7.2	17.147	17.159	17.171	17.183	17.195	17.207	17.219	17.231	17.243	17.255
7.3	17.266	17.278	17.290	17.302	17.314	17.326	17.338	17.349	17.361	17.373
7.4	17.385	17.396	17.408	17.420	17.431	17.443	17.455	17.466	17.478	17.490
7.5	17.501	17.513	17.524	17.536	17.547	17.559	17.570	17.582	17.593	17.605
7.6	17.616	17.628	17.639	17.650	17.662	17.673	17.685	17.696	17.707	17.719
7.7	17.730	17.741	17.752	17.764	17.775	17.786	17.797	17.808	17.820	17.831
7.8	17.842	17.853	17.864	17.875	17.886	17.897	17.908	17.919	17.931	17.942
7.9	17.953	17.964	17.975	17.985	17.996	18.007	18.018	18.029	18.040	18.051
8.0	**18.062**	**18.073**	**18.083**	**18.094**	**18.105**	**18.116**	**18.127**	**18.137**	**18.148**	**18.159**
8.1	18.170	18.180	18.191	18.202	18.212	18.223	18.234	18.244	18.255	18.266
8.2	18.276	18.287	18.297	18.308	18.319	18.329	18.340	18.350	18.361	18.371
8.3	18.382	18.392	18.402	18.413	18.423	18.434	18.444	18.455	18.465	18.475
8.4	18.486	18.496	18.506	18.517	18.527	18.537	18.547	18.558	18.568	18.578
8.5	18.588	18.599	18.609	18.619	18.629	18.639	18.649	18.660	18.670	18.680
8.6	18.690	18.700	18.710	18.720	18.730	18.740	18.750	18.760	18.770	18.780
8.7	18.790	18.800	18.810	18.820	18.830	18.840	18.850	18.860	18.870	18.880
8.8	18.890	18.900	18.909	18.919	18.929	18.939	18.949	18.958	18.968	18.978
8.9	18.988	18.998	19.007	19.017	19.027	19.036	19.046	19.056	19.066	19.075
9.0	**19.085**	**19.094**	**19.104**	**19.114**	**19.123**	**19.133**	**19.143**	**19.152**	**19.162**	**19.171**
9.1	19.181	19.190	19.200	19.209	19.219	19.228	19.238	19.247	19.257	19.266
9.2	19.276	19.285	19.295	19.304	19.313	19.323	19.332	19.342	19.351	19.360
9.3	19.370	19.379	19.388	19.398	19.407	19.416	19.426	19.435	19.444	19.453
9.4	19.463	19.472	19.481	19.490	19.499	19.509	19.518	19.527	19.536	19.545
9.5	19.554	19.564	19.573	19.582	19.591	19.600	19.609	19.618	19.627	19.636
9.6	19.645	19.654	19.664	19.673	19.682	19.691	19.700	19.709	19.718	19.726
9.7	19.735	19.744	19.753	19.762	19.771	19.780	19.789	19.798	19.807	19.816
9.8	19.825	19.833	19.842	19.851	19.860	19.869	19.878	19.886	19.895	19.904
9.9	19.913	19.921	19.930	19.939	19.948	19.956	19.965	19.974	19.983	19.991

Ratio $\left(\dfrac{x}{x_0}\right)$	0	1	2	3	4	5	6	7	8	9
10	**20.000**	**20.828**	**21.584**	**22.279**	**22.923**	**23.522**	**24.082**	**24.609**	**25.105**	**25.575**
20	26.021	26.444	26.848	27.235	27.604	27.959	28.299	28.627	28.943	29.248
30	29.542	29.827	30.103	30.370	30.630	30.881	31.126	31.364	31.596	31.821
40	32.041	32.256	32.465	32.669	32.869	33.064	33.255	33.442	33.625	33.804
50	33.979	34.151	34.320	34.486	34.648	34.807	34.964	35.117	35.269	35.417
60	35.563	35.707	35.848	35.987	36.124	36.258	36.391	36.521	36.650	36.777
70	36.902	37.025	37.147	37.266	37.385	37.501	37.616	37.730	37.842	37.953
80	38.062	38.170	38.276	38.382	38.486	38.588	38.690	38.790	38.890	38.988
90	39.085	39.181	39.276	39.370	39.463	39.554	39.645	39.735	39.825	39.913
100	**40.000**	–	–	–	–	–	–	–	–	–

Table F.2. Amplitude Ratios > 10

APPENDIX G

CONVERSION CHARTS, TABLES etc.

Conversion of Length

m	cm	mm	ft	in
1	100	1000	3,281	39,37
0,01	1	10	0,0328	0,3937
0,001	0,1	1	0,00328	0,03937
0,3048	30,48	304,8	1	12
0,0254	2,54	25,4	0,0833	1

800184

Conversion of Velocity

m/s	km/h	ft/min	mile/h
1	3,6	196,85	2,2369
0,2778	1	54,68	0,6214
$5,08 \times 10^{-3}$	$1,829 \times 10^{-2}$	1	$1,136 \times 10^{-2}$
0,4470	1,6093	88	1

800185

Conversion of Acceleration

g	m/s^2	cm/s^2	ft/s^2	in/s^2
1	9,81	981	32,2	386
0,102	1	100	3,281	39,37
0,00102	0,01	1	0,0328	0,3937
0,03109	0,3048	30,48	1	12
0,00259	0,0254	2,54	0,0833	1

800186

Conversion of Area

m^2	cm^2	ft^2	in^2	yd^2
1	10^4	10,764	1550	1,196
10^{-4}	1	1,0764 x 10^{-3}	0,1550	0,0011
9,29 x 10^{-2}	929	1	144	0,1111
6,452 x 10^{-4}	6,452	6,944 x 10^{-3}	1	0,0008
0,8361	8361	9	1296	1

Conversion of Volume

m^3	l = (dm)^3	ft^3	gal (UK)	gal (US)	yd^3
1	10^3	35,315	219,98	264,28	1,308
10^{-3}	1	0,035315	0,21998	0,26428	0,0013
2,8317 x 10^{-2}	28,317	1	6,2290	7,4805	0,0370
4,546 x 10^{-3}	4,546	0,1605	1	1,2011	0,0059
3,785 x 10^{-3}	3,785	0,13368	0,8326	1	0,0050
0,7646	764,56	27	168,16	201,97	1

Conversion of Mass

kg	tekma	g	lb	oz
1	0,102	1000	2,2046	35,274
9,807	1	9807	21,6205	345,93
10^{-3}	1,02 x 10^{-4}	1	2,205 x 10^{-3}	3,527 x 10^{-2}
0,45359	4,625 x 10^{-2}	453,59	1	16
2,835 x 10^{-2}	2,8908 x 10^{-3}	28,35	6,25 x 10^{-2}	1

Conversion of Specific Mass (density)

kg/m^3	lb/ft^3
1	6,243 x 10^{-2}
16,0185	1

Conversion of Force

N	kp	lb ft/s² (pdl)
1	0,102	7,2329
9,807	1	71,0
0,1379	$1,405 \times 10^{-2}$	1

800188

Conversion of Pressure

Pa	mbar	mm $H_2$0	atm	in WG	lbf/in²
1	10^{-2}	0,102	$9,869 \times 10^{-6}$	$4,02 \times 10^{-3}$	$1,4504 \times 10^{-4}$
100	1	10,917	$9,869 \times 10^{-4}$	0,402	$1,4504 \times 10^{-2}$
9,807	$9,807 \times 10^{-2}$	1	$9,678 \times 10^{-5}$	$3,937 \times 10^{-2}$	$1,4223 \times 10^{-3}$
$1,013 \times 10^5$	1013	$1,0332 \times 10^4$	1	406,77	14,696
249,10	2,491	25,4	$2,453 \times 10^{-3}$	1	$3,605 \times 10^{-2}$
6908,9	69,089	704,49	$6,805 \times 10^{-2}$	27,736	1

800630

Conversion of Work, Energy and Heat

J = Ws	kWh	kpm	kcal	Btu	ft lbf
1	$2,778 \times 10^{-7}$	0,1020	$2,39 \times 10^{-4}$	$9,48 \times 10^{-4}$	0,7376
$3,6 \times 10^6$	1	$3,6710 \times 10^5$	860	3413	$2,655 \times 10^6$
9,807	$2,7241 \times 10^{-6}$	1	$2,3423 \times 10^{-3}$	$9,2949 \times 10^{-3}$	7,233
4187	$1,163 \times 10^3$	427	1	3,9685	3087,4
1,055	$2,93 \times 10^4$	107,59	0,25198	1	777,97
1,3558	$3,766 \times 10^{-7}$	0,1383	$3,239 \times 10^{-4}$	$1,285 \times 10^{-3}$	1

800629

Conversion of Power

kW	kpm/s	hk	kcal/h	ft lbf/s	hp
1	102	1,36	860	738	1,34
$9,81 \times 10^{-3}$	1	$1,33 \times 10^{-2}$.	8,44	7,23	$1,32 \times 10^{-2}$
0,735	75	1	632	542	0,986
$1,16 \times 10^{-3}$	0,119	$1,58 \times 10^{-3}$	1	0,858	$1,56 \times 10^{-3}$
1,36	0,138	$1,84 \times 10^{-3}$	1,17	1	$1,82 \times 10^{-3}$
0,745	76	1,014	642	550	1
$2,93 \times 10^{-4}$	$2,99 \times 10^{-2}$	$3,99 \times 10^{-4}$	0,252	0,216	$3,93 \times 10^{-4}$
3,52	35,9	0,479	3024	259	0,471

800628

Temperature:

$$F = \frac{9}{5}C + 32 \qquad C = \frac{5}{9}(F - 32)$$

Single Degree of Freedom System

m = mass (kg)
k = Stiffness (N/m)

Resonant frequency

$$f_0 = \frac{1}{2\pi} \sqrt{\frac{k}{m}} = \frac{1}{2\pi} \sqrt{\frac{g}{\Delta_{st}}}$$

where

g = gravitational acceleration
Δ_{st} = static deflection of the mass

For Single Frequency (Sinusoidal) Vibration

Acceleration	Velocity	Displacement
$a_0 \cos 2\pi ft$	$\dfrac{1}{2\pi f} a_0 \sin 2\pi ft$	$-\dfrac{1}{4\pi^2 f^2} a_0 \cos 2\pi ft$
$-2\pi f v_0 \sin 2\pi ft$	$v_0 \cos 2\pi ft$	$\dfrac{1}{2\pi f} v_0 \sin 2\pi ft$
$-4\pi^2 f^2 d_0 \cos 2\pi ft$	$-2\pi f d_0 \sin 2\pi ft$	$d_0 \cos 2\pi ft$

Frequency, acceleration, velocity, displacement nomograph
(SI Units)

Velocity, Displacement and Acceleration, RMS values (or peak values)

Frequency

271453

APPENDIX H

Standards Related to
Vibration and Shock Measurements

H.1. General

Austria	Österreichisches Normungsinstitut Leopoldsg. 4 1020 Wien
S 9001	Mechanische Schwingungen; Erschütterungen
S 9100	Schwingungslehre; Kinematische Begriffe
C.S.S.R.	Office for Standards and Measurements, 11347 Praha 1, Václavské Námésti 19
ČSN 01 1312 1975	Quantities and units pertaining to mechanical vibration and shocks
ČSN 01 1390	Methods of Measurements of mechanical vibrations
ČSN 01 1391	Mechanical vibration measuring equipment. General terminology
ČSN 01 1400 1975	Mechanical vibrations and shocks. Terminology
ČSN 01 1401	Balancing of rotating machine elements. Terminology
ČSN 02 8902	Characteristic data for design of elastic bearing elements
ČSN 12 3062	Measurement of noise and vibration from ventilators
France	L'Association Française de Normalisation (AFNOR) Tour Europe, 92 Courbevoie
NF E 90-001 1972	Vibrations et chocs mécaniques — vocabulaire
C 20408 Jan. 1974:	Méthodes d'essais. Essais généraux climatiques et mécaniques. Guide pour l'essai de chocs. spectres de chocs et autres caractéristiques des formes de chocs
Germany (BRD)	Beuth Verlag GmbH. Burggrafenstr. 4 — 10 1000 Berlin 30
DIN 1311	Schwingungslehre Teil 1: Kinematische Begriffe Teil 2: Einfache Schwinger Teil 3: Schwingsysteme Teil 4: Schwingende Kontinua
DIN 4150 T. 1	Erschütterungen im Bauwesen, Grundsätze ...
DIN 45667	Klassierverfahren für das Erfassen regelloser Schwingungen
Germany (DDR)	Amt für Standardisierung, Meßwesen und Warenprufung der Deutschen Demokratischen Republik 1026 Berlin Wallstraße 16
TGL 0-1311/01 1963	Schwingungslehre; Benennungen
TGL 0-1311/02 1963	Schwingungslehre; Einfache Schwinger
TGL 0-1311/03 1963	Schwingungslehre; Schwingungssysteme mit endlich vielen Freiheitsgraden
TGL 22312/01 1971	Arbeitshygiene; Wirkung mechanischer Schwingungen auf den Menschen; Begriffe
TGL 22312/02 1971	Arbeitshygiene; Wirkung mechanischer Schwingungen auf den Menschen; Grenzwerte für Ganzkörperschwingungen

TGL 22312/03 1971	Arbeitshygiene; Wirkung mechanischer Schwingungen auf den Menschen; Meßmethodik für Ganzkörperschwingungen
TGL 22312/04 1972	Arbeitshygiene; Wirkung mechanischer Schwingungen auf den Menschen; Grenzwerte für Teilkörperschwingungen
TGL 22312/05 1972	Arbeitshygiene; Wirkung mechanischer Schwingungen auf den Menschen; Meßmethodik für Teilkörperschwingungen
TGL 22312/06 1974	Arbeitshygiene; Wirkung mechanischer Schwingungen auf den Menschen; Bewertungsfilter für Ganz- und Teilkörperschwingungen
Great Britain	British Standards Institution, 2, Park Street, London W. 1
BS 3015 1958	Glossary of terms used in vibration and shock testing
Hungary	Magyar Szabványugyi Hivatal, Budapest 1X, Ullúl út.25
M.Sz.4900/2 -78	Fizikai mennyiségek neve és jele. Rezgések
Netherlands	Nederlands Normalisatie-Instituut, Polakweg 5, Rijswijk (Z-H)
NEN- ISO 1925	Same as (ISO 1925-1974)
NEN- ISO 2041	Same as (ISO 2041-1975)
NEN10 050(20)	Same as (IEC 50(20)-1958)
Poland	Polski Komitet Normalizacji i Miar, ul. Elektoralna 2, 00-139 - Warszawa
PN-75 M-53527	Instruments for mechanical vibration measurements. Terms and definitions
Sweden	Sveriges Standardiseringskommission, Box 3295, 10366 Stockholm
SS 4011401	Ordlista, Vibrationer och Stöt
U.S.A.	American National Standards Institute, 1430 Broadway, New York, NY 10018
S1.1-1960 (R 1976)	Acoustic Terminology (including Mechanical Shock and Vibration)
ANSI S2.6- 1963 (R 1976)	Nomenclature and Symbols for Specifying the Mechanical Impedance of Structures
ANSI S2.7- 1964 (R 1976)	Terminology for Balancing Rotating Machinery
ANSI S2.10- 1971 (R 1976)	Methods for Analysis and Presentation of Shock and Vibration Data
ANSI S3-W—39 - 1960	The Effects of Shock and Vibration on Man
U.S.S.R.	Komitet Standartov, Leninsky Prospekt 9 b, 117049 Moskva M-49
Gost 13731-68	Mechanical vibration. General requirements for measurement performances
Gost 16819-71	Vibrometers. Terms and definitions

International (I.E.C.)	International Organization for Standardization, 1, Rue de Varembé, Geneva, Switzerland
50	International Electrotechnical Vocabulary
50(20) (1958)	Scientific and industrial measuring instruments
50(411) (1973)	Rotating machines
International (I.S.O.)	International Organization for Standardization, 1, Rue de Varembé, Geneva, Switzerland
R.1925-1974	Balancing — Vocabulary
R.2041-1975	Vibration and shock — Vocabulary
DP 4863	Flexible couplings — Guide for specifications, selection and application
DP 4865	Analog analysis and presentation of vibration and shock data
DP 4866	Evaluation and measurement of vibration in buildings
DP 5345	Definitions relating to rotating rigid bodies
DIS 5805	Vocabulary of mechanical Vibration and shock affecting man. Supplement to ISO 2041 1975
DIS 5982	Vibration and shock — Mechanical driving point impedance of the human body

H.2. Vibration Rating Recommendations

Austria	Österreichisches Normungsinstitut Leopoldsg. 4 1020 Wien
S 9010	Wirkungen von Erschütterungen auf den ganzen Menschen
S 9020	Wirkungen von Erschütterungen auf Bauwerke
C.S.S.R.	Office for Standards and Measurements, 11347 Praha 1, Václavské Náměsti 19
ČSN 01 1410 1971	Permitted limits for unbalanced solid machine elements
Denmark	Arbejdsmiljøfondet Vesterbrogade 69 1620 København V
	Hvide Fingre Vibrationsskader fra håndværktøjer
Finland	Valtion Painatuskeskus PL 516, 00101 Helsinki 10
	Yleiset koneteknilliset turvallisuusohjeet
France	L'Association Française de Normalisation (AFNOR), Tour Europe, 92 Courbevoie
E 90-400 1971	Exposition des individus aux vibrations et aux chocs — guide pour l'estimation de l'exposition des individus à des vibrations globales du corps

E 90-600 1970	Equilibrage et machine à équilibrer — qualité d'équilibrage des rotors rigides
E 90-601 1973	Description, caractéristiques et possibilités des machines à équilibrer
Germany (BRD)	Beuth Verlag GmbH Burggrafenstr. 4 — 10 1000 Berlin 30
DIN 4150	Erschütterungen im Bauwesen T. 2: Einwirkung auf Menschen T. 3: Einwirkungen auf bauliche Anlagen
VDI 2056	Beurteilungsmaßstäbe für mechanische Schwingungen von Maschinen
VDI 2057	Beurteilung der Einwirkung mechanischer Schwingungen auf den Menschen + Neuentwurf Blatt 1: Grundlagen, Gliederung, Begriffe Blatt 2: Schwingungseinwirkung auf den menschlichen Körper Blatt 3: Schwingungsbeanspruchung des Menschen
Great Britain	British Standards Institution, 2, Park Street, London W. 1
DD 23	Guide to safety aspects of human vibration experiments
DD 32	Guide to the evaluation of human exposure of whole body vibration
DD 43	Guide to the evaluation of exposure of the human hand/arm system to vibration
Hungary	Magyar Szabvángügyi Hivatal Budapest 1X Ullul út.25
KGST 715-77	Motoros kéziszerszámok rezgésjellem zőinek megengedett értékei és hőszigetelő védőbevonata
KGST 1932-79	Munkahelyen megengedett rezgés szintek
Netherlands	Nederlands Normalisatie-Instituut, Polakweg 5, Rijswijk (Z-H)
NEN- ISO 1940	Same as (ISO 1940-1973)
NEN- ISO 2372	Same as (ISO 2372-1974)
NEN 22 373	Same as (ISO 2373-1974)
NEN- ISO 2631	Same as (ISO 2631-1974)
Poland	Polski Komitet Normalizacji i Miar, ul. Elektoralna 2, 00-139 - Warszawa
PN-73 E-06020	Rotating electrical machines. Vibration limits
U.S.A.	American National Standards Institute 1430 Broadway New York, NY 10018
ANSI S2.19 —1975	Balance Quality of Rotating Rigid Bodies
U.S.S.R.	Komitet Standartov, Leninsky Prospekt 9 b, Moskva M-49
Gost 17770-72 Gost 13731-68 Gost 16519-70 Gost 16844-71 Gost 16436-70	Hand tools. Acceptable vibration levels

GOST 23552 -79	Civil aeroplanes. Acceptable levels of sound shock intensity on the ground and measuring methods
International (I.S.O.)	International Organization for Standardization, 1, Rue de Varembé, Geneva, Switzerland
R.1940-1973	Balance quality of rotating rigid bodies
2372-1974	Mechanical vibration of machines with operating speeds from 10 to 200 rev/s — Basis for specifying evaluation standards
2373-1974	Mechanical vibration of certain rotating electrical machinery with shaft heights between 80 and 400 mm — Measurement and evaluation of the vibration severity
R.2631-1974	Guide for the evaluation of human exposure to whole-body vibration
DP 4867	Code for the measurement for reporting of shipboard — Vibration data
DP 4868	Code for shipboard — Local vibration measurements
DP 5343	Criteria for flexible rotor balance
DIS 5349	Principles for the measurement and the evaluation of human exposure to vibration transmitted to the hand
DP 6897	Guide to the evaluation of the response of occupants of fixed structures, especially buildings, and off-shore structures to low frequency horizontal motion (0,063 Hz to 1 Hz)

H.3. Vibration Measuring Equipment

C.S.S.R.	Office for Standards and Measurements, 11347 Praha 1, Václavské Náměsti 19
ČSN 01 1391 1970	Mechanical vibration measuring equipment. General terminology
ČSN 35 6850 1972	Instruments for vibration measurements. Technical requirements
ČSN 35 6858 1975	Instruments with piezoelectric pick-ups for service vibration measurements. Metrologic testing
Finland	Suomen Standardisoimisliitto PL 205, 00121 Helsinki 12
SFS 2882	Same as IEC 184 (1965)
SFS 2883	Same as IEC 222 (1966)
France	L'Association Française de Normalisation (AFNOR), Tour Europe, 92 Courbevoie
E 90-100 1973	Instruments de mesure des caractéristiques d'intensité vibratoire des machines tournantes ou alternatives
E 90-110 1973	Descriptions et caractéristiques des appareils pour l'équilibrage in situ
E 90-200 1970	Abaque destiné au tracé des caractéristiques des ensembles générateurs de vibrations (Exp.)

E 90-210 1970	Caractéristiques des ensembles générateurs électrodynamiques de vibrations (Exp.)
E 90-211 1970	Caractéristiques des générateurs électrodynamiques de vibrations (Exp.)
E 90-213 1970	Caractéristiques des amplificateurs de puissance pour générateurs électrodynamiques de vibrations (Exp.)
Germany (BRD)	Beuth Verlag GmbH Burggrafenstr. 4 — 10 1000 Berlin 30
DIN 45661	Schwingungsmeßgeräte; Begriffe, Kenngrößen, Störgrößen
DIN 45662	Eigenschaften von Schwingungsmeß-geräten, Angaben in Typenblättern
DIN 45664	Ankopplung von Schwingungsmeßgerä-ten und Überprüfung auf Störeinflüsse
DIN 45666	Schwingstärkemeßgerät; Anforderungen
DIN 45669 Teil 1 Entwurf	Messung von Schwingungsimmissionen (Schwingungsmesser)
Germany (DDR)	Amt für Standardisierung, Meßwesen und Warenprüfung der Deutschen Demokratischen Republik 1026 Berlin Wallstraße 16
TGL 22747/01 1975	Geräte und Einrichtungen zur Messung nichtelektrischer Größen; Schwingungsmeßeinrichtungen; Begriffe
TGL 22747/02 1975	Geräte und Einrichtungen zur Messung nichtelektrischer Größen; Schwingungsmeßeinrichtungen; Kenngrößen
Netherlands	Nederlands Normalisatie-Instituut, Polakweg 5, Rijswijk (Z-H)
NEN 10 217	Same as (IEC 217–1967)
NEN - ISO 2371	Same as (ISO 2371–1974)
NEN - ISO 2953	Same as (ISO 2953–1975)
NEN - ISO 2954	Same as (ISO 2954–1975)
NEN 10 348	Same as IEC 348–1971, 348 A–1974)
Spain	Instituto Nacional de Racionalización y Normalización (IRANOR) Zurbano, 46 Madrid 10
21 328 75(1)	Características relativas a los transduc-tores electromecánicos destinados a la medida de choques y vibraciones
21 328 75(2)	Clases de captadores de vibración y elementos sensibles empleados en estos captadores
21 328 75 (3)	Métodos para la especificación de las características relativas al equipo auxi-liar para la medida de choques y vibra-ciones
U.S.A.	American National Standards Institute, 1430 Broadway, New York, NY 10018
ANSI S2.2-1959 (R 1976)	Methods for the Calibration of Shock and Vibration Pick-Ups
ANSI S2.3-1964 (R 1976)	Specifications for High-Impact Shock Machine for Electronic Devices

ANSI S2.4-1976	Method of Specifying the Characteristics of Auxiliary Equipment for Shock and Vibration Measurements
ANSI S2.5-1962 (R 1976)	Recommendations for Specifying the Performance of Vibrating Machines
ANSI S2.11—1969 (R 1978)	Selection of Calibrations and Tests for Electrical Transducers used for Measuring Shock and Vibration
ANSI S2.14—1973 (R 1978)	Methods for Specifying the Performance of Shock Machines
ANSI S2.15-1972 (R 1977)	Specifications for the Design, Construction and Operation of Class HI Shock-Testing Machines for Light-Weight Equipment
ANSI Z24.21-1957 (R 1978)	Methods for Specifying the Characteristics of Pick-Ups for Shock and Vibration Measurements
	Instrument Society of America 400 Stanwix Street Pittsburg, PA 15222
ISA S37.2 1964	Guide for Specifications and Tests for Piezoelectric Acceleration Transducers for Aerospace Testing
U.S.S.R.	Komitet Standartov, Leninsky Prospekt 9 b, 117049 Moskva M-49
Gost 5.295-69	Electromechanical vibrator type LV-22 (power 0,8 kw) for general use
Gost 5.304-69	Electromechanical vibrator type IV-19 (power 0,27 kw) for general use
Gost 15939-70	Vibration measuring equipment with piezoelectric transducers
Gost 16826-71	Vibrometers Basic parameters
International (I.E.C.)	International Organization for Standardization, 1, Rue de Varembé, Geneva, Switzerland
184 (1965)	Methods for specifying the characteristics of electro-mechanical transducers for shock and vibration measurements
217 (1967)	Electronic voltmeters
222 (1966)	Methods for specifying the characteristics of auxiliary equipment for shock and vibration measurement
225 (1966)	Octave, half-octave and third-octave band filters intended for the analysis of sounds and vibrations
348 (1978)	Safety requirements for electronic measuring apparatus
International (I.S.O.)	International Organization for Standardization, 1, Rue de Varembé, Geneva, Switzerland
R.2371-1974	Field balancing equipment — description and evaluation
R.2953-1975	Balancing machines — description and evaluation
R.2954-1975	Mechanical vibration of rotating and reciprocating machinery — Requirements for instruments for measuring vibration severity
DIS 3719.2	Balancing machines — Symbols for front panels

DIS 5344	Electrodynamic test equipment for generating vibration — Methods of describing the characteristics of the equipment
DP 5347	Standard methods for the calibration of vibration and shock pickups
DP 5348	Mechanical mounting of vibration transducers (pickups)
DIS 6070	Characteristics of auxiliary tables for vibration generators

H.4. Measurement of Vibration of Machines

Austria	Österreichischer Arbeitsring für Lärmbekämpfung, Regierungsgebäude, 1012 Wien
ÖAL-Richtlinie Nr. 4	Körperschallgedämmte Aufstellung von Maschinen
ÖAL-Richtlinie Nr. 7	Schwingungsgedämmte Maschinenaufstellung
Bulgaria	Institut de Normalisation, 8, rue Sveta Sofia, Sofia
BDS 5626-65	Measurement of vibration on electrical rotating machines
C.S.S.R.	Office for Standards and Measurements, 11347 Praha 1, Václavské Námĕsti 19
ČSN 02 8902 1971	Elastic foundation characteristics of elastic mounting and isolators
ČSN 12 3062 1961	Measurement of noise and vibration from ventilators
ČSN 12 3063 1971	Fans. Prescription for measurement of vibration
France	L'Association Française de Normalisation (AFNOR), Tour Europe, 92 Courbevoie
E 90-300 1973	Vibrations mécaniques des machines ayant une vitesse de fonctionnement comprise entre 10 et 200 tours par seconde — évaluation de l'intensité vibratoire
E 90-310 1973	Vibrations mécaniques des machines électriques tournantes de hauteur d'axe comprises entre 80 et 400 mm — évaluation de l'intensité vibratoire
H 00-042 1971	Essais de choc vertical par chute libre
H 00-043 1971	Essai de vibration
NFC 20616 AVR. 1973	Méthodes d'essais applicables aux composants. Essais généraux climatiques et mécaniques. Vibrations
Germany (BRD)	Beuth Verlag GmbH Burggrafenstr. 4 — 10 1000 Berlin 30
DIN 45665	Schwingstärke von rotierenden elektrischen Maschinen der Baugrößen 80 bis 315. Meßverfahren und Grenzwerte

358

DIN 45668	Ankopplung für Schwingungsaufnehmer zur Überwachung von Großmaschinen
DIN ISO 2373	Mechanische Schwingungen von umlaufenden elektrischen Maschinen mit Achshöhen von 80 — 400 mm
VDI 2059 Entwurf	Wellenschwingungen von Turbosätzen Bl.1: Grundlagen für die Messung und Beurteilung Bl.2: Dampfturbosätze für Kraftwerke Bl.3: Industrieturbosätze Bl.4: Gasturbosätze
VDI 2060	Beurteilungsmaßstäbe für den Auswuchtzustand rotierender starrer Körper

Great Britain	British Standards Institution, 2 Park Street, London W. 1
BS.4675: 1971	Recommendations for a basis for comparative evaluation of vibration in machinery
BS.4999: 1972	Part 50: Mechanical performance-vibration

Hungary	Magyar Szabrányügyi Hivatal, Budapest IX Ullül út.25
M.Sz.19426-77	Forgogépek rezgéserősségének mérése
KGST 716-77	Motoros kéziszerszámok rezgésjellemzőinek mérési módszerei

Netherlands	Nederlands Normalisatie-Instituut, Polakweg 5, Rijswijk (Z-H)
NEN - ISO 3080	Same as (ISO 3080—1974)
NEN - ISO 3945	Same as (ISO 3945—1977)

Poland	Polski Komitet Normalizacji i Miar, ul. Elektoralna 2, 00-139 - Warszawa
PN-73 E-04255	Electrical rotating machines. Measurement of vibrations

Roumania	Oficiul de stat pentru Standarde, Str. Edgar Quinet 6, Bucarest 1
STAS 7536-66	Measurement of vibration from electrical rotating machines

U.S.A.	Anti-Friction Bearing Manufacturers Association 60 East 42nd Street New York, NY 10017
AFBMA Standard No. 13 (1968)	Rolling bearing vibration and noise

U.S.S.R.	Komitet Standartov, Leninsky Prospekt 9 b, Moskva M-49
Gost 12379-66	Measurement of vibration on electrical rotating machines
Gost 16529-70	Agricultural mounted machines, methods of determination oscillating and noise characteristics
Gost 23719-79	Passenger and transport aeroplanes and helicopters. Methods of measuring vibration parameters in saloons and crew cabins

International (I.S.O.)	International Organization for Standardization, 1, Rue de Varembé, Geneva, Switzerland

R.1940-1973	Balance quality of rotating rigid bodies
R.2372-1974	Mechanical vibration of machines with operating speeds from 10 to 200 rev/s — Basis for specifying evaluation standards
R.2373-1974	Mechanical vibration of certain rotating electrical machinery with shaft heights between 80 and 400 mm — Measurement and evaluation of the vibration severity
R.3080-1974	Guide for the mechanical balancing of marine main steam turbine machinery for merchant service
3945 - 1977	Mechanical vibration of large rotating machines with speed range from 10 to 200 rev/s — Measurement and evaluation of vibration severity in situ
DIS 5406	The mechanical balancing of flexible rotors

H.5. Vibration Testing

Belgium	B.I.N. (Belgisch Instituut voor Normalisatie) VZW Brabançonnelaan 29 1040 Brussel Tel.: 02/734.92.05
	I.B.N. (Institut Belge de Normalisation) ASBL Avenue de la Brabançonne 29 1040 Bruxelles Tel.: 02/734.92.05
C 06-206	Fundamentele klimatologische en mechanische beproevingsmethoden: Deel II: Proeven; Proef Fc: (Sinusvormige) trillingen Essais fondamentaux climatiques et de robustesse mécanique: Partie II: Essais; Essai Fc: Vibrations (sinusoidales)
C 06-229	Idem: Proef Eb: Trilproef Idem: Essai Eb: Secousses

France	L'Association Française de Normalisation (AFNOR), Tour Europe, 92 Courbevoie
UTE C 20-408 1974	Guide pour l'essai de chocs — Spectres de chocs et autres caractéristiques des formes de chocs (11 pages)
NF C 20-508 1975	— Essai 8: Chocs (Enr.) (10 pages)
NF C 20-523 1975	— Essai 23: Accélération constante (Enr.) (8 pages)
NF C 20-524 1975	— Essai 24: Secousses (Enr.) (7 pages)
NF C 20-526 1975	— Vibrations aléatoires (Essai Fd) (Enr.) (17 pages)
NF C 20-527 1975	— Vibrations aléatoires (Essai Fda) (Enr.) (25 pages)
NF C 20-528 1975	— Vibrations aléatoires (Essai Fdb) (Enr.) (25 pages)
NF C 20-529 1975	— Vibrations aléatoires (Essai Fdc) (Enr.) (14 pages)
NF C 20-608 1974	— Essai 8 B: Chocs (Enr.) (10 pages)

NF C 20-616 1973	— Essai 16 B: Vibrations (Enr.) (10 pages)
NF C 20-623 1973	— Essai 23 A: Accélération constante (Enr.) (6 pages)
NF C 20-624 1973	— Essai 24 A: Secousses (Enr.) (7 pages)
NF C 90-163 1967	— Essai Nr. 163: Essai de vibrations (Enr.) (10 pages)
E 90-200 1970	Machines pour essais de vibrations et de chocs — abaque destiné au tracé des caractéristiques des ensembles générateurs de vibrations
E 90-210 1978	Machines pour essais de vibrations et de chocs — caractéristiques des ensembles générateurs électrodynamiques de vibrations
H 00-043 1971	Emballages d'expédition complets et pleins — essai de vibration

Germany (BRD)	Beuth Verlag GmbH Burggrafenstr. 4 — 10 1000 Berlin 30
DIN 40046	Klimatische und mechanische Prüfungen für elektrische Bauelemente und Geräte der Nachrichtentechnik Teil 7: Prüfung E. Stoßen Teil 8: Prüfung F. Schwingen
DIN 50100	Dauerschwingversuche. Begriffe, Zeichen. Durchführung. Auswertung
DIN 51228	Dauerschwingprüfmaschinen

Great Britain	British Standards Institution, 2 Park Street, London W. 1
BS.3015: 1958	Glossary of terms used in vibration and shock testing
BS.2011: 1980	Part 1.1 Basic Environmental Testing Procedures. GENERAL Part 2.1 ea Test ea Shock Part 2.1 eb Test eb Bump Part 2.1 fc Test fc Vibration (sinusoidal) Part 2.1 fd Random Vibration — Wideband General Req. Part 2.1 fda Random Vibration — Wide-band Reproducibility high Part 2.1 fdb Random Vibration — Wideband Reproducibility medium Part 2.1 fdc Random Vibration — Wideband Reproducibility low
BS.3G100: 1969	Part 2: General requirement for equipment in aircraft

Hungary	Magyar Szabvángügyi Hivatal Budapest 1X Ullül út.25
KGST 1367-78	Forgógépek rezgéserősségének vizsgálata és értékelése
KGST 1368-78	Nagy forgógépek rezgéserősségének helyszini vizsgálata és minősitése

India	Indian Standards Institution, Manak Bhavan 9 Bahadur Shah, Zafar Marg, New Delhi 110002
2106	Environmental tests for electronic and electrical equipment: Part VII Bump Test (1964) Part VIII Impact or shock test (1964) Part IX Drop test (1964) Part XIV Constant acceleration test (1966) Part XVI Vibration test (1971)

Japan	Japanese Standards Association 1-24, Akasaka 4 chome, Minato-ku Tokyo
JIS C 0911 (1960)	Vibration testing procedures for electric machines and equipment
JIS C 0912 (1960)	Shock testing procedures for electric machines and equipment
JIS 1601 (1967)	Vibratile testing methods for automobile parts
JIS B 6003 (1962)	Methods of vibration testing for machine tools
JIS W 6051 (1954)	Vibration testing method for aeronautical instruments
JIS W 6053 (1955)	Shock testing methods for aeronautical instruments
JIS W 6054 (1955)	Acceleration testing method for aeronautical instruments

Poland	Polski Komitet Normalizacji i Miar, ul. Elektoralna 2, 00-139 - Warszawa
PN-75 0-79166	Transport packages. Methods of vibration tests

Sweden	Sveriges Standardiseringskommission, Box 3295, 10366 Stockholm
SEN 431600	Miljöprovning av elektronikkomponenter, allmänt
SEN 431605	Miljöprovning av elektronikkomponenter, skakprov
SEN 431606	Miljöprovning av elektronikkomponenter, vibration

U.S.A.	Naval Publication and Forms Center, 5801 Tabor Avenue, Philadelphia, PA. 19120
MIL STD 810 C	Environmental Test Methods (Equipment)
MIL E 4158 E	Electronic Equipment Ground; General Requirements for
MIL E 5272 C	Environmental Testing. Aeronautical and Associated Equipment, General Specifications
MIL E 5400 P	Electronic Equipment, Airborne; General Specifications for
MIL T 5422 F	Testing, Environmental, Aircraft, Electronic Equipment
MIL E 16400 G	Electronic, Interior Communication and Navigation Equipment, Naval Ship and Shore, General Specifications for
MIL T 21200 L	Test Equipment for use with Electronic and Electrical Equipment, General Specifications for
MIL STD 202 E	Test Methods for Electronic and Electrical Components
NATO STANAG 3518	Environmental Test Methods for Aircraft Equipment and Associated Ground Equipment

International (I.E.C.)	International Organization for Standardization, 1, Rue de Varembé, Geneva, Switzerland
68	Basic environmental testing procedures
68-1 (1968)	Part 1. General

68-1 A (1974)	First supplement to publication 68-1 (1968)
68-2	Part 2. Tests
68-2-6 (1970)	Test Fc: Vibration (sinusoidal)
68-2-7 (1968)	Test Ga: Acceleration, steady state
68-2-27 (1972)	Test Ea: Shock
68-2-29 (1968)	Test Eb: Bump
68-2-34 (1973)	Test Fd: Random vibration wide band — General requirements
68-2-35 (1973)	Test Fda: Random vibration wide band — Reproducibility high
68-2-36 (1973)	Test Fdb: Random vibration wide band — Reproducibility medium
68-2-37 (1973)	Test Fdc: Random vibration wide band — Reproducibility low

H.6. Measurement of Dynamic Properties of Materials

France	L'Association Française de Normalisation (AFNOR), Tour Europe, 92 Courbevoie
NFS 31049 FEV. 1979	Mesure du pouvoir d'isolation acoustique des éléments de construction et de l'isolement des immeubles. (fidélité)
NFS 31050 FEV. 1979	IDEM (postes d'essais)
NFS 31051 FEV. 1979	IDEM - Pouvoir d'isolation acoustique au bruit aérien des éléments de construction
NFS 31052 FEV. 1979	IDEM - Mesure en laboratoire de la transmission du bruit de choc par les planchers
NFS 31053 FEV. 1979	IDEM - Mesure de la réduction de la transmission du bruit de choc par les revêtements de sol et les dalles flottantes

Germany (BRD)	Beuth Verlag GmbH Burggrafenstr. 4 — 10 1000 Berlin 30
DIN 52214	Bauakustische Prüfungen. Bestimmung der dynamischen Steifigkeit von Dämmschichten für schwimmende Böden
DIN 53426	Prüfung von Schaumstoffen; — Bestimmung des dynamischen Elastizitätsmoduls und des Verlustfaktors nach dem Vibrometerverfahren
DIN 53440	Prüfung von Kunststoffen und schwingungsgedämpften geschichteten Systemen. Biegeschwingungsversuch. Teil 1: Allgemeine Grundlagen Teil 2: Bestimmung des komplexen Elastizitätsmoduls Teil 3: Mehrschichtsysteme
DIN 53445	Prüfung von Kunststoffen; Torsionsschwingungsversuch.
DIN 53513	Bestimmung der visko-elastischen Eigenschaften von Gummi bei erzwungenen Schwingungen außerhalb der Resonanz
DIN 54119	Ultraschallprüfung, Begriffe

Great Britain	British Standards Institution, 2 Park Street, London W. 1
BS.1881: 1970	Part 5: Methods of testing concrete. Methods of testing hardened concrete for other than strength
BS.AU 125: 1966	Automobile series specification for methods of test for panel damping materials
DD 47	Vibration isolation of structures by elastometric mountings

Netherlands	Nederlands Normalisatie-Instituut, Polakweg 5, Rijswijk (Z-H)
NEN - ISO 2017	Same as (ISO 2017-1972)

Roumania	Oficiul de stat pentru Standarde Str. Edgar Quinet 6, Bucarest 1
STAS 8048-67	Measurement of dynamic stiffness of vibration absorbing materials in building acoustics

U.S.A.	American Society for Testing and Materials, 1916 Race St., Philadelphia, Pa. 19103
ASTM C215-60	"Standard method of test for fundamental transverse, longitudinal and torsional frequencies of concrete specimens". Annual ASTM Standards Part 10
ASTM C597-71	"Standard method of test for pulse velocity through concrete". Annual ASTM Standards Part 10
ASTM D1577-66	"Standard methods of test for linear density of textile fibers". (Vibroscope method) Annual ASTM Standards Part 25
ASTM D2231-71	"Standard recommended practice for forced vibration testing of vulcanizates". Annual ASTM Standards Part 28
	American National Standards Institute 1430 Broadway New York, NY 10018
ANSI S2.8— 1972 (R 1978)	Guide for Describing the Characteristics of Resilient Mountings
ANSI S2.9— 1976	Nomenclature for Specifying Damping Properties of Materials

International (I.S.O.)	International Organization for Standardization, 1, Rue de Varembé Geneva, Switzerland
2017-1972	Vibration and Shock — Isolators — Specifying characteristics for mechanical isolation (Guide for selecting and applying resilient devices)
DP 5405	Nomenclature for specifying damping properties of materials

INDEX